Better Homes
and Gardens

BABY BOOK

A handbook for parents by

The Better Homes & Gardens

Child Care and Training Department

lorraine fox

About th

FIFTH REVISION

COPYRIGHT 1943, 1945, 1946, 1947, 1948, 1949, 1950, 1951

BETTER HOMES & GARDENS

MEREDITH PUBLISHING COMPANY, DES MOINES

PRINTED IN THE UNITED STATES OF AMERICA

On the proper rearing of children depends the future of humanity. Our children must be helped to grow and keep strong and healthy, and to develop socially and emotionally in such a way as to make a happier world.

You cannot rely on your intuition and instinct alone to guide you in all the phases of your child's development. Such knowledge is largely acquired. To this end, a source book of information is very helpful. Perhaps not all your questions can be answered in such a book, though many of the less complex ones may be.

This book is designed and prepared to be a comforting and authoritative place to turn when doubts and fears arise. Its purpose is to preserve the health and happiness of your child, and it should serve well as a guide.

Unfortunately, we still have serious illness and death from those diseases against which we have satisfactory means of protection. The importance of these safeguards is stressed here. As medical and scientific knowledge increases, a larger proportion of the infectious diseases to which children are subject can be brought under control.

Authorities differ in opinion as to the details of child care, but they agree on the basic general principles. The advice in this book has been found to be good and trustworthy.

Babies are not miniature adults. Their requirements are of a type wholly different from those of an adult person. In the development of the baby, early progress is rapid, much more so than later. Part of the development consists of habit formation. A baby's behavior and activities are largely instinctive at birth, but habit development begins immediately, and the response depends enormously on the environment and management.

This book stresses the importance of adapting the schedule to the baby, rather than the reverse. While schedules tend to conform to general pattern, each baby is an individual and should be permitted, within limitations, to make his own schedule.

Childhood feeding problems can be frequently traced to adoption of a too-rigid schedule in infancy. The appetite of a baby varies from time to time just as does that of anyone else. If a solicitous mother should insist that all of each feeding be taken as has been prescribed, an antagonism to food may develop, and may be the beginning of an emotional disturbance in regard to food.

Expert medical advice is desirable for the feeding of an infant, and each physician has his preference. However, it is well that parents understand not only what foods to give and how they should be given, but also why these foods are given.

The record section of the book also deserves commendation. Records of this type serve several useful purposes. They are always of interest to parents. They serve as a source of reference. They are particularly valuable to the physician who uses them in his assessment of the health, growth, and the development of his young patient.

Philip C. Jeans, M. D.,
professor of pediatrics,
College of Medicine,
State University of Iowa

To the proud parents

Let us congratulate you upon the happiness awaiting you in your new baby, and assure you of our interest in the welfare of your family.

Since its publication in 1943, the *Better Homes & Gardens* Baby Book has gone through many printings and revisions. As this revision goes to press, we are proud to state that, to date, the parents of a million babies have used the *Better Homes & Gardens* Baby Book as a supplement to the advice given by their doctors.

In developing the Baby Book and continuing to improve it, we have asked a great many mothers what they would like in a book of this type. We have had the counsel and assist-ance of distinguished obstetricians, pediatricians, physicians, and child psychologists. This book, then, is authoritative.

To help you plan your days, we've included at the end of each chapter typical daily routines. These are offered only as guides, and your baby may vary considerably from these in his daily schedules, just as his development may not correspond exactly to that of the different ages described. Let him follow his own pattern.

We hope you will agree with the many parents who have called the Baby Book a welcome help and a faithful friend in the everyday care of their youngsters.

Ann Usher

Director, Child Care and Training Department
Better Homes & Gardens

Acknowledgments

We wish to express our appreciation to these authorities on infant
and child care, maternal health, and child development
who have worked with us in the preparation and revision of this book:

P. C. Jeans, M. D.,
*professor of pediatrics,
College of Medicine,
State University of Iowa*

Arthur J. Horesh, M. D.,
*assistant clinical professor of pediatrics,
Western Reserve University, director,
Pediatric Allergy Clinic, University
Hospitals, Cleveland, Ohio;
associate pediatrist, Babies and
Childrens Hospital, Cleveland, Ohio*

Parker K. Hughes, M. D.,
*chief of obstetrics, Iowa Methodist
Hospital and Iowa Lutheran
Hospital, Des Moines, Iowa;
member, American Board of
Gynecology and Obstetrics*

Dennis H. Kelly, M. D.,
*Des Moines, Iowa, fellow of the
American Academy of Pediatrics*

Van C. Robinson, M. D.,
*member of the staffs of Iowa Methodist
Hospital, Iowa Lutheran Hospital,
and Broadlawns Polk County
Hospitals, Des Moines, Iowa*

Lawrence E. Kelley, M. D.,
*member of the staffs of
Iowa Methodist Hospital, Iowa
Lutheran Hospital, and Mercy
Hospital, Des Moines, Iowa*

**Ralph H. Ojemann, Ph. D.,
H. V. Meredith, Ph. D.,
Wendell Johnson, Ph. D.,**
*members of the staff of the
Iowa Child Welfare Station,
University of Iowa*

Contents

Section Three *Your child from two to six years*

Section Four *General*

Section Five *A record*

Section I

Before baby comes

Looking

e future

You are embarking upon one of the most exciting and most satisfying of human experiences—the birth and rearing of your child.

It will be an adventure rather than a job, for service given lovingly, understandingly, and cheerfully is not work. It is pleasure. And the love and appreciation you receive in return from your child can't be called "pay" or "reward." It is fulfillment. It is the proud yet humble knowledge that you have had a share in starting your youngster's feet sturdily and confidently upon the path of life.

In this period when you are waiting for your child to be born, and during the years he is in your care, you can help him most by informing yourself as fully as possible about every phase of his development before his birth and after. If you know the "why" of his behavior patterns and growth stages, the "how" of guiding and taking care of him becomes simpler.

According to Chinese custom, a baby is considered one year old the day of his birth. This is very nearly correct. For nine months previous to birth, he has been living, developing, and growing. You cannot see him, but you can feel his movements and listen to his heartbeats.

On the following pages, your baby's development is described, starting with his earliest beginnings inside your womb.

He's sturdier than you think, this unborn baby of yours. He is protected by the fluid with which wise Nature has surrounded him in his uterine nest. Nothing you see, hear, or think during this phase of this existence can affect him in the slightest.

But you can think ahead to his future well-being by talking over with your mate your philosophy of parenthood—the acceptance, love, and understanding you will bestow on this baby who is even now a part of your world.

Remember that your baby's coloring, features, and sex were determined the moment he was conceived. So don't fix your dreams on attributes he may not have. Instead, look forward with happy anticipation to this special baby who will actually be a nine-months-old individual the day he is born. And even though he will be *yours*, above all, he will be *himself!*

The egg moves slowly through the Fallopian tube into the uterus. This journey takes about 3 days

increase in uterine glands. The purpose of this activity is to provide nourishment for the new life. Once this job is completed, the ovary springs to new activity. The tiny crater from which the egg erupted rapidly fills with a yellowish, waxy stuff—the corpus luteum. It, too, produces a hormone—progesterone. It is the job of this chemical to quiet the rhythmic contractions of the uterus—otherwise, the fragile egg might be injured or discarded.

In a sense, all of this activity is like preparing a house—the uterus—for an honored guest. If the guest—a fertilized ovum—does not arrive, all the preparations have been in vain. Excess tissue breaks down and is discarded. But in the case we are interested in, the guest *does* arrive, right on schedule.

Once the fertilized egg reaches the uterus —a muscular organ approximately the size and shape of a small pear—it leads an apparently aimless existence for six days. It drifts around the uterine cavity, carried by fluid currents. Were any foreign body placed in the uterus, that organ would contract to expel it. But it makes no effort to discard the new life.

Embryo is separate being

This six-day period of apparently aimless— or at least unexplained—drifting represents a highly critical period for the fertilized egg. By now its food supply, the microscopic yolk of the original egg, is near exhaustion. The life it carries is dangerously near extinction. The egg reacts to this hazard. It selects a spot on the red, velvet-smooth uterine wall. It apparently secretes something—possibly an enzyme—which eats a tiny niche in the wall. Then it shoots out tiny feelers with which to draw nourishment. Now, at last, the embryo is safe. It has a nest, and has tapped an always dependable source of food.

Fom this point out, one wonder piles rapidly on top of another. The rounded clump of cells becomes the *morula*—which is Latin for mulberry. Then this minute berry of life grows into a tiny hollow sphere, which is filled with fluid. Over it, a membrane forms which will become the placenta. Through this placenta the growing life will take nourishment from the mother, and will discharge its body wastes—to be excreted by her kidneys. From now on, until the moment of birth, it will live a submarine life, immersed in a bath of amniotic fluid—the watery stuff that fills the sac in which the baby is forming. At one point in its development, the baby will even have primitive gill slits—a reminder of the fact that all life sprang from the seas.

By the end of the third week, the growing life is a tiny fleck of grayish tissue. But even at this point, it has a primitive heart, a tiny puslating tube; and its own system of blood vessels. Already it is manufacturing its own blood which is quite independent of the blood supply of the mother, separated from the

Fertilized egg attaches itself to uterine wall, then shoots out tiny feelers through which it feeds

mother's circulatory system by the placental barrier. The baby's blood, note in passing, may be an entirely different type blood from that of the mother.

During this third week, other striking things have happened. A rudimentary nervous system has been forming; a brain of microscopic proportions, a threadlike spinal cord, even smaller nerves.

The first evidences of a bony structure don't appear until the end of the sixth week. Up to this point, the embryo has been indistinguishable from the embryos of other mammals. But by the end of the sixth week, it is recognizable, even to the unaided eye, as a human being. The head is forming, and during the following week, fingers and toes will appear. By the end of the ninth week, the face, a tiny miniature, is completely formed. Still, the baby is almost unbelievably small. At this point, it weighs only 1/15 of an ounce.

By the end of the third month, most organs are completed and functioning, but the head is large in proportion to the rest of the body. If born at this time, and placed in a bowl of warm water, the infant will make feeble movements in a vain struggle for life. But it is not nearly ready for an independent existence in a hostile world.

Up to this point, the mother is aware of the new life only by external signs. She may feel morning sickness and has, of course, ceased menstruating. Now she can feel a small lump just above the pelvic area—the rapidly enlarging uterus. At first, pear-shaped, the uterus assumes a globular form, then, later on, an ovoid, or bottle shape. By now, the uterus has undergone almost unbelievable expansion. By volume, it has increased 500 times! It has pushed other organs aside, almost filling the abdominal cavity, and even pushing against the diaphragm to cause breathing difficulties.

There is a general misconception that the forming infant leads a cramped life, that it is folded tightly within the uterus. This is not true. At least in its early stage of development, it floats lazily about in the amniotic fluid—which acts as a kind of shock absorber. A prospective mother may undergo violent injury—she may fall down stairs, out a window, or be involved in an auto crash—but there is little likelihood of her baby suffering, even up to the time that birth is imminent. The watery bath in which the baby lives takes up shocks which might otherwise be fatal.

By the middle of the fourth month, the infant can twist its face into a grimace and con-

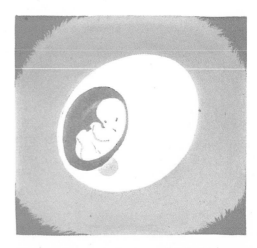

Human characteristics have developed at two months, yet embryo weighs only 1/15 of an ounce

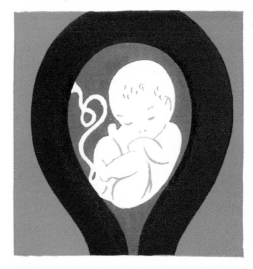

Infant can swallow at 4½ months, and has a thin, red covering for skin. Mother can now feel it move

tract eyes into a wink—even though eyelids are still fused together. It can swallow, and it discharges urine into the fluid in which it floats. At this time, the mother feels the first stirrings of life within her. The baby thrashes arms and legs but lacks energy—and oxygen —for sustained movement. It cannot gulp air into its lungs to get oxygen it needs for any extended exercise—it has to depend on the supply available in the mother's blood. So, after a short period of wakefulness, it is tired and goes back to sleep.

By the fifth month, it has hair, eyebrows, and lashes, and weighs nearly two pounds. Its heartbeat is now detectable by ordinary clinical means such as the stethoscope. Earlier, the faint beat could be heard only with elaborate amplifiers. In this connection, let's straighten out another common misconception. There is a widespread, and erroneous, belief that hearts of girl babies beat more rapidly than those of boys—and that the physician can thereby tell the sex of the unborn child with his stethoscope. There is no clinical support whatsoever for this belief.

By now, the baby is an altogether remarkable individual. The original single cell has grown to a point where the new life now has its full lifetime complement of nerve cells—a staggering total of 12 billion of them!

By the seventh month, the baby is complete enough to stand a good chance of survival if born prematurely. An old wives' tale states that a seven-months baby has a better chance of survival than an eight-months baby. This isn't true. The longer a baby stays within its mother, the better its chances for life. In a sense, the eighth and ninth months are nature's safety factors. The child has a chance if born before, but it has a far better chance if given these two months in the womb to grow sturdier and stronger.

During this period, the placenta has assumed other tasks besides those of nourishing the baby and disposing of wastes. It has also become a gland of internal secretion. It would be impossible for the ovaries to secrete enough progesterone to keep the enormously enlarged uterus quiet, to keep it from contracting and expelling the fetus. Hence, the placenta starts manufacturing progesterone. The placenta also starts making estrogen, another ovarian hormone, which is needed to stimulate tissue-building in the uterus. Evidence now arrives that there is a third female sex hormone—one called relaxin. Its job is what its name implies: to relax tendons and tissues in the pelvic area to facilitate birth.

In its final stages of development, the baby takes the first steps toward acquiring a personality. He swallows and even makes breathing motions with his chest. He may even be subject to hiccups, or take up thumbsucking.

The forming baby reacts to external environment. If its mother smokes a cigarette, it derives enough nicotine from her blood to speed up its heart. Some sounds apparently cause irritation—or at least excitement—to the baby. Research men have found that certain sounds cause rapid movement of the baby's arms and legs. Yet, as always, there is a pattern and a wisdom here. Only by such selfishness can the baby insure his own survival. The mother can seek help from a hundred or a thousand people. The baby is completely dependent on one. Thus, the baby prepares himself for the supreme moment of his life: his birth.

Body prepares for birth

Once again, the mother's body has undergone elaborate preparations for the event. Nothing has been forgotten in the whole, vastly complex procedure. The placenta has generated enough surplus hormones to prepare the breasts for their waiting job. The breasts contain a treelike structure of milk ducts, the nipples representing the trunks. Under pressure of increased hormone production, these tree structures become enormously enlarged—shooting out thousands of new branches and twigs.

Everything is in readiness to provide food for the new life. Actual milk production, however, won't start until the pituitary gland at the base of the mother's brain gives the

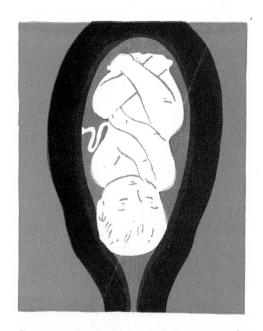

In preparation for birth, the baby turns to this head-down position. Flexible tissues in the head allow infant to pass through the birth canal easily

word. A few hours after birth, it gives this word. It starts producing minute amounts of the hormone, prolactin. This, in turn, starts the breasts functioning.

Other dramatic things have happened within the mother's body. The normally hard cervix, or mouth of the womb, through which the baby must pass, has changed in consistency. Medical students are taught that it is normally of the approximate hardness of the tip of the nose, but that during pregnancy it becomes softened like the lips. The birth canal itself has been provided with a new supply of blood vessels, and with a special lubricant to facilitate passage of the infant. Nothing has been forgotten. The moment of birth is at hand.

What starts labor?

How does the body decide that the child is ready to be born? Physicians would dearly love to have a sure answer for this question. If they knew what triggered labor, they might find a means of stopping labor when it started too early. As things stand, there are only guesses—some of them feeble—as to how the body decides the moment has come.

One theory is that the vastly enlarged uterus has been stretched beyond its endurance. The uterus expresses itself by contracting in an effort to expel the irritant—the baby. Another theory is that the body chooses this moment to produce a mysterious chemical which inaugurates labor, but no such chemical has ever been found.

A third theory has some support in experimental evidence. Just before the birth process begins, there is a dramatically sharp decline in the amounts of sex hormones circulating in the blood. It appears possible that the placenta has become senile and is no longer able to produce the hormones which have made the uterus lie quiet for nine months. In any case, this rapid decline of hormones in the blood stream is a signal that labor is about to begin. The uterus, which is made up almost entirely of muscular tissue, starts rhythmic contractions.

How birth takes place

The head of the baby—over 95 percent of all babies are head downward at the time of birth—pushes with increasing force against the cervix. This opening, no larger than a pencil lead in nonpregnant women, must expand to four or five inches. To achieve this, relatively enormous forces are required. It has been shown, for example, that a pull of as much as 100 pounds is required for a forceps delivery.

Once again, the uterus has prepared itself for the job awaiting it. As pregnancy advanced, it grew thicker and stronger at its upper levels, adding new strands of muscle tissue. At lower levels, it grew thinner. Thus, when the moment arrives, it will be able to apply the greatest forces where they are most needed.

So a new life comes into the world—to greet the world with a cry of rage with its first lungful of air. It is not a wonder that there are so many people on this earth. It is a wonder that there are any at all. For the process which created each man or woman is a miracle almost beyond comprehension.

Chapter II

Care during the waiting period

The good care you're determined to give your baby begins, not the day he is born, but the day you realize that he has probably been conceived. And even before that—for in the years prior to this time, your good health, good nutrition, and good physical development have all been building up to contribute to your baby's well-being.

Right now, taking care of your baby means putting yourself immediately under the guidance of the doctor you have chosen, and following his instructions for keeping yourself in good health and rested and, most important of all, *well nourished*.

Happily, this kind of prenatal care pays double dividends. First, you're giving your baby the best chance to be strong and healthy; and second, you are helping to make your pregnancy comfortable, and your labor and delivery as easy as possible.

The first rule is to go to a doctor as soon as you think conception has taken place. Even though you have had children before, have come through without any difficulty whatever, and have no reason to feel you'll have difficulty this time, you will still be better off for consulting your doctor without delay. He would rather have you consult him at the very beginning so he can manage and make this period in your life as comfortable for you as possible.

He will give you a thorough examination and will take a specimen of your blood for testing early in your pregnancy.

He'll make note of your initial weight, blood pressure, measurements, and urinalysis. These records will be an invaluable aid to him in later months in determining your weight gain, and whether there has been any important change in your urine.

Many serious complications can sometimes be avoided by the early examination your doctor makes, and regular checkups thereafter.

Signs of pregnancy

How can you tell if you're pregnant?

Usually, the first sign is a missed period. If you're very regular, and go over 10 days or more, you'll begin to surmise that conception has taken place. If you miss two periods, it's fairly certain. If you've gone over your period and begin feeling nauseated in the mornings, or start urinating frequently, you'd better see your doctor.

There are other signs by which your doctor judges—for one, the breasts grow larger, and the brown circle around the nipple widens—though sometimes it's hard for him to be sure before about the third month. In times of stress especially, women sometimes simulate the symptoms of pregnancy. It's not at all uncommon for a bride, though she isn't pregnant, to skip a period and even feel morning nausea because the possibility of pregnancy is in her thoughts.

If you must find out immediately whether you're really pregnant, there's the rabbit test which is about 95 percent accurate. You might ask your doctor about it. There is no need for it, however, unless you've a reason for wanting an early, accurate diagnosis.

During the first half or so of pregnancy, if all goes well, you should visit your doctor once a month. In the latter half, he may ask you to come every two or three weeks, and in the last month or so, perhaps every week. When you first go to your doctor, ask him about his charges. Have an understanding as to how his fee is to be paid—whether in advance, as you go, or at the conclusion of your pregnancy.

Your doctor's part, as he'll no doubt emphasize, isn't so much to treat you as a patient, as to manage your pregnancy so you'll remain comfortable and happy.

When to expect your baby

The doctor will probably give you a date on which your baby may be expected, but don't hold him to it too closely! The lengths of pregnancies may vary and still be normal, and sometimes there are other factors which make close calculation difficult. The doctors usually figure on 280 days, or 10 lunar months. The method is simple. Count back three calendar months from the first day of your last menstrual period, and add seven days. Let's say that your last period began on December 16. Count back three months to September 16, and add seven days, which makes the expected date of your baby's birth next September 23. Remember, though, that this is only a stab in the dark, since neither your doctor nor anyone else knows just how long it will take your baby to get ready to be born. With a first baby especially, two weeks one way or the other is nothing at which to be surprised.

Your frequent trips to the doctor toward the end, and his examination of the baby's heartbeats, will assure you that all's well, and that when your baby gets ready, he'll be coming along! Don't urge your doctor to hurry things. If he decides the birth should be hastened, he'll take proper measures.

Activities which are permitted

What you do at this time depends upon what you have been in the habit of doing previously. If you are accustomed to playing golf and driving a car, you may continue in moderation, provided your doctor consents and you feel no ill effects. Swimming should not be risked unless the water is unquestionably clean and not cold. Violent exercise, such as horseback riding, tennis, and dancing, may be harmful. The important thing is to avoid exhaustion. A good rule is to stop *before* you're tired, not after.

Be sure to talk these matters over with your doctor. Ask him also about driving a car after the sixth month. He may consider it all right in your case, but under some circumstances he may prefer that you don't.

If you're accustomed to doing your own housework, you'll benefit by continuing to do it, provided you delegate the heavy tasks to others and don't overtire yourself.

The "stop *before* you're tired" rule applies to housework as well as any other form of exercise. If you feel that you are becoming tired during a task, stop and rest awhile before completing it.

If you continue working at a job during your pregnancy, take advantage of rest periods and really rest! Lie down, if facilities are available, even though it is only for short periods.

If you're not accustomed to exercise or housework, it may prove unwise for you to begin at this time. On the other hand, some exercise is a necessity, but it should conform, as nearly as possible, to your usual habits.

The best answer to the exercise problem is to take two walks a day, in the morning and evening, beginning with short ones and gradually increasing them to any amount which doesn't tire you. The rest of the time, stay in the open air as much as you can. Most doctors advise a healthy woman to walk every day even though she's doing some housework.

Should you travel?

Your doctor must decide how much traveling you ought to do, and pass upon the means of transportation. Long auto trips tire many pregnant women, and in some cases, perhaps, have been instrumental in producing miscarriages. If there's a good reason why you should take one, plan to take it by easy stages. Boat trips are all right if the water isn't rough.

Airplane travel seems to do no harm unless you suffer from nausea.

If you must travel, trains or planes are recommended. During the last two months of pregnancy, it's wise for you to stay in your own city, or to go to the locality where you are expecting to be confined and remain there.

You need fresh air

The old theory that the expectant mother must eat twice as much as usual has been exploded. But it's coming to be understood that the expectant mother must breathe for two. Hence it's very essential that you have plenty of pure air. You should be outdoors in the daytime as much as you can. The rooms in which you spend any time during the day must be well ventilated, as your bedroom should be at night.

Smoking and liquor

Opinion is divided as to the effects of smoking during pregnancy. A cigarette now and then would seem to do no harm. If you're a heavy smoker, doctors advise that you cut down to a great extent, but you needn't quit entirely, unless your doctor recommends it.

Alcoholic drinks place an added strain on the kidneys at this time and should be indulged in rarely, if at all. It's best to consult your doctor about this matter, too.

Intercourse

Sexual relations are permitted up to the last six weeks of pregnancy. It is advisable to avoid intercourse during the time each month when you would be having your menstrual period if you were not pregnant. There's a greater tendency to miscarry at these times; so it's best not to take any chances. Refrain from intercourse altogether during the last six weeks of pregnancy.

Baby grows on what you eat

Since your baby, before birth, grows and develops according to what you eat, your diet is most important.

We know now that as an expectant mother you don't need any more food than at any other time, but the quality of the food you eat is enormously significant.

It's true that you're eating for your baby as well as yourself, yet you mustn't get fat. Excess weight may cause complications during your pregnancy and at the time of delivery, and is mighty hard to get rid of afterward! The up-to-date doctor therefore "weighs in" his patients when they come for their regular examinations, and in most cases insists that they don't gain more than 18 pounds.

This means that without eating any more than you did before, you must include all the food elements your baby needs for the very best development.

The dangers of a poor diet during pregnancy

Studies made in recent years in hospitals and research centers have proved conclusively that the baby's development can be seriously affected if the mother's diet during pregnancy is deficient, particularly in certain minerals and vitamins. These babies may be light in weight and too short. The development of their bones and teeth may be hampered. And they are believed to be more subject to infant illnesses than the babies of mothers who have had good diets.

In addition to the possible effect of a poor diet on the baby, it can also cause trouble for you. It may result in more difficult labor, major complications, even the loss of your baby because of prematurity or stillbirth. Moreover, a poor prenatal diet can interfere with your ability to nurse your child.

So, you see, the importance of the best possible diet all through your pregnancy cannot be overemphasized.

Your baby is developing continuously and needs these vital food elements every day. Many of the needed vitamins *cannot* be stored up, so you can't just eat a good diet one day, then backslide for a few days, thinking you've done your duty.

Learn the good foods

On the next few pages, the foods you should and should not have are discussed. Learn the good foods, then stick to them every day. Father-to-be can help by adopting this best-food plan, too. If you don't have to order or prepare foods you shouldn't have, you'll be less tempted to eat them. Not only will you and the baby benefit, but your husband will be healthier as well.

You need milk for calcium

Milk contains the minerals needed for the baby's skeleton and teeth, and in a form that makes it easy for both you and the baby to use. It's also a rich source of proteins, which build tissues; carbohydrates needed for energy; and important vitamins.

Whole milk, it's true, is fattening. You allow for that by cutting out other fattening foods which are sweet and starchy, and which don't begin to give you as much nourishment in proportion to their calories.

If you seem to gain more weight than you should, in spite of cutting out sweets, starches, and other fattening foods, ask your doctor about substituting skimmed milk for whole milk. Whole milk is preferred for the vitamin A in its butterfat. If you use skimmed milk, your doctor will suggest some additional source of vitamin A.

You should have a quart of milk each day.

It may be taken as a beverage with your meals or between meals, or you may drink part and use the remainder in foods, such as cream soups, custards, creamed vegetables, and the like. Drink your milk as a beverage if possible, though. It's much the simplest way of getting your full quota every day.

The milk may be fresh pasteurized, or evaporated. Evaporated milk supplies the same elements as fresh milk.

In fact, it's a good idea to take at least part of your daily milk requirement in evaporated milk. Physicians who specialize in the study of allergies tell us that large amounts of any one food can sensitize your unborn baby and make him allergic to that food. This is especially true in families with a history of allergies. They recommend that part of the large milk intake during pregnancy be in "allergenically denatured" form. Evaporated milk is considered to be allergenically denatured because of its heat-processing. A pint (16 ounces) of evaporated milk diluted with an equal amount of water is the equivalent of a quart of whole milk.

If you don't like to drink milk, try slightly diluted evaporated milk in cooking or on your cereal. Since it is concentrated, it will give you more nutritional value with less fluid. Or mix powdered milk with other foods, thus getting your milk in a highly concentrated form.

Some years ago it was thought that calcium, taken in capsules or wafers, might replace milk in the diet of those who dislike it, but this substitution isn't wholly satisfactory, since calcium is but one of the minerals supplied by milk. In milk, you get needed minerals, vitamins, and growth protein. So, unless you're markedly allergic to milk, you're advised to get your calcium from milk or cheese, which has food value similar to milk. Cheese made from whole milk, such as American (cheddar) cheese, may be substituted for part of your milk requirement. A 1-ounce cube of yellow American cheese, about an inch and a quarter square, has about the same amount of calcium, phosphorus, proteins, and vitamins as a 6-ounce glass of whole milk. Cheese, because it is such a concentrated food, shouldn't be used to replace more than one glass of milk in your day's diet.

Cottage cheese is rich in protein but not as rich in calcium. It would take about 10 tablespoons of cottage cheese to get the calcium contained in a glass of milk. Therefore, while cottage cheese is an excellent food, it should be used in addition to instead of in place of milk.

If you gain too much weight, cut down on something else—not on milk. If you find milk constipating, try the suggestions made later under the care of the bowels. But don't cut out milk!

You need iron, too

Second in the list of needs for you, and especially for your baby, comes iron. There's some tendency toward anemia on a mother's part during pregnancy. This is counteracted by iron. Also, your baby is storing iron in his liver to last him for some months after he's born. So you must eat iron-rich foods. In addition, your doctor may supplement your diet with iron in pure form.

Here are the foods that are considered excellent sources of iron:

Eggs (particularly egg yolk)

Liver, heart, kidney, lean meat, ox tongue, turkey, beef juice

Oysters, fish

Milk

Barley, whole wheat, wheat germ, bran, farina, rolled oats, enriched breads and cereals

Dried apricots, dried peaches, dried figs, prunes and raisins, molasses, sorghum

Navy, soy, and kidney beans, lentils, dried peas

Yeast extracts

Broccoli, Brussels sprouts, cabbage

Green leafy vegetables, i.e., chard, spinach, collards, kale, mustard greens, turnip greens, wild greens, salad greens

Potatoes, boiled or baked in the skin.

You need adequate iodine

Your baby depends on you for his iodine compounds during the prenatal and nursing periods. So essential is it, that a deficiency of iodine can retard mental development and cause serious physical defects in your child. But since iodine is lacking in the soil of certain localities and therefore in the food raised there, this element may not be supplied by your diet and must be provided in some other form. The best sources of iodine are iodized salt, cod-liver oil, and sea-water fish. It is sometimes necessary to supplement the diet with a medicinal source of iodine, but this must be done only on the advice of your physician.

You need vitamins more than ever

Vitamins are substances which are present in minute quantities in food and yet are indispensable for life, health, and growth. They are essential for everyone, but the demand for all vitamins is greatly increased during pregnancy and the nursing period. Since the average American diet is frequently deficient in certain vitamins, you must keep them in mind and see that all the vitamins are amply supplied by your diet. Vitamins are so important that your doctor may supplement those you receive in your food with "multivitamin" capsules, as an added measure of safety.

Set out below are the vitamins most likely to be deficient in your diet, what each is needed for, and the foods which supply them best. Many of the foods listed above as being rich in calcium, phosphorus, or iron, also supply some of the vitamins. Where they are particularly good sources of certain vitamins, we will name them again.

Vitamin A

Needed for: Normal growth; smooth, soft skin; healthy mucous membrane; strong bones and teeth; good nerve and eye development; resistance to infections.

Best sources: Butterfat; cream; whole milk; cheese; egg yolk; liver; yellow vegetables, especially carrots; green leafy vegetables; fish-liver oils; food products fortified with vitamin A.

Vitamin B₁ (thiamin)

Needed for: Normal functioning of nerves, heart; proper use of carbohydrates by the body; healthy appetite; good digestion of food; good elimination; growth; resistance to infection; prevention of fatigue.

Best sources: Pork; heart, liver, and kidney; whole-grain and enriched breads and cereals;

wheat germ; peas; soy and Lima beans; egg yolk; tomatoes; baked potatoes; oranges, grapefruit, pineapple; dried brewer's yeast.

Vitamin B₂ (riboflavin) (also called vitamin G)

Needed for: Growth; vitality; appetite and digestion; nervous system; skin and eye tissues.

Best sources: Liver, kidney; egg yolk; whole milk; cheese; green leafy vegetables; dried soy and Lima beans, dried peas; dried brewer's yeast; wheat germ; enriched cereals.

Niacin (another component of the vitamin-B complex, also called nicotinic acid)

Needed for: Normal digestion and assimilation; healthy skin; the nervous system; growth. Prevents, and is a remedy for pellagra.

Best sources: Milk; egg yolk; lean meat, meat extracts; heart, kidney, liver; chicken; canned salmon; wheat germ; enriched cereals; whole wheat and rye; brown rice; mushrooms; tomatoes; yeast.

Vitamin C (ascorbic acid)

Needed for: Growth; healthy bones, teeth, gums; intracellular material; strong blood vessels; blood regeneration; tissue respiration; healing of wounds; resistance to infections.

Best sources: Oranges, grapefruit, lemons; tomatoes; potatoes (particularly new potatoes); berries; cantaloupe; fresh raw cabbage; green peppers.

Vitamin D

Needed for: Growth; strong bones and teeth; helping body utilize calcium and phosphorus.

Best sources: Fish-liver oils or their concentrates; foods fortified with vitamin D; the "dispersible" varieties of vitamin D, in solution or dry form, which may be added to milk; exposing the skin to sunlight.

Vitamin E

Needed for: Thought to be necessary for the normal development of the fetus and the completion of pregnancy.

Best sources: Its distribution is so widespread that vitamin E is generally supplied by any balanced diet. Lettuce, water cress, and wheat germ are foods high in this vitamin.

Vitamin K

Needed for: Normal clotting of blood and prevention of hemorrhage.

Best sources: Most diets contain adequate quantities. Egg yolk, liver, spinach, kale, soy-bean oil, tomatoes, and cauliflower are all good sources of this vitamin. An injection of this vitamin may be given before delivery.

Save the vitamins and minerals

Since many of the vitamins are lost on exposure to heat and air, uncooked fruits and vegetables should be included in the diet every day. Some of the vitamins and minerals may be absorbed by the water in which foods are cooked. Cook foods quickly, in a covered container and in a small amount of water. And use the water in sauces and soups.

Cook foods in their skins to save minerals.

Use the freshest possible fruits and vegetables. Keep them in a cool place to prevent wilting, or vitamins may be lost. Avoid reheating cooked foods when possible.

Vitamin C is lost very rapidly when exposed to air; so prepare citrus fruit juices and salads just before eating.

Canned, glassed, or frozen vegetables and fruit juices can be used as well as fresh ones. Save the liquid from canned foods to use in soups and desserts.

Proteins build the new life

The calcium and phosphorus in milk supply the framework of your baby's body, but proteins provide the actual building materials. So proteins in adequate amounts are essential in your diet. Formerly, there was a tendency to restrict the protein in the diet during pregnancy in the belief that this would lessen the chances of toxemia. Now, there appears to be no foundation for this idea. On the other hand, it has been found that liver damage, edema, and anemia may be the result of too little protein in pregnancy. Actually, the woman who is pregnant requires about 50 percent more protein than she normally would. So doctors now feel that a large amount of protein is usually desirable.

Meat, eggs, milk, and cheese are our richest sources of protein. These last two have already been discussed. Meat and eggs are practically equal in value as sources of protein.

Eggs, besides being concentrated protein, are rich in iron and vitamins. Remember, you're harboring a little iron-hoarder; so eat at least one egg every day (unless you're allergic to eggs). Most doctors also advise a serving (about $\frac{1}{4}$ pound) of lean meat every day, with liver at least once a week. Chicken, lamb, mutton, veal, kidney, heart, lean pork, and lean beef are allowed.

Liver contains iron, copper, and valuable vitamins in addition to its protein, so it gives extra value. Oysters are only a little behind liver in these respects and may be eaten liberally when you can get them.

Fresh fish is also excellent, and sea food is especially good because it contains iodine. Boil or broil the fish. Or you may fry it, if you drain off the extra fat.

Choose the best carbohydrates

Carbohydrates, the energy foods, are needed in pregnancy as at other times. These include cereals, breads, potatoes, and various sweets. While they're fattening foods and need to be taken rather sparingly, they have a definite place in your diet, especially whole-grain breads and cereals.

Recent research has shown that vitamin B, found in the germ and shell of wheat, is particularly vital to pregnant women; so you'll need more vitamin B now than at other times. Choose the breads and cereals you eat, therefore, from either the whole-wheat or enriched variety, so you'll get these needed vitamins along with the energy. Eat at least three slices of whole-wheat or enriched breads, buttered, every day. Eat a whole-grain or enriched cereal every day for breakfast or supper.

Need for vitamin D

No matter how much milk you drink, vitamin D is needed to help your body use the bone-building calcium and phosphorus milk contains. You may get some vitamin D by taking sunbaths in summertime, but it's an added precaution to take a teaspoon of cod-liver oil every day in summer, and 2 teaspoons of cod-liver oil daily the rest of the year.

Vitamin D can be obtained in other forms besides cod-liver oil, and your doctor may prescribe one of these. He will tell you also the amount to take, as it varies with the product chosen. There are other fish-liver oils, vitamin D concentrates, vitamin D tablets and capsules, dispersible vitamin D in solution or dry form which can be added to your milk or other foods, and "multivitamin" capsules, which supply other vitamins as well as vitamin D. Many doctors now prescribe multivitamin capsules, as this is one of the simplest ways to be certain you'll get adequate vitamin D plus other needed vitamins. One multivitamin capsule a day is the usual recommendation.

In addition, most canned milk and some pasteurized fresh milk is now being "fortified" by the addition of vitamin D when the milk is processed. If you consume a full quart of fortified fresh milk or a 13-ounce can of fortified evaporated milk, you will get 400 International Units of vitamin D. However, since the recommended amount of vitamin D during pregnancy is 400 to 800 International Units daily, your doctor may prescribe additional vitamin D supplement to your diet.

Dietary "musts" in pregnancy

Here are the foods which you should eat *every day* for your own well-being, and to enable your baby to grow as you would like him to do:

1. Milk. One quart. (Or its equivalent in evaporated or powdered milk, and cheese.)

2. Vegetables. Two or more servings of cooked vegetables and one liberal serving of raw vegetables. A serving is 4 heaping tablespoonfuls or ½ measuring cup. Include some dark green leafy or deep yellow vegetables every day. One small potato, boiled or baked in the skin. (Potato, in addition to its other nutritional value, furnishes vitamin C and iron.)

3. Fruit and fruit juices. One measuring cup (8 ounces) of unstrained orange juice, or the juice of other citrus fruit or tomato in amounts that will supply as much vitamin C as 1 cup of orange juice. For instance, ¾ measuring cup (6 ounces) of grapefruit juice equals ½ cup of orange juice; 1 cup of tomato juice equals ½ cup of orange juice; ½ cup of strawberries, ¼ cantaloupe, or 2 tangerines are also equal to ½ cup of orange juice. In addition to meeting your vitamin C requirements, eat at least one other serving of fruit each day. Dried fruits are excellent sources of iron—apricots, especially—and they're also high in vitamin A.

Liberal amounts of fruits also help prevent constipation.

4. Meat, fish, or fowl. At least one serving.

5. At least one egg.

6. Whole-grain or enriched cereals. One serving.

7. Whole-wheat or enriched breads. Three slices.

8. Butter or fortified margarine. About 3 teaspoonfuls.

9. Vitamin D as prescribed by your doctor.

Amount of liquids daily

If your weight gain is too rapid, or your doctor tells you to limit liquids, restrict your total daily intake of all liquids to 6 to 8 glasses. This will include milk, fruit juices, tea, coffee, water, soups, and other beverages.

Foods NOT to eat

Avoid foods rich in fats, sugars, and starches, such as gravies, bacon, mayonnaise, fat meats, doughnuts, potato chips, macaroni, spaghetti, rice, pies, pastries, cakes, rich puddings, ice cream, candy, ginger ale, other soft drinks, popcorn, peanuts, and the like. Reject food that's highly spiced or seasoned, and condiments of all kinds.

Use salt sparingly because it encourages retention of water in the tissues, and there's considerable tendency to that anyway during pregnancy. When you're cooking, cut down on the amount of salt you normally add to foods and don't add any more at the table. Foods, such as bacon, ham, salt pork, salt fish, chipped beef, and other salty prepared meats and dark rye bread should not be used.

A good diet during pregnancy

Breakfast:

4 ounces of orange juice (or its equivalent in citrus fruits)

¾ cup whole-grain cereal, with sugar or honey and whole milk

1 slice buttered toast (whole-wheat or enriched bread) (1 teaspoon of butter or fortified margarine)

1 egg

1 cup coffee

10 a.m.

1 glass of milk

Luncheon:

Sandwich (2 slices whole-wheat or enriched bread with filling of tuna, salmon, cheese, lean meat, or egg)

1 serving raw or cooked vegetable

1 glass of milk

½ cup any kind of fruit or berries, or 1 piece of melon, or 1 peach, pear, apple, or the like

3 p.m.

1 glass of milk

Dinner:

4 ounces (¼ pound) lean meat, fish, or fowl

1 small potato, cooked in skin

½ cup cooked vegetables

1 liberal serving raw vegetable salad

1 glass of milk (may be taken at bedtime)

½ cup orange juice or its equivalent in citrus fruit

1 multivitamin capsule, or vitamin D in the form that has been prescribed by your doctor

Iron or other vitamin supplement if prescribed by your doctor

(The remaining 2 teaspoonfuls of butter or fortified margarine allowed each day may be used on your cooked vegetables; or 1 teaspoon of olive or vegetable oil may be substituted in a dressing for your salad).

Ideally, it's probably a better practice to have your large meal at noon, and a lighter one at night. The majority of American families, however, have their dinner at night, and the point is not important enough for you to prepare one kind of meal for your family and another for yourself.

If your family's large meal is at noon, eat the "dinner" which has been suggested for that time, and the meal called "luncheon" at suppertime.

Care of the bowels

It's easy to understand that you need to keep your bowels functioning regularly, since the waste products of the baby's body as well as of your own must be carried off through your excretory system. As far as possible, the bowels should be controlled through diet and regular habits.

If you choose your foods from the list just given and eat large quantities of vegetables and fruits, you should have little trouble. Should you have a tendency to constipation, the following foods will be especially helpful: cream, oatmeal, green vegetables, figs, dates, stewed fruits, prunes, oranges, baked apples, and whole-wheat bread.

The other constipation preventive is regularity in going to the toilet. If you haven't already done so, you should form the habit of going to the toilet every morning after breakfast and staying there for some time. Don't strain to force the movement. Instead, relax as much as possible. This practice, combined with the diet described, will in most cases establish a daily movement.

If you need further help, try this regimen:

1. Drink a glass of warm water when you get up.

2. Eat a coarse, laxative cereal, such as oatmeal, for breakfast, with one of the laxative fruits just mentioned. Marmalade on your toast is also a stimulus to bowel action.

3. Eat some fruit before going to bed at night.

4. Use mineral oil in dressing for your salad, *but only if constipated*. Mineral oil decreases absorption of vitamins. Don't take any other laxative (mineral oil is really only a lubricant) except on doctor's orders.

Care of the kidneys

The importance of the kidneys at this time is recognized in the regular examination of urine which every reliable doctor gives his obstetrical cases. Aside from having this examination, you usually need to do nothing except drink the six to eight glasses of liquids a day already mentioned and observe the other hygienic rules. In early and late pregnancy, there's a tendency to urinate frequently because at these times the uterus presses upon the bladder and urethra. There's nothing abnormal about this. If, however, the urine becomes scanty, hard to pass, dark colored, or has a strong odor, have your doctor examine a specimen at once.

Signs of danger

If any of the following occur between your visits to the doctor, don't delay, but let him know *AT ONCE!*

1. Swelling of the face, hands, or feet

2. Dimness or blurring of vision

3. Pain in the abdomen

4. Fever

5. Any vaginal bleeding

6. Persistent vomiting

7. Continuous headache

8. A rush of water from the vagina

9. A hard fall. If you have one, go to bed, notify your doctor, and be examined for any signs of danger.

These may be of slight importance, but on the other hand, they may indicate a condition that needs immediate attention. Only your doctor can decide.

Take care of your teeth

There is a tendency toward decay in the teeth of pregnant women. This may be because the fetus helps himself to the stores of calcium in his mother's body if his needs are not supplied by her diet; or it may be that the child-bearing years occur at the same periods when teeth ordinarily show signs of decay. Whatever the cause, you should be under the watchful eye of your dentist as well as of your doctor.

It won't injure your baby in any way for the dentist to work on your teeth, and it's wise to arrest any decay that shows itself.

Consult your dentist early in pregnancy and have a thorough dental checkup. It's desirable to have the necessary work done as early in pregnancy as possible. Try to make dental appointments for times other than the period of each month when you would usually be menstruating, as you may be more emotionally upset at those times than generally. If it's necessary to have a tooth extracted, arrange the extraction so as to avoid those periods—for the same reason. It is better to have teeth extracted under local anesthetic rather than under gas. Gas deprives the body of oxygen, and thus would decrease the amount of oxygen available to the fetus from your blood stream.

Brush your teeth after every meal, and use an alkaline mouthwash night and morning. Ask your dentist if he recommends any particular type of tooth paste or powder, or mouthwash.

Care of the nipples

The condition of your nipples when your baby is born will have a good deal to do with your success or failure in nursing him. If your nipples are stiff and hard, it will be difficult for the baby to get milk from them. Later, in the section dealing with the feeding of the newborn baby, the way to handle the nursing to make it as pleasant as possible will be described. But now's the time to condition your nipples for the task ahead.

The first requisite is absolute cleanliness. The nipples should be washed every morning with mild soap and water. Then dash cold water over them lightly to toughen them. If the nipples are stiff or hard, you may cover them with petroleum jelly, lanolin, or warm cocoa butter. Place little squares of clean linen or gauze over them to protect your clothes.

Any time from the fourth month on, some fluid may come from the nipples, sometimes enough that your clothes must be protected by pads. If the fluid stays on the nipples, it may make them sore. They should be washed often. If crusts form, wash the nipples gently with tepid boiled water, then anoint as has been described.

If you have inverted nipples—that is, if they sink into the breast instead of pointing out—spend five minutes each day gently drawing them out between thumb and finger. You may use cocoa butter for this massage.

Use an uplift type of brassiere, which pulls the breasts up and out and doesn't press on the nipples. Never wear a brassiere which presses the nipples in, as this makes nursing more difficult for your baby.

If cracks appear in your nipples, wash them

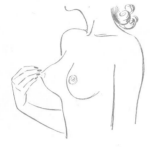

If you have inverted nipples, spend five minutes a day drawing them out gently

with tepid boiled water and keep them covered with sterile gauze. Report the condition to your doctor.

Streaks on the abdomen

The streaks or lines which often appear on the abdomen, and even down on the thighs, result from overstretching of your skin. You may succeed in keeping these streaks (which are called "striae") to a minimum if you watch your weight diligently. Don't gain too rapidly. And unless your physician directs otherwise, limit your daily fluid intake to 6 glasses of all liquids. Excess fluids are frequently retained in your tissues and the resulting overdistention can cause striae.

The streaks may be lessened also by wearing a girdle which supports the weight of your expanding abdomen.

Some authorities recommend massaging your abdomen with cocoa butter or cold cream every day during the last four months to ease the stretched condition of your skin. This may or may not help avoid the streaking, but it does no harm to try it.

The marks will lighten in time, after delivery, but never disappear entirely.

Baths

A daily bath is desirable. However, it should not be either steaming hot or so cold that you become chilled, and you must be careful not to slip in the tub, or in getting in or out of the tub. Place a mat or towel in the bottom of the tub to prevent accidents.

During the last six weeks of pregnancy, shower baths are preferable to avoid introducing infection into the vagina. If you have

no shower, take all-over sponge baths standing at the washbasin, or put a few inches of water in the tub and kneel in it to bathe.

Clothing

Rules for dressing at this time are simple:

1. No tight elastic or other bands, either at the waist or around the legs.

2. All clothing to hang from the shoulders as much as possible, so its weight does not come at the waist.

3. Nothing tight or confining, especially over the breasts, waist, and abdomen.

Unless your physician recommends otherwise, you may get adequate support and comfort from an ordinary "two-way stretch" girdle. It should be of a size large enough for absolute comfort. Discontinue wearing one size as soon as there is the least suggestion of snugness, and obtain another girdle in a sufficiently larger size. There should be no re-

An uplift type of brassiere should be worn if support is needed. Take care that your brassiere does not press on your nipples or bind at the bottom

inforcing panels or stays in such a girdle, and it should not be the panty-type girdle.

If you have any discomfort from backache, or feel the need for more support, a well-fitted maternity girdle will help. The best practice is to ask your doctor to recommend one for you.

The best type of shoe for pregnancy is a low-heeled, broad-toed one. You'll have a tendency to a swaybacked and teetering posture anyway, since you're carrying so much extra weight in front. High heels would throw you even more off balance. However, if you're used to wearing high heels and feel uncomfortable in any other kind, medical authorities allow you a heel not more than an inch and a half high. Wedge-soled sandals are not advisable.

Ingenious maternity dresses and slack suits may be bought or made which will help your morale greatly. For street wear, a three-quarter length flaring coat is good. Under it your figure may swell and swell!

Well-designed maternity clothes are good for morale. Make them yourself or buy inexpensive ready-mades

Some of the loveliest figures you see belong to mothers of one or more tots. Soon yours will be slender again

Your underwear or "briefs" should fit closely around your thighs, as a sanitary precaution. However, they must not bind at the waist or legs. Be sure to dress warmly enough, as it's important to avoid becoming chilled.

You'll be sylphlike again

As you get more and more ungainly, you may be haunted by a fear that you're going to stay that way. The walking or other mild exercises prescribed for you will help keep good muscle tone. Your abdomen may sag for a time after your baby's birth, but that's a temporary condition, too. Good posture, attention to diet, and exercises as described on pages 51-54, if your doctor agrees, will bring your waistline into bounds again. Many of the lovely figures you see going up and down the street belong to women who have had one or more babies.

Follow instructions about not getting heavier than is necessary, and don't worry!

Take precautions but live normally

Your pregnancy is exciting to you and, if it's your first, it's even a little mysterious and awe-inspiring. That's as it should be. On the other hand, pregnancy is no excuse for making an invalid of yourself or for upsetting your normal life. Proof of this is the number of women who have worked outside their homes all through their pregnancies, some right up to the very day of delivery. They're well and happy the whole time, and their babies are fine, healthy youngsters.

Common sense dictates that you take some precautions. Otherwise, follow your usual daily routine. Here are the few precautions you need to observe:

1. Avoid anyone with a cold, and especially anyone with an infectious or contagious disease. Because many diseases are transmitted before definite diagnosis can be made, stay away from any person who seems to be coming down with an illness.

An infection, while it may not affect you at all, can be a serious danger to your baby. This is particularly true of German measles (rubella). This disease lasts but a few days, and may not make you very ill, but can have damaging effect on the fetus, especially if you contract the disease during the first three months of pregnancy. If you know that one of your own children, or a child in your household, has been exposed to German measles, turn over the care of the youngster to another adult and stay well away from him.

2. Plenty of rest is important. You should have at least eight and preferably nine hours' sleep every night, and a rest during the day. During the early months especially, you may have spells of unusual drowsiness during the day. Don't fight the sleepiness. Just go ahead and take a nap, no matter how short. If you are working and can't rest during the day, get in an extra hour or more of sleep at night.

3. Pay particular attention to your doctor's diet instructions. Familiarize yourself with the foods that are best for good nutrition and why each group of foods is essential; see pages 24-28.

4. Avoid violent exercise; activities that require jumping or sharp, jerky motions, and lifting or pushing heavy objects. Don't climb stairs any more than is absolutely necessary, and avoid running up- and downstairs.

5. Avoid standing still for long periods, and long drives or trips.

6. Get as much fresh air and sunshine as possible.

7. Avoid becoming chilled.

8. Refrain from intercourse during the time each month when you would normally menstruate, and do not have intercourse at all during the last month or six weeks before delivery.

9. Continue your outside interests, including seeing friends, as much as possible.

10. See your doctor at the regular times he has set, and report to him immediately any unusual symptoms.

Don't worry if a friend's doctor has recommended something different for her than your physician has for you. Your doctor knows your case best and has your welfare in mind. He has his own reasons for whatever instructions he has given you. It's just as well *not* to compare notes with other pregnant women, or friends who have had babies.

Life

Toward the end of the fourth month of pregnancy, your baby will begin to stir inside you. Your awareness of his first movements is often referred to as "feeling life." It will feel something like the fluttering of a bird. Later, as he gains strength, you will think your unborn urchin is turning somersaults.

If you're a working woman

Your condition will become rather readily apparent by the fifth month. If your appearance is important in your work, you'll want to quit, or arrange to work at home after that.

Perhaps it doesn't matter whether or not you look pregnant, but your work may keep you on your feet or be otherwise physically tiring. Then you should quit two months before your baby's birth and spend the time resting and getting things ready for him in leisurely fashion. However, if yours is a "sitting" job and you enjoy it enough to stay on, follow your own wishes about keeping or discontinuing it.

Don't plan to return to work until your baby is at least 6 weeks old, and not then if you are nursing him. Unless it is absolutely necessary for you to work, think it over carefully before you leave your baby in the care of someone else every day. He needs you! And the job may not really pay after figuring expenses.

Arrange with the hospital

Your doctor will probably recommend a hospital to which he wants you to go. Many doctors prefer to make their own arrangements. If yours does not, it is best to go in person to the hospital, learn the rates, and indicate your choice. You would be wise to attend to this important matter early.

It may be necessary for you to share a room with another woman, or even with several. Many mothers have found that this helps the time to go more pleasantly. Hospital rates are quoted according to the kind of room you get, and whether or not you share it with one or more other persons. They include board and nursing service, but there's an extra charge for the delivery room, medicines, drugs, and dressings. In a normal delivery, the hospital's nursing service is quite adequate.

When you arrange for your room, ask what you're to bring for yourself and for the baby. Different hospitals have different rules about this.

Rooming-in

In the last few years, many hospitals have started what is known as "rooming-in" programs. The term rooming-in means that the newborn baby, very soon after delivery, is placed in a crib at his mother's bedside. There he stays as long as his mother remains in the hospital. He is removed from his mother's bedside only if he is so noisy at night as to disturb his mother and other patients, or if either he or his mother becomes ill.

Rooming-in has been enthusiastically approved, because it permits an intimate association between mother and baby almost from birth on. With this arrangement, you can reach your baby and the materials for his care. You change him, nurse him, or cuddle him as needs be. During the first twenty-four hours after delivery, the nurses take care of most of the baby's needs and, in the process, demonstrate to you the technique of nursing and attending to him. After that, you perform the routine care of your baby yourself.

Most mothers who have had their babies at their side in this fashion have enjoyed it immensely and go home feeling very confident of their ability to take over on their own. The babies are very contented rooming-in with their mothers and gain rapidly. And breast feeding seems to be established more easily with this system.

Your hospital may not as yet have arrangements for rooming-in; but if you're interested in it and want more information, or would like to have it, ask your doctor and your hospital if they have such accommodations.

Anesthetics or no anesthetics

You're probably wondering if you should have an anesthetic during labor and delivery. And if so, what kind? Since there are so many different kinds today, how do you know which is the safest and most effective?

During one of your regular visits to your doctor, ask him what his usual practice is in regard to anesthetics. He will tell you his preference and explain the reasons for his choice.

Each doctor has many things to consider before he decides which anesthetic to give his patient. Remember that whatever your doctor decides to do, he does because it's best for you and your baby. When the time comes, just relax and do what he tells you.

Analgesia and anesthesia may be two words you've heard frequently, but don't quite know the difference in meaning. They are the methods of relief used most often.

Analgesia

Analgesia means relief from pain or discomfort without loss of consciousness.

Analgesics are given in many forms—pills, capsules, hypodermically, rectally, or by inhalation. Since you are conscious, they do not prevent you from doing your share in the birth process during the second stage of labor.

Amnesia

There are also amnesiac drugs which allow the patient to remain conscious, but with little or no memory of discomfort.

Anesthetics

During anesthesia there is either partial or total unconsciousness. Anesthetics are administered hypodermically, rectally, or by inhalation. The list is growing each year as new discoveries are made, but the first and best-known is ether. Some others that your doctor may select are chloroform, nitrous oxide-oxygen, ethylene-oxygen, cyclopropane-oxygen, and sodium pentothal.

Caudal anesthesia

In recent years you've heard a lot about caudal anesthesia. It is a continuous injection of a drug at the base of the spine which blocks the nerves at the site of the delivery. Caudal anesthesia eliminates discomfort, yet allows the mother to remain conscious during delivery. Moreover, it does not depress the breathing of mother or baby.

Caudal anesthesia is not suitable for all women. First of all, it interferes with muscular action needed to push the baby downward through the birth canal. There are other individual circumstances, too, under which caudal anesthesia is not advisable. And finally, specially trained personnel are needed for administration.

Saddle block

Saddle block is the latest drug method known, and like caudal, is a local anesthesia. It, too, allows the mother to stay conscious and does not depress the baby's respiration.

The technique of administering this type of anesthesia is brief and simple. While the patient sits over the side of the bed, a fine needle is passed through the spine between two of the lower vertebrae, injecting a small amount of anesthetic such as nupercaine. The needle is removed, the patient lies down, and all discomfort disappears.

Like caudal anesthesia, saddle block cannot be used in all deliveries. It's not for people with diseases of the nervous system or spine, nor for those with low blood pressure.

Saddle block may cause a moderate to severe headache afterward, and the patient will require absolute bed rest for several days.

Both methods have definite advantages over inhalation anesthesia. They are most useful in the second stage of labor, while analgesic and amnesiac drugs are used during the first stage.

Twilight sleep

What does twilight sleep really mean? It's simply another name for amnesia (a state in which you remain conscious to assist in labor, yet have no memory of discomfort later).

Natural childbirth

In recent years you've heard a great deal about the natural process of childbirth as set forth by an English physician, Dr. Grantly Dick Read. He claims that if you know what is taking place and how to relax during the process, you'll feel very little discomfort. In other words, when you relax during labor, the muscles of the uterus are free to expel the child. Even though your doctor wishes to give you an anesthetic during delivery, you should take advantage of a course on natural childbirth if your community offers one.

Generally, such a course consists of lectures by physicians and nurses. Part of the time is devoted to instruction and part to exercising. They show you exactly what takes place during delivery. You learn muscular techniques and postural and breathing exercises to use during labor. If the course is given in the hospital where you are to be delivered, you may be shown the labor and delivery rooms, and introduced to the hospital nurses and doctors. Then when you enter for confinement, you'll be in a familiar place.

If you would like to know more about natural childbirth, and there are no classes available in your community, you can obtain an excellent book describing the instructions and exercises. It is *A Way to Natural Childbirth*, written by Helen Heardman, and published in the United States by Williams and Wilkens of Baltimore, Maryland.

Additional reading

Childbirth, by Carl Henry Davis, M. D., and Donita Ferguson, Harper & Brothers.

Expectant Motherhood by Nicholas J. Eastman, M. D., Little, Brown & Company.

Getting Ready to Be a Mother by Carolyn Van Blarcom and Hazel Corbin. Information about a home confinement. The Macmillan Company.

Getting Ready to Be a Father by Hazel Corbin. The Macmillan Company.

Manual for Teaching Midwives, Publication No. 260, of the U. S. Children's Bureau. Superintendent of Documents, Washington, D. C.

Chapter III

Routine and special tests
during pregnancy

Probably on your first visit to your doctor, or as soon as it is certain that you are pregnant, your doctor will check on your pelvic measurements. This is to determine whether your pelvis (the bony structure between your hips) is of adequate size for the baby to pass through. He will record your weight and blood pressure at every visit, and sometime during your pregnancy, he will make an internal examination by way of the vagina. This helps him determine the shape of your uterus, the construction of your pelvis, and whether or not everything concerning your Fallopian tubes, ovaries, cervix (the mouth of your uterus), and the vaginal passage is satisfactory.

As your pregnancy progresses, your doctor will make regular external examinations of your abdomen to listen to the baby's heart sounds, and to learn the size of your enlarging uterus, and the position of the baby.

In addition, he will make other tests, all of them for your welfare and that of your baby. To help you understand these tests, here are the most usual ones and why they are done:

Urinalysis

At each visit to his office, your doctor will probably request a specimen of your urine. He may have you bring a sample in a small bottle, or he may have arrangements in his office by which a fresh specimen of your urine can be obtained.

This regular examination of your urine is to check for albumin, which could indicate a developing toxemia; sugar, which might be a sign of diabetes; and pus cells and casts, which may mean a kidney infection.

Blood pressure

Your doctor will check your blood pressure during your regular examinations. This is a precaution so that any unusual rise above your normal pressure can be detected and treated.

Blood test for syphilis

Early in your pregnancy, your doctor will probably take a specimen of your blood for a Wasserman test to determine whether or not you may have syphilis. This test is compulsory in many states. The fact that your doctor has your blood tested does not mean that he suspects you may have the disease, although some women may have syphilis without being aware of it. If you should have it, your doctor must know it to begin treatment immediately. This is simply a precautionary measure to protect you and your child.

Hemoglobin concentration

Your doctor will also have your blood tested for its hemoglobin concentration. This is done because many women have anemia, and a low hemoglobin estimation will show it. Your doctor can then treat the anemia to prevent it from causing any difficulty.

The RH factor

Another test which your doctor may have made is for the RH factor. And he may examine the blood of your husband to determine his type.

RH is the name given by doctors to a factor found in the red blood cells of most people, which causes the cells to clump together when they come in contact with blood that doesn't contain the same factor. Persons who have this factor are called RH positive. Those who do not have it are known as RH negatives. It was named for the Rhesus monkeys because it was first detected in experiments with these animals.

If an RH negative person is given a transfusion of RH positive blood, antibodies are built up in the patient to attack the RH factor in the blood from the positive donor. Now that this reaction is known, physicians giving transfusions are always careful to use blood of the same type as the person receiving the transfusion.

In some pregnancies, a clash between the RH factor and the negative antibodies may have a harmful effect on the unborn child. But the chances of this complication occurring are very slight.

No complications from the RH factor can arise where both parents are the same type. Only when you are RH negative, and your husband and your child are RH positive, is there any possibility of trouble.

Even when this combination of blood types occurs, there is no likelihood of any complication in a first pregnancy, unless you have previously received a transfusion of RH positive blood.

Difficulty sometimes arises if an RH negative mother has had one or more pregnancies or an RH positive transfusion. When this is the case, the doctor may give injections during pregnancy to break down the antibodies in the mother's blood. However, many physicians do not feel that these shots have any effect.

In the very small percentage of such cases where a clash of blood types is found to have a serious effect on the newborn baby, doctors now give the baby a complete blood transfusion within 24 hours after birth, substituting RH negative blood for the baby's RH positive. This treatment usually results in a dramatic recovery.

Since complications due to the RH factor are so uncommon, your doctor may forego the tests for your RH type unless something in your history indicates its desirability.

Special tests

Other tests which your doctor may suggest you take are: a basal metabolism test which determines the activity of your thyroid gland; kidney function test; electrocardiograph examination of your heart activity; complete blood count if anemia is suspected; blood sugar test if your urinalysis indicates the possibility of diabetes; X-rays to check for tuberculosis, or to determine the structure of your pelvis.

Don't hesitate to follow your doctor's recommendations in such matters. Although you may be reluctant to spend the money on special tests, your doctor has your best interests in mind when he suggests them. Early detection and treatment of any unusual condition will be both to your advantage and to the advantage of your baby.

Chapter IV

If you don't feel well

Many women go through the whole period of pregnancy feeling better and looking lovelier than they ever did before. But you may have various discomforts which can be lessened by proper care. Serious complications sometimes develop, but these, too, may be avoided if you follow your doctor's instructions carefully.

Nausea and vomiting

The most common minor discomfort of pregnancy is "morning sickness," so called because it usually occurs immediately after you get up in the morning. However, you may feel nauseated at other times as well.

Although one-half to two-thirds of all expectant mothers have experienced nausea, especially in the first months of pregnancy, doctors today feel that much of the morning sickness in early pregnancy stems from a psychological rather than a physical cause. They believe that it results from the deep emotions that are aroused when a woman becomes aware she is pregnant. Some doctors think, too, that the fact that many women expect to be nauseated and vomit when they're pregnant may account for "morning sickness."

However, if you're experiencing this discomfort, it would be hard for anyone to convince you that you're imagining things! But, unless you have pernicious vomiting (which requires constant medical care), you can obtain considerable, if not absolute, relief by combining special diet and rest.

The idea of a diet to overcome morning sickness is to keep the stomach full of solids. It calls for six meals a day, each meal high in carbohydrates and low in fats. When you're on the diet for nausea, you won't be able to keep your weight gain to a minimum as you would like.

When the nausea is overcome, or disappears, which usually happens at the end of the first three months, you may cut out the excess carbohydrates and lose some of the weight you have gained on the diet to overcome morning sickness. In this way, while you may gain a lot at first, you'll be able to keep your weight within bounds when it becomes necessary because of the baby's increasing size.

Since butter encourages the tendency to nausea, it should be used sparingly while the condition lasts. If you are taking cod-liver oil and it seems to upset you, ask your doctor about a vitamin D substitute.

In addition to the six meals a day prescribed for nausea, have a supply of crackers handy and eat them whenever your stomach gets uneasy. Keep some beside your bed at night, and eat one or two first thing in the morning before you've so much as raised your head from the pillow. Then rest quietly for twenty minutes or so. Follow the same course —lie down and eat a cracker—any time during the day that your stomach begins to act up. If you're working, keep some crackers in your desk and munch one when you feel a spell of nausea coming on.

After the first attacks have stopped, you may have a "regular" dinner at night of lean meat; green vegetable; potato; lettuce and tomato or fruit salad; and dessert.

Here's the high calorie diet (recommended *only* if you are troubled with nausea):

Diet for nausea

7:30 a.m. 2 soda crackers.

8:00 a.m. Stewed prunes (6 large), or baked apple.

Cooked whole-wheat or enriched cereal with sugar or honey, and very small amount of cream.

Cup of chocolate with sugar (if coffee increases nausea).

2 slices of whole-wheat toast, spread with honey. No butter.

10:30 a.m. 2 slices of toast (with marmalade or jelly, no butter), or 2 crackers, 1 glass of milk, cocoa, hot malted milk, or tea.

12:30 p.m. Vegetable, cream of celery, or potato soup, with crackers.

2 slices of whole-wheat or enriched bread.

Lettuce, ½ head.

1 cup of custard, cornstarch pudding, apple tapioca, ice cream, or 3 ounces of gelatine dessert.

4:00 p.m. Fruit juice, or tea with sugar.

2 slices of whole-wheat toast, honey or marmalade, no butter.

1 slice of sponge cake.

6:30 p.m. 1 cup of cream of pea soup, or other soups as at lunch.

2 crackers, or 2 slices of toast.

Baked sweet or white potato (large) or 3 ounces of rice.

3 ounces of stewed carrots, or beets.

Desserts as at lunch, 1 ounce of dates, or 1 ounce of raisins.

9:30 to 10:00 p.m. Toast or crackers.

1 glass of milk, cocoa, or malted milk.

The above diet is to be used only while nausea is a problem. As soon as you're over it, change gradually to the diet on pages 28-29.

Rest lots if you're nauseated

Rest is quite as important as diet. Diet does little good unless you go to bed at 8 or 9 o'clock—never later—every night, and rest some during the morning and afternoon. You will probably be able to do your regular housework, but outside activities must be curtailed. If guests come in the evening, excuse yourself when you are ready to go to bed, otherwise the morning after may be painful.

As every nausea victim knows, the unpleasantness leaves as if by magic when the three months are up, although it may recur temporarily if there's too long an interval between meals or if you become overly tired.

Other digestive discomforts

Gas, heartburn, indigestion, and the heart palpitation often felt are all largely caused by something in the diet. The first step in relieving them is to determine what food is causing the difficulty. Then eliminate it.

Heartburn can often be prevented by taking a tablespoon of cream one-half hour before meals. The cream shouldn't be taken at mealtime, however. If the heartburn persists, consult your doctor. He can give you something to relieve it. *Never take baking soda during pregnancy*, for heartburn or any other reason.

Rapid heart action, often experienced in pregnancy, may be due to indigestion or pressure of the uterus on stomach or heart. Attention to diet and exercise usually helps.

Varicose veins

Sometimes certain veins in the legs become swollen and painful. This seldom happens in a first pregnancy, but may be a problem in succeeding ones. This condition should be called to your doctor's attention.

Varicose veins result from poor circulation. You were cautioned in the section about clothing (page 31) never to wear tight garters or rolled stockings. In spite of these precautions, veins may still become dilated.

Proper bandaging with elastic bandages may give some relief. These may be purchased in any drugstore. Some women prefer fitted elastic stockings, although these are more expensive than the bandages. Whichever you use, put them on the first thing in the morning, before getting out of bed. Wrap the bandage once or twice around the instep, around the ankle, and continue in an overlapping spiral all the way up the leg to just below the knee. The bandage should be snug and fastened with a safety pin, just below the knee.

Enlarged veins may be helped by lying down as often as possible during the day. Prop your legs up with pillows so they're higher than your hips. And when you're sitting, try to rest your legs on a high footstool.

Hemorrhoids

Hemorrhoids have been called "varicose veins of the rectum." They are engorged veins at the opening of the rectum. They often itch and bleed and may be extremely painful. Generally, they result from straining over the hard stools of constipation. So the best preventive is to avoid constipation. Mention to your doctor any indication that you are developing hemorrhoids. A more laxative diet (see page 29) and a daily dose of mineral oil may be all that's needed to correct them. If the hemorrhoids become extremely painful, get in touch with your doctor at once.

Lying down frequently during the day and sitting with your legs raised level with your body is beneficial if you have hemorrhoids.

Itching of the body and vagina

Occasionally a woman who is pregnant complains that the skin all over her body itches. This may be helped by adding baking soda to your bath water, but should be reported to your doctor as it may be a symptom of a food or drug allergy.

Advise your doctor of any itching of the vagina, so that he can determine the cause and treat it. Don't use any douches unless your doctor orders them.

Vaginal discharge

In the latter part of your pregnancy, you may have a thin, pale yellow discharge from the vagina. This is normal and requires only the wearing of a sanitary pad and a thorough washing of the vagina once or twice a day. If the discharge is thick or profuse, or accompanied by itching, consult your doctor.

Skin spots and brittle hair

You may notice brown spots developing on your face, particularly if you're a brunette. Occasionally, the brownish tinge spreads over the whole face. This is the "mask of pregnancy," and the spots disappear shortly after delivery.

In the latter part of your pregnancy, you may notice your hair becoming dry and breaking off. Don't be concerned if this happens. Your hair will return to its normal state after your baby is born.

Brush your hair and massage your scalp regularly. Hot oil scalp treatments before shampoos will be helpful, too. Permanent waving may not be successful at this time because of the brittleness of your hair.

Muscle cramps

Toward the end of pregnancy, you may have a tendency toward cramps in your thigh and leg muscles. This is associated with insufficient circulation of blood, and to the use of muscles not usually called into action.

It may also be the result of a calcium deficiency. Mention it to your doctor as he may want to prescribe additional calcium.

A good maternity corset and low-heeled shoes will help you avoid these cramps. If they occur, you may get relief by massaging your legs and by walking about the room without shoes. Stretching your leg out in front of you and pushing downward with your heel sometimes relaxes the cramped muscles.

Sometimes the baby's head presses on certain nerves and causes shooting pains down the legs. Changing your position may help.

Swelling of feet and ankles

Toward the end of pregnancy, your feet and ankles may swell noticeably, particularly after you have been sitting in one position or standing a long time. The swelling will usually disappear if you lie down and raise your legs with pillows. If your feet and legs are constantly swollen, and lying down doesn't seem to help, get in touch with your doctor.

Shortness of breath

As the baby grows and presses upon your vital organs, shortness of breath is to be expected. This is a normal condition and causes only minor discomfort. If it interferes with sleep, prop your head and shoulders up with pillows. Extreme shortness of breath, however, should be reported to your doctor.

Serious complications

In addition to the annoying symptoms described, more serious conditions sometimes develop. Your regular visits to your doctor will enable him to detect them.

Early symptoms of one or more of the complications of this type were described on page 30. Briefly, they are a constant headache that doesn't yield to ordinary headache remedies, swelling of face or hands, blurred vision, bleeding from the vagina, fever, and pain in the abdominal region. They should be reported at once to your doctor, as should vomiting which persists.

Bleeding from the vagina may indicate a threatened miscarriage or premature labor. Call your doctor at once, lie down, and don't take any medicine until the doctor gets there.

Chapter V

Things to have ready for your baby

When your baby arrives, he'll not only need a layette, but various pieces of equipment as well. Fortunately, most items manufactured and advertised nationally for babies have been prepared with an infant's comfort and well-being in mind. Some have been approved by the American Medical Association. This approval is shown by a little seal which these items carry. The baby section of a good department store, moreover, is a service department where a special effort is made to give inexperienced mothers reliable information. If you'll tell the saleswoman how much you want to spend, she'll try to help you get the most value for your money.

A room of Baby's own—if possible

A room of Baby's own should go at the top of your list. If you are not permanently located at the time, it may not be possible to have everything just as you'd like.

If you can give him a room that's exclusively his, by all means do so. A room of his own will help Baby build better sleeping habits and will also give you more rest. It may be ever so tiny as long as it's well ventilated and quiet so he can have his naps undisturbed. During the first weeks of his life, your baby should be in a room adjoining yours, so that you will hear him if he cries and can give him the attention he needs.

Articles that will not be needed in the care of the baby should be taken out of the room. All furnishings should be such that they can be easily cleaned. Linoleum is a good floor covering as it can be washed frequently.

If you can't provide a separate room for Baby, give him a corner where his clothes and equipment can be kept handy, and he can rest in peace and quiet. Should you have just one bedroom, plan to put him in it for his naps. When you go to bed, wheel or carry his bassinet out into the room next to yours if it's warm enough.

His room should be warm

The room your baby uses should be easy to heat, for during the first few weeks the temperature shouldn't go below 70 degrees. Special care should be taken to keep the humidity at a proper level, so his nose and mouth membranes won't become dry. Keep water in the furnace humidifier or set shallow pans of water near the radiators or register in his room. Fill the pans daily.

Should be well ventilated

At the same time your baby's room should be well ventilated. Ideally, it should be cross ventilated, but his bed shouldn't be in a draft. You can prevent drafts by placing ventilators or cloth screens in the windows when they're open, or keeping a screen between his bed and the draft. If a screen is used, be sure that it cannot topple over.

A room with a fireplace is a nice one for Baby, because the open chimney provides a constant stream of fresh air without drafts.

Baby's furniture

The nursery may be furnished as simply or as elaborately as you wish. Don't have a daz-

By substituting a matching junior bed for the crib, nursery furniture like this serves for your child long after infancy

← A folding bath table, with a tub attached, is convenient. But an ordinary table will do

If you haven't a folding tub, → one like this, big enough for all-over baths, will do nicely

← Baby's room, though warm, should be well ventilated. Use glass or window board

← Baby's bassinet can be made from a laundry basket, if you use materials that wash well

It's handy, though, to have the → first bed on wheels. This, or oblong-type bassinet, is good

zling white color scheme, which is hard on your baby's eyes. Any soft color will do.

For your baby's first bed, a bassinet on wheels is very convenient, since it can be taken anywhere in the house and wheeled out on a porch for naps. However, a big laundry basket, well padded, does very well. The first bassinet should be at least 30 inches long.

Whatever kind of bed you use, be sure it's long enough and wide enough to let the baby kick and squirm all he likes. When purchasing a full-size crib, choose the type with a side which can be raised and lowered. The latch which unfastens the side should be placed where Baby cannot reach it as he gets older.

Another convenience in a crib is an adjustable mattress base which can be moved up and down. The mattress should be at your hip height during the first months, so that you don't have to stoop low to lift Baby.

If you can't obtain a crib with this adjustable feature, raise the crib to the proper height by screwing wood doorstops into legs.

How to make up Baby's bed

It will make little difference to your baby whether his room is an elaborate nursery or a little corner, but the way his bed is made up will matter a great deal.

Mattress. First of all, the mattress must be firm, for a baby's bony structure is soft, and easily develops a sag. Cotton felt, horsehair, or foam rubber are ideal materials for the mattress filling. A number of mattresses today are waterproofed. If the one you buy isn't, you'll want to cover it with a protective waterproof sheet that's large enough to tuck well under the mattress.

Absorbent pads. The mattress pad for your baby's bed should be both soft and absorbent. You'll need 2 or 3 of these pads for changing when they become soaked or soiled. They should be large enough to tuck well under the mattress.

Sheets. Over the absorbent pad goes the sheet, which should be large enough to tuck under the mattress. Fitted sheets are now made with mitered corners, and slip over the ends of the mattress so they're held firmly in place, wrinkle-free. You'll want 4 to 6 sheets.

Small waterproof and absorbent pads. For extra protection, and extra comfort for your baby, place a small waterproof sheet—these are made in several convenient sizes—in the spot where he'll lie, and place over this a small absorbent pad. This will soak up excess mois-

ture and cut down the number of times it will be necessary to change the large pad.

Four cotton blankets. These should be long enough to tuck under the mattress. It's better to have several light blankets that launder easily than only one or two heavy ones.

Two comforters.

Wardrobe and chair

You'll want a wardrobe or chest of drawers in which to keep your baby's clothes. The picture of the nursery on page 42 shows two types. Or you can repaint an old chest of drawers or contrive one yourself. It will be all the same to your baby.

A comfortable chair is indispensable in the nursery. Baby must be held in your arms for nursing and feeding. A good easy chair will make this your opportunity for relaxing comfortably. A footstool on which to rest your feet will be welcome, too!

You should have a small, steady table at the side of your armchair. This will hold the items needed during a feeding, and the bottle when Baby needs "bubbling."

Other nursery furnishings

You will need a place to change and dress Baby. This, like the crib mattress, should be your hip height to eliminate tiring strain to your back. The top of a low chest of drawers will do, if it's the correct height. It should be well padded, as should a wooden table. The top of the canvas bath table may be used, too, and does not require padding.

A scale to check Baby's weight gains is a big comfort, but it is not a necessity. Your doctor will weigh the baby each month during his checkup and that will be sufficient.

A shaded lamp will enable you to peek at Baby at night without disturbing him. If this lamp can be connected with a silent mercury switch placed just inside the door of Baby's room, there will be no click to wake him.

A wastebasket, a 2- or 3-gallon covered pail, and a soiled clothes hamper will be needed. The pail and hamper may be kept in the bathroom. If you intend to use a diaper service, the covered pail will not be necessary as the diaper service furnishes the container.

Bath articles

Keep your baby's bath articles in his room or in the bathroom, whichever's more con-

Have ready a bath basket or tray ➡
with things Baby will need for his toilet

⬅ You'll need to weigh
Baby often at first

venient. As the bathroom is usually warm, it's often the best place to bathe your baby. The following articles should be secured:

Bath table. The folding variety, with bath attached, is very convenient. When not in use, it can go into a closet or behind a door.

If you don't have a folding table, use any table that's a convenient height. An ordinary table, however, will need to be thickly padded to keep the hard surface from making the baby uncomfortable. A pad, or folded blankets, will do the job.

Tub. If you haven't the bath table and tub combined, you'll want a tub. For the first sponge baths after the baby gets home from the hospital, a washbasin will do. When he's ready for tub baths, a regular baby tub or container of adequate size which can be cleaned easily will be needed. A long, oval shape is best.

Bath tray. A square enameled basket is the most practical for this purpose. See illustration at top of page. It should contain:
Bath thermometer
Mild, pure soap
Baby cream or lotion
Baby or olive oil
Shallow, covered soap dish or jar
Shallow, covered oil dish or jar
Small jar (covered) of sterile water
Nursing bottle of boiled water with sterile
   nipple, covered
Covered jar of extra sterile nipples
Safety pins, assorted sizes
Toothpicks
Surgical gauze squares in a covered jar
Sterilized cotton balls in a covered jar
Washcloths—squares of cheesecloth or
   other soft material; or regular baby
   washcloths
3 bath towels, large enough to warp around

Baby. (Or you can buy 36-inch-wide, extra-soft bath toweling and cut it into two-yard lengths, hemming the ends. This makes towels of excellent size.)
1 large bath apron
The bathroom closet or cabinet should contain these articles, ready for use when needed:
Rectal clinical thermometer. (During the first four years at least, the temperature should be taken rectally.) Small hot-water bottle, to warm Baby when necessary. Baby syringe (for enemas when needed).

Baby's layette

Your baby's clothing needs are few, for his wardrobe has been simplified until it approaches the vanishing point. The basic dress, in summer or winter, is shirt and diaper. The old custom of swathing the tiny baby in wool and flannel, even in hot weather, has fortunately gone out. Most babies get along with no wool at all, except in outside garments, such as sweaters or other light wraps.

The warmth of your baby's clothing depends upon the climate where you live and the heating arrangements in your home.

Keep in mind that the purpose of clothing him is to make him comfortable, not to prevent colds or other infections. These are contracted through germs carried to your baby by some other person—not by the weather.

Of course, Baby should not become chilled. If your climate and home heating arrangements are such that warm shirts will be needed to keep him comfortable, get them. Fabric is still a matter of choice.

Your baby should not be overdressed. Babies are more likely to be too warm than too cool. Good sense will guide you.

If yours is a warm, evenly heated house,

shirts of cotton or similar light materials will be adequate for a new baby's needs.

If your baby is to be born at home, you'll want to provide three abdominal bands to hold the navel dressing in place till the navel is healed. This band is made of a strip of soft flannel or gauze, 18 to 20 inches long and 4 to 5 inches wide. Most babies born in hospitals, however, no longer need these bands by the time they're taken home. (Whether or not a band is needed is a point to be determined by your own doctor.)

The absolute essentials of your baby's wardrobe are:

4 shirts—either long- or short-sleeved
    Size 2 (6 months size)
4–6 sacques or kimonos (cotton knit or cotton flannel for winter, cotton crepe for summer)
6 pinning blankets or outing flannel squares 36x36 inches
2 wool sacques or sweaters
3–4 dozen diapers
1 hood
Safety pins.

The first few months, when the baby is tiny and has to be changed frequently, sacques or kimonos can be used instead of nightgowns. As he gets stronger and more likely to kick off his covers at night, you'll need 3 to 6 nightgowns. Cotton knit gowns are comfortable and easy to launder. They should be long and have long sleeves. If they tie at the cuffs and hem, Baby is covered even though he throws off his bedclothes.

In these early months, too, a lint-free blanket is more satisfactory as an outer wrap than a baby coat or "baby bunting." These garments are usually too large for a tiny infant. And if they are small enough now, he'll outgrow them very quickly. When he becomes more active, you may need a coat or bunting for him.

Quite a variety of materials and styles are available in diapers. The square of outing flannel or birds-eye, folded twice triangularly, has given way quite largely to an oblong shape, 20 or 21x40 inches. New, absorbent materials have been perfected that are easy to launder and quick-drying. The oblong shape can be folded in different ways as the baby grows, and the new materials are so soft that the 21x40-inch size isn't too large even for a tiny baby. Whatever material you select, you'll need a minimum of three to four dozen diapers for convenience. There are also pads for cribs and your lap in the same soft, absorbent material.

Adjustable, fitted diapers with gripper-type fastenings are available, too. They are higher-priced than standard diapers, and may not fit a very young baby even when adjusted to the smallest size. However, they're very nice for an older baby.

In addition to these garments, there are several brands of disposable diapers. Whether you want to use these all the time or not, it's smart to have a supply on hand for those periods when you want to omit diaper washing for a time.

There are also paper inserts to place in a cloth diaper which eliminate the worst of the soiling.

Most communities now have diaper laundry services. These are a boon to many mothers. If you intend to use a diaper service, inquire about it several months before your baby is born. Otherwise, as it's very much in demand, you may not be able to get this service when you need it.

Make sure the diaper service you select has high standards of sanitation in handling and laundering the diapers. The doctor who will take care of your baby can advise you about this. Ask other customers, too, whether or not they've been satisfied with the service.

If you have a diaper service, it will supply the diapers; so you will not have to buy any.

Hip-length sacques are becoming popular for baby wear. The absence of skirts means less wet clothing. If the short garments are used, legs and feet are kept warm by wrapping baby in an outing flannel square or a cotton flannel "receiving" blanket.

Dresses and underslips may be worn occasionally. If a garment must slip over the baby's head, be sure the opening is large enough so it will go on easily.

← Baby needs a warm sweater or two and warm hood for winter

Long nightie has drawstrings in the hem and in the cuffs ↓

Chapter VI

Your part before
and after delivery

The ninth month finally comes. This last period of waiting may seem longer than all the rest. You are heavy and awkward. And you may not sleep well. But if you continue your regular routine and interests, you'll forget yourself and the calendar.

Use these last few weeks to observe and help any mothers of your acquaintance who have young babies. You'll learn firsthand how to take care of your baby when he arrives. Your husband will be interested in this, too. He's going to be eager to help with the baby and will feel more confident if he has some beforehand knowledge.

Many communities have prenatal classes for expectant mothers and fathers. You'll both benefit by attending these classes if they're available. Even though this may not be your first child, you can brush up on your technique and learn some newer methods.

Read ahead in this book, through the chapter "Your Baby From Birth to One Month," so you'll feel familiar with everything necessary for your baby's care and comfort.

Keep on your diet and continue any exercise your doctor recommends. Soak up as much fresh air and sunshine as you can. Your doctor will give you your final checkup, and soon the great day will come.

You may go as much as two weeks past the expected date for delivery. This is perfectly normal, so don't worry about it.

Have your doctor's home and office telephone numbers by your telephone. If you have no telephone, be sure to make arrangements for someone to get a message to the doctor for you. Decide now how you will get to the hospital when the time comes.

Arrange the matters discussed under the next five headings now, so they'll be taken care of before you go to the hospital.

The doctor to supervise Baby's care

The doctor who delivers you may handle obstetrics only. If so, he will not continue taking care of Baby after you leave the hospital. In that case, you should select the doctor you wish to take care of the baby. To save yourself time and worry get in touch with him now to make sure he will be available when your baby is born. Then ask your obstetrician to call him to the hospital after the baby is born. They will go over Baby together, and the new doctor will be familiar with everything concerning his care.

What to take to the hospital

When you enter the last month of pregnancy, it's time to pack your bag with everything you'll need and have it ready. It's impossible to tell precisely when your baby will arrive. Pack whatever articles the hospital asked you to bring for the baby.

Baby will need an outfit to wear home, but this can be brought to the hospital later. Assemble it in a certain place at home so your husband can find it easily to bring when needed. The outfit should include a shirt, 2 diapers, safety pins, a waterproof outer diaper, a sweater and bonnet, and a wrapping blanket.

For your stay at the hospital, you'll want the following things:

Nightgowns or pajamas. For the first few days, you'll wear the hospital gowns, but after that you'll want to have your own pretty ones.

You're likely to perspire a good deal and—as your milk may seep through—you'll need a fresh gown or pajamas every day. If you don't want to buy so many, arrange to have someone launder them for you during your stay.

You may wear just pajama tops in bed, but bring the trousers for when you're up.

Bed jacket

Dressing gown or bathrobe. If you take a pretty negligee, you should also have a warm robe, for hospital corridors are sometimes drafty.

Slippers

Watch or clock

Fountain pen, stationery, and stamps

Hand mirror

Comb and brush

Manicuring set

Cleansing tissues

Cosmetics

Cologne—nice for back rubs

Bath powder. Bath powder is particularly refreshing to dust on your neck, shoulders, and arms when you perspire.

Toothbrush and paste

Three nursing brassieres

Sanitary belt

Sanitary napkins. Hospitals may provide these. Inquire.

Take any special books you'd like to read. Your husband or friends can supply you with others, and many hospitals have libraries for the patients, the staff of which delivers books to your bedside.

You may want to take a portable radio. Generally, hospitals have radios available which you can rent reasonably.

Arrange for help when you come home

You should have someone to help you at home for several weeks after you return from the hospital. Perhaps a relative can assist you. Arrangements should be made before you go to the hospital.

Home confinement

If the delivery is to be at home, you should obtain from your doctor—well in advance of confinement—a list of articles needed in the home at that time. Have them assembled, sterilized, and wrapped, ready for use when needed. Select the best-lighted room in the house for the place of delivery. Be sure it is thoroughly cleaned and stripped of every thing except the essential pieces of furniture. Remove curtains, draperies, and carpeting.

Mentioned at the end of Chapter II are two publications which will give you detailed instructions concerning a home confinement.

Arrange for diaper service

If you intend to use a diaper laundry, check to make sure the service is available.

Enjoy yourself

With all the foregoing details taken care of, you can relax with a free mind. Don't hesitate to go to the theater or visiting. Invite friends to your house in the evening. Getting out and seeing people is good for you. Dr. Nicholas J. Eastman, obstetrician-in-chief of Johns Hopkins Hospital, says he likes to get a delivery case straight from a bridge party, so to speak, for it means that the woman is in a relaxed frame of mind, and has been thinking of something outside herself.

Lightening

"Lightening" (when the baby sinks down and forward) may occur any time during the last month with a woman having her first baby. This forward movement of the uterus relieves the pressure on the abdomen, and you'll be able to breathe easier. But this change in the position of the uterus causes greater pressure below. With succeeding pregnancies, lightening may not come until the last week, perhaps not until labor begins.

Signs that labor is starting

1. Labor usually starts with a slight backache that comes and goes at regular intervals. The backache may be accompanied by weak cramps in your abdomen. Your abdomen will become hard and then soft again, as the uterus contracts. Each contraction lasts from 10 to 40 seconds. At first, the contractions will be from 10 to 30 minutes apart. Later, the intervals between contractions will be much shorter.

2. The "show." This is the passage from the vagina of a small amount of mucus streaked with blood.

3. Breaking of the bag of waters. This is signaled by a rush of water from the vagina. It doesn't always occur by itself, though, and may have to be induced by your doctor. (Only in a small percentage of cases does the bag of waters break prior to the onset of labor.)

At one or all of these signs, get in touch with your doctor. He'll tell you when to start for the hospital.

And now, the hospital

When you arrive at the hospital, you'll be taken to a "Prep" room where you'll be prepared for delivery, and given an enema and bath.

In a short time, your doctor or, at his direction, an interne will give you an examination which will indicate to them how near you are to actual delivery. The baby, propelled by the contraction of your muscles, is pushing down on the opening of your uterus—which is slowly dilating to permit him to descend.

After you have been examined, you may be left by yourself in a "labor" room. Don't worry, though; you'll have a buzzer right at hand to summon the nurse immediately if the contractions become harder or more frequent. Someone will check on you often.

Many times after the first signs of labor, the contractions subside. If this occurs, relax and sleep if you can. Several hours may pass before they begin again. The doctor or nurse may suggest that you don your robe and slippers and walk in the corridor. The exercise will be good for you. Whether your husband can visit with you at this time depends upon the hospital's rules.

You will, in all probability, receive very little food and rarely any solids.

Labor

The contractions of the muscles of the uterus preceding childbirth are a natural function, and their purpose is to open the mouth of the uterus to permit passage of the baby. In the second stage of labor, after the uterus has opened sufficiently to allow the baby to pass, the contractions continue to propel the baby out until birth is completed.

Doctors have found that when mothers understand the purpose of labor contractions, they can be relaxed and unworried.

The labor period varies from 12 to 24 hours for a first baby, to less than 6 or 8 hours for later ones. Much of this period is free from even the slightest discomfort.

As you are prepared for delivery, your doctor may give you an injection of Vitamin K. Usually this shot is given as a precaution—to lessen the chances of bleeding for both you and your child.

If the contractions are frequent enough to keep you awake, the nurse may give you a sedative in capsule form to help you sleep. You'll wake up a few hours later as the contractions become stronger and more frequent. This time you'll probably get a hypodermic containing amnesiac drugs. (Remember, they are the drugs which eliminate most, often all, memory of any discomfort.) You may go to sleep again.

When you awaken this time, the doctor will examine you to see how far the cervix (the opening of the uterus) has dilated. If it is completely dilated, he knows that you are in the second stage and must stay awake to assist in the birth process. The second stage begins as the baby's head passes through the cervix. The pressure on the birth canal gradually increases as the child moves down through the muscle bed at the bottom of the pelvic area.

Father's waiting period

After your arrival at the hospital, your husband may be told that it will be many hours before delivery. Your doctor or nurse may advise him to go back to the office or home and keep in touch with the hospital. Some hospitals permit the husband to remain with his wife during labor. This helps him feel he is participating in this important event.

However, it isn't necessary for your husband to be there. You will be sleeping some of the time, and many doctors feel that you will relax more and rest better if your husband is not present.

If your hospital doesn't allow your husband to be with you during the labor period, don't be upset about it. If his remaining at the hospital makes you and him feel better, he may stay in the waiting room provided for expectant fathers.

In the delivery room

The birth of your baby is near. You will be encouraged to work with your contractions to help push the baby down. During this period you will probably be given light whiffs of an anesthetic (if you are receiving inhalation-type anesthesia). Just as the baby is about to be born, you may be given a complete anesthetic. If the anesthetic is of the inhalation type, such as nitrous oxide-oxygen, you will be unconscious, or nearly so, from then on. If you have a caudal or saddle-block anesthetic, you'll be conscious but will have no sensation in the birth area.

Your doctor may perform an episiotomy.

This means that he makes a cut in the vagina to avoid any irregular tears which might be difficult to repair later. After the baby and the placenta have been delivered, your doctor repairs the cut with absorbable sutures (stitches which do not have to be removed).

If you should lack the strength to push the baby out, the doctor will help you with forceps. There is no need to be concerned about a forceps delivery. It just means that the doctor inserts into the vaginal opening first one, then the other, of the separate prongs of the forceps, and joins them so the baby's head is held with gentle pressure. Then he carefully pulls your child out.

After your baby is delivered, contractions of the uterus separate the afterbirth, or placenta, and push it into the vagina during the third stage of labor. This happens anywhere from 3 to 15 minutes after birth, and if you have an anesthetic, you won't feel any sensation. Your physician will expel it from the vagina by applying gentle pressure on the upper part of the uterus.

After delivery is finished and the doctor allows you to see and hold your baby for the first time, you'll feel that you have taken part in the most rewarding experience of your life.

Birth registration

Generally, your doctor fills out and files the birth certificate. In many states, it is compulsory that this be done, usually within a certain number of days after birth. Ask your doctor if the birth has been registered. Obtain a copy of the birth certificate and keep it in a safe place, so that it may be available whenever needed. On page 212 of the Record Section in this book is space for a photostatic or certified copy of the birth certificate.

Circumcision

If a baby boy is to be circumcised, it should be done before the end of the second week.

In circumcision the movable fold of skin which covers the end of the penis is clipped away. One of the purposes is to aid the boy to maintain cleanliness. If circumcision is not performed, ask your doctor about cleansing under the foreskin.

To help establish breast feeding

Although your milk will not appear until the third or fourth day, most physicians put the baby to the breast sometime during the first 24 hours after birth, and at regular periods from then on.

The first fluid which comes from the breast is called colostrum. It is yellow, and differs from the real milk which will usually appear on the third or fourth day. The baby should nurse regularly until the breast milk is "in," as the colostrum is considered important for body-building and possible immunizing benefits. Also, Baby's nursing stimulates the flow of milk. Very little milk is obtained these first few days, so boiled water is offered between nursings. He's expected to lose $\frac{1}{2}$ pound, or slightly more, during this period. As much as a pound may not be cause for alarm, but more than that should be looked into by the doctor.

Supplementary feedings should not be started during the first few days unless they're absolutely necessary, as they spoil Baby for working at the breast.

Ask your doctor to leave orders at the hospital that your baby is *not* to get any supplementary bottle feedings, unless he has ordered them. If they should be needed, however, his instructions will be followed.

If your baby is premature, he will not be brought to you for nursing. He'll be kept in a heated incubator and given special feedings. However, regular emptying of your breasts with a breast pump may maintain your supply of milk so he can be breast-fed when he graduates from the incubator.

How to help Baby nurse and how to make nursing comfortable is discussed on pages 60 through 63.

You may feel depressed

Often after a new mother returns home and the care of the baby becomes her responsibility, she develops a feeling of helplessness.

You may have this sense of discouragement. You may worry about the baby without any reason. You may feel that you'll never look as attractive as you did before you became pregnant. You may think you and your husband won't become adjusted to this changed life. It may seem to you that your husband isn't as interested in you as he once was.

Don't let this "blue" feeling get you down. Remember it's a common experience. Many other new mothers have felt the same way. The reaction passes as strength and confidence return.

Remember, too, that your husband *is* going

through a time of adjustment, the same as you are. The household where he was formerly the leading man now revolves around a tiny baby. He wants the baby to have your care and attention, but he needs to feel important, too. Help him to understand that he still comes first. Include him in the care and enjoyment of Baby, so he won't feel left out.

Try to arrange an outing for yourself—in the evening with your husband, or downtown with friends during the day. If Baby is in good hands, getting away will relax you.

For a few women, the after-childbirth depression becomes so deep that medical help is needed—the sooner the better. Fortunately, these cases are very rare. Other mothers may have so little depression, they're scarcely aware of it. But knowing that it may happen, and is not unusual, helps you to overcome it when it occurs.

Preparing to go home

Before you leave the hospital, the nurse may show you how to bathe and care for Baby.

If he's a formula-fed baby, your hospital may furnish a day's supply of his formula.

If your baby was born at home, have the nurse show you how to bathe and dress Baby, and how to prepare his formula, if he is not breast-fed.

Send extra packages and luggage home the day before you leave the hospital. Most hospitals now prefer that you leave around noon rather than in the evening.

For the first week or two, it's best for you and the baby if you have no visitors (even loving relatives), except the person who is to help with the housework and baby care. You'll rest better without visitors, and Baby needs to be protected from colds and other infections which they might bring in.

Your doctor will tell you what he wishes you to do to care for yourself at home. It might be well to write down everything he says so you will remember.

Rest

Even though your doctor allows you to get up and move about within three or four days after Baby's birth, rest as much as you can.

Stay in bed as much as possible the first few days at home. Don't go up and down stairs at all for a week or two, and keep stair-climbing to a minimum for a month.

After you have taken over the full care of the baby, arrange your day so you can lie down for a half-hour twice a day. When Baby is sleeping would be the best time.

You can get additional rest during nursing or bottle feedings. Sit in a comfortable armchair at these times, with a table beside it. Rest your feet on a hassock.

You may lie down while feeding the baby, but don't do it if you are drowsy. You might drop off to sleep with him in your arms.

If you can afford it, hire someone to do heavy cleaning and laundry for the next few months. If not, forget about unusual and seasonal house cleaning for the time being. A rested, well mother is the most important need right now.

Baths

Take either shower or sponge baths during the first month after your baby is born. At the end of that time, you may take tub baths, provided that you no longer have any blood-tinged discharge. Don't take any douches unless your doctor orders them.

When will menstruation reappear?

Generally, menstruation does not occur for several months after the birth of your baby. And after it does appear, it may be irregular. It may be some time before your regular monthly cycle is re-established.

Some mothers do not menstruate at all as long as their baby is nursing. If you should, however, don't discontinue nursing because of menstruation.

Sometimes breast milk is not as plentiful during these periods as at other times, or Baby may seem restless. Give him a bottle for a few feedings if he seems unduly upset during menstruation. Your breasts may then be emptied by hand or pumped to relieve fullness. It is well to accustom Baby to an occasional bottle, anyway, after the first month or so, even though he is entirely breast-fed.

Many women believe that they cannot become pregnant if they are nursing and have not resumed menstruating. This is not correct. Conception can occur during this period.

Resuming intercourse

It's advisable to refrain from intercourse until your doctor has examined you a month or six weeks after delivery. Ask him then if it's all right.

Exercises after delivery

You can start exercising the first few days, flat on your back in bed. Here are some exercises to begin on which do not require much exertion: Cross ankles, tighten hip muscles, and press muscles on inside of thighs together. Relax. Then tighten rectal muscles as if stoping bowel action. Relax and repeat 6 times.

Flat on your back, raise and lower head, touching chin to chest. Repeat as often as you wish without tiring yourself.

Still on back, flex feet up, down, and sideways, and wiggle your toes.

Then in a day or so, while still in bed, you can progress to the exercises pictured, if your doctor permits. Continue them, in bed or on the floor, at home.

Lie on back, knees bent. (a) Inhale slowly, expanding chest and abdomen (b) Pull abdomen in, spreading ribs apart. Exhale. (c) Pull abdomen in, press lower back to bed. Hold; relax. Repeat each 10 times

On hands and knees, swing your hips like a dog wagging its tail. Turn head every time in direction you're swinging so that waistline is well tucked in on side to which you're looking. Repeat 5 times, and then rest

On hands and knees, pull abdomen up toward spine, tightening hip muscles. Tuck head in to look at your knees. Your back should be completely rounded. Alternate with the exercise at right. Repeat 5 times

In same position as exercise at left, lift head and look toward ceiling, hollowing back and letting hip muscles go slack. Repeat 3 times; and then rest your head on your forearms. Repeat 3 times, 4 times daily

Exercises to be starte

Lie on back, knees bent, feet flat on floor. Raise head and shoulders off floor. Reach forward with hands outside left knee. Repeat, reaching beside right knee. Repeat each movement 3 times. Rest

Same position as exercise 1. With chin in, lift head off floor as far as possible, then lower it slowly. Repeat, stretching arms forward, raising shoulders off floor. Try to raise entire back. Repeat 5 times

"Knee-chest" position. Kneel, bend forward, until chest and side of face are resting on floor, knees 12 to 18 inches apart to allow air to enter vagina. Remain in this position five minutes, twice a day

ter six weeks

On hands and knees, swing right arm under the left side of body, then sideways and up toward ceiling, turning body and head to look up at hand. Swing each arm 5 times. Repeat 5 times daily

Same position as exercise above. Swing right arm under left side of body, reaching as far over back as possible. Turn head in direction you're reaching. Rest, and repeat 5 times with each hand

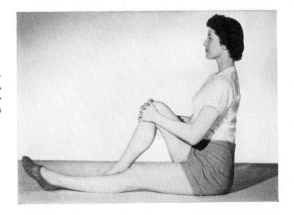

Sit on floor, right knee bent, foot flat on floor. Clasp hands around knee. Using back muscles, stretch toward ceiling, abdomen pulled in, shoulders loose. Repeat 10 times, alternating knees

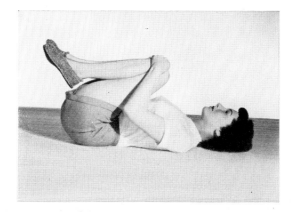

Lie on your back, knees flexed on abdomen, hands clasping bent knees. Pull knees toward chest; hold; then lower legs slowly to floor. Relax. Repeat 6 to 10 times. Try to touch knees to chest

Sit on stool against wall, back, buttocks, and head touching wall. Keep chin in, feet flat on floor. Raise arms; pull abdomen in so lower spine is pressed to wall, arms touching ears. Repeat 5 times

"The Camel Walk." Bend over from standing position; rest palms on floor, feet 12 to 18 inches apart. Keeping knees and elbows straight, walk around on all fours. Repeat 5 times a day

Section II

Your baby from birth to two years

The future is

ur hands

Your baby is here. From birth until he reaches maturity, the responsibility of guiding and caring for him is yours. There is no greater trust imposed on mankind than the obligations of parenthood.

Yet, this trust shouldn't be a burden. It shouldn't frighten you. It is the greatest joy with which human beings are blessed. Right now, the job ahead and the decisions you'll be called on to make may seem bewildering. Have confidence in your own ability as a parent. Millions of people have had the same problems you will meet, and have come through with flying colors. If they did it, you can.

Have fun with your baby. Show him your love but don't hover over him nor fear to let him develop independence as he grows. Treat him as a human being and respect him as an individual.

Make *understanding*, *respect*, and *affection* the keynotes in your relations with your mate, and in the attitude of both of you toward your child. If a family reflects these three attributes, all other things will take care of themselves.

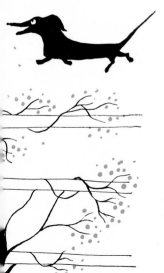

Interested, loving relatives and friends may not always approve the methods you adopt in raising your youngster. This often disturbs inexperienced parents. Just keep in mind that this is *your* baby—not anyone else's. You're not going to please everyone. It can't be done.

Don't be alarmed by conflicting advice. You have picked a doctor in whom you have confidence for your child. Be guided by what he tells you.

Health, wisdom, happiness, self-confidence, love of God, and love for his fellow man should be your goals for your youngster. If you instill in him these qualities, he will face the future unafraid; and you will look with pride on a task well done.

Chapter 1

Your baby from birth to two months

When you hold a tiny baby, support his wobbly little head and back with your arm and hand. Even the tiniest tot quickly recognizes Dad's firm grasp of the situation and looks on him as a favorite

For the first few weeks, weight will be a very important consideration in your baby's life. His weight may be expected to decrease during the first three days, or until your milk comes in, but the loss is usually made up by the tenth day. After that, if he gets enough milk or a formula adapted to his needs, he should gain at least 4 ounces a week. He may gain 6 to 8 ounces a week or even more for the first 6 months. The gain will probably slow down to from 3 to 6 ounces a week after that.

The legendary "average" baby doubles his birth weight at 5 months and triples it at a year. Remember, though, that no baby is average. Plenty of variations are possible in your baby's gain, all perfectly proper and normal. If he weighs 9 pounds at birth, which is more than average, he may not double it at 5 months, and still be all right. A small baby will probably more than double his weight at 5 months.

How much should he eat?

Babies differ in their rate of growth and in bodily needs. Their appetites differ from day to day and from meal to meal, as those of adults do. Daily exposure to fresh air and sunshine increases appetite and encourages growth. So does cold weather. Hot weather, however, cuts appetites. Race and sex also play a part in growth.

Don't, therefore, insist on any particular amount of food at a particular time. The baby's weight tells the story. As long as your baby gains between 4 and 8 ounces a week, be satisfied with his progress.

Consideration for your doctor

Try not to take your doctor's time by asking him to perform services you can do yourself.

Before calling or seeing a doctor, write down whatever you think you should tell him and any questions you wish to ask him so that you will not forget about them and have to make another call. Jotting down the doctor's instructions during each visit will protect you against forgetting or misunderstanding them.

The doctor should examine your baby thoroughly at birth. If there are any nursing or feeding difficulties, he'll tell you just what to do.

Again when your baby is a month or 6 weeks of age, take him back to his doctor for another checkup. Then be guided by his directions as to times for regular examinations.

These routine visits enable the doctor to know your baby. Any time anything unusual comes up, get your doctor on the telephone and tell him about it. He'll want you to do this.

Help Baby to nurse well

At first there may be difficulty in getting your baby to take your nipple. Ask the nurse to stay with you to help you. Baby has an instinctive rooting reflex. As soon as he smells milk, he will move his head toward you and attempt to find it. When his cheek touches your breast, he'll start rooting for the nipple with his mouth.

Hold him so that his mouth can reach your nipple, and lift your breast from beneath, so the nipple is directed to his mouth.

Help him take the brown circle behind the nipple in his mouth, as well as the nipple. This will help keep your nipples from becoming sore.

While Baby is nursing, hold your breast away from his nose so that he can breathe comfortably. After he has finished nursing, remove the nipple gently by pressing his mouth open with thumb and forefinger on each cheek near corners of lips. Don't pull the nipple away abruptly, as this may injure it.

Babies are often too sleepy at first to nurse. If he stops nursing, tickle him gently on the cheek. This will stimulate him to begin again, and soon he'll have the habit of working steadily until he has enough. Don't let him continue to hold the nipple in his mouth after he's had his fill, as this makes the nipple sore.

It will hurt at first to have your baby's lips tugging at your nipples. Don't let this discourage you, as they will soon become toughened. Five minutes is long enough for each nursing period the first few days. Generally, one breast is offered at one nursing, the other one the next. Continue to alternate at each period. However, your doctor may prefer dividing the time between both breasts at every nursing.

If breasts are painful

The coming of milk into your breasts may make them tender and sore. The breast binder, which offers support, relieves this condition. If the breasts are full and extremely painful, hot applications are helpful. Wring out several layers of heavy flannel in hot water (not hot enough to burn) and lay over the breasts, changing cloths as they become cool.

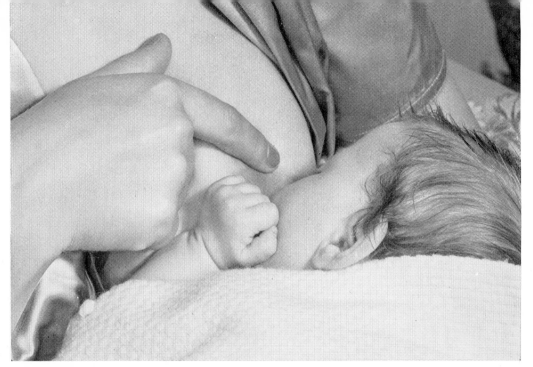

Start nursing off in the right way. To protect nipple from getting sore, be sure Baby takes the whole nipple in his mouth, including brown part behind it. Hold breast away from his nose so he can breathe easily. If Baby falls asleep before he's finished, tickle his cheek to keep him working steadily until he has taken enough

Do this for about an hour two or three times a day.

Care of your nipples in nursing

Your nipples should be washed with sterile water and cotton before and after each feeding. In working with the breasts or nipples, the greatest care should be used to keep them sterile, as infected breasts or infections for the baby may result from carelessness. Between nursings, plastic shields may be placed over the nipples to keep the binder from rubbing them. Lead shields should not be used because of the danger of giving the baby lead poisoning. If soreness is severe, the nipples may be sponged off with rubbing alcohol after nursing. This should be carefully removed before the baby is put to the breast again.

Just keep in mind that this initial tenderness of your nipples is nothing to be alarmed about.

Watch his gains

Baby's expected gain is 6 to 8 ounces a week for the first 6 to 8 weeks. If you have a scale, weigh your baby two or three times a week with diaper on. Failure to gain is usually due to insufficient breast milk. It's rare for a mother to have unsuitable breast milk. One

pediatrician with a large practice says that he has never yet encountered any. Milk varies in women chiefly in fat content and in amount. It's how much you have that's important.

Breast feeding is worth working for

Most mothers can nurse their babies, and the baby reared on breast milk has a number of advantages over the formula-fed baby. After all, human milk is intended for human babies, so why shouldn't it be best?

Breast-fed babies in general have fewer stomach upsets, less diarrhea, no constipation, fewer respiratory infections, and scarcely any skin rashes. Infant mortality is also strikingly lower among breast-fed babies. An older breast-fed baby has noticeably firmer skin and better muscular development than bottle-fed babies.

Breast milk is the most convenient kind, too. It eliminates long hours of bottle washing, sterilizing, and formula preparation. There are no refrigeration, warming, or transportation worries with your milk, and no concern about changing the proportions of the mixture to keep pace with your baby's growth. Nature takes care of all these things for you.

Another advantage of nursing is that it's good for you, too. The uterus and other birth organs of a nursing mother return to normal

62

size much more quickly than those of a mother who does not nurse her infant. Also, mothers who breast-feed their babies seem to feel better.

Perhaps even more important than all its physical benefits are the psychological values of breast feeding. There's no faster way for you and your baby to get acquainted with each other. And there's nothing more reassuring to your little newcomer than the soft warmth of your breast and the security of your embrace, as he satisfies his physical hunger as well as his basic need to suck and nuzzle and root for his food.

Mothers of today *want* to nurse their babies. But they need help.

Older people can help by keeping their opinions to themselves.

Doctors can help by telling the expectant mother how to prepare for nursing. They can help most of all by convincing her that there's no reason why she can't nurse her baby.

Hospitals, nurses, and doctors can help by giving the new mother all possible cooperation in establishing breast feeding while she is at the hospital.

At the present time, many young mothers are being defeated in their efforts to nurse their babies because hospitals and doctors are too quick to offer a formula as a supplement to mother's milk in the early stages of nursing, and because babies are given bottles of formula in the nursery as a matter of convenience to stop their crying. As a result, the babies aren't hungry when the're brought to their mothers, or they are spoiled for nursing at the breast because they have found it much easier to draw milk from a rubber nipple on a bottle.

Just to prove that you *can* nurse your baby if you are helped, here are some figures from recent studies of breast-feeding. In a survey of 31 hospitals, 4 hospitals, whose mothers want to nurse their babies and are given help doing it, reported 67 to 80 percent breast-fed babies. Another survey of 900 mothers showed that 6 out of 7 were able to nurse their babies.

When you and your baby get home, your husband can do a great deal to help you continue breast feeding. He helps by being especially considerate; by being enthusiastic about the nursing project; by lending a hand at housework and baby care; by overlooking a not-quite-immaculate house. And he'll help most of all by keeping you calm, relaxed, and free from worry.

All you need is the conviction that you can do it, that it's best for your baby, and that it will make you more beautiful rather than less lovely. And then you need to keep trying even though it takes many weeks before you succeed.

To avoid sore nipples

Your nipples may hurt a little at first from the suction Baby applies to extract his food. This soreness won't continue after your nipples become accustomed to nursing. And here are precautions that will keep them from becoming painfully sore:

1. See that Baby takes in his mouth the brown circle behind the nipple as well as the nipple itself.

2. When first put to the breast, he will probably not nurse more than four or five minutes. This is long enough until your nipples become used to it. Gradually let him nurse for longer intervals, but until your nipples become quite hardened, 12 minutes is long enough for one breast at a time. After your nipples are conditioned, 15 to 20 minutes is sufficient for one breast at a nursing.

3. Don't let Baby lie with the nipple in his mouth after he has finished nursing.

4. Protect your nipples from soiling, infection, or injury by always washing your hands with soap before touching them. Wash your nipples with sterile cotton and warm boiled water before nursing. Cover them between nursings with a clean handkerchief or plastic shields.

5. Wear a well-fitted nursing brassiere (one that opens in front for convenience) to support your breasts. If your breasts are very heavy, it's a good idea to wear a comfortable brassiere while you sleep.

If Baby doesn't empty the breast after he has nursed a sufficient length of time, empty it yourself with a breast pump or your hand.

If it becomes unduly painful for Baby to nurse, you should have your doctor examine your nipples. If they're cracked, Baby should not nurse until they're healed. You can either pump out or express the milk by hand, giving it to Baby in a bottle until your nipples are healed.

Tell your doctor immediately if any tender bumps or redness develops.

Frequent nursing and emptying of the

For the first few weeks after you get home from the hospital, lie down to nurse your baby. Lie on your side with Baby resting on your arm. Make yourself comfortable, but don't go to sleep while Baby is in your bed

breast at each feeding stimulates the production of milk. If your baby doesn't seem to get enough milk to satisfy him at a feeding, try offering the second breast for five minutes after he has emptied the first. Then start the next feeding with the unemptied breast.

After the first two weeks, let Baby nurse as long as he wants, provided he's actually getting milk. About 20 minutes nursing time usually satisfies, but some babies need longer.

Comfortable position helps in nursing

At first, of course, you'll nurse your baby lying down. Arrange yourself comfortably on one side, holding the baby on your arm. It's a good idea to continue this practice for at least six weeks after Baby's birth, and as much longer as you wish. The more rested and relaxed you are, the better your milk supply. But be sure you do not go to sleep while he is in your bed, as you may roll over on Baby and smother him.

After you no longer feel like reclining, choose a low, comfortable chair for your "nursing" chair. Rest your feet on a footstool, and put a pillow behind your back. Support the baby's head and back with your arm, and let your arm in turn rest upon your upraised knee. Hold him close to your breast and lean forward a bit, thus assisting the milk to flow more easily.

How to increase your breast milk

If your breast milk is scanty, you may be able to increase it by the following measures:

1. Take extra fluid and foods. Every day you'll need one quart more fluid and one-fourth more solid food than you ordinarily eat, or from 500 to 1,000 extra calories. A quart of milk will supply the fluid and 672 calories of food as well, so, one quart of milk a day added to your ordinary diet will give you both the solids and the fluids needed for nursing your baby. Milk is valuable because of its richness in calcium, which must be furnished the baby to form bones and teeth. If you can't drink all of the milk as a beverage, use it in soups, custards, malt drinks, or cocoa. Drink extra glasses of water daily, too.

   Continue the multivitamin capsules you took during pregnancy.

   Eat meat (beef, lamb, chicken, fish, bacon) twice a day, and three times if you want it; eggs; cooked cereal with sugar and cream once a day; potatoes; at least two vegetables besides potatoes; and fruit twice a day. Limit your desserts to fruits, puddings, and gelatines.

2. Let baby nurse frequently. The more milk your baby gets from your breast—or that you expel with pump or fingers—the more

there will be. Wait until your baby is a month old to start the "relief bottle." Then when you do begin, the 6 p.m. feeding is a good time to give it.

3. Rest and freedom from worry. Remember that the more relaxed and rested you are, the better your milk supply. So, rest as much as you can. Arrange a nap in the afternoon and get 8 to 9 hours sleep each night. Try to avoid excitement and worry.

Is your breast milk enough?

There's only one way to tell whether or not you have enough milk for your baby—by his weight. If each week he gains between 4 and 8 ounces or more, it's ample. But if you're doing all the things just listed and he still fails to gain 4 ounces a week, weigh him before and after each feeding, for a 24-hour period. Write down the amounts by which his weight increases after each feeding, and total them for the 24 hours. This will indicate how much milk he is receiving from you each day.

Inform your doctor of the amount. He may wish to examine the baby, or he may suggest giving formula to supplement breast milk.

Supplementary bottles should be offered only after Baby has nursed full time at the breast. Then give the bottle immediately and let him take what he wants.

Breast milk is usually thin, floury-looking, and bluish. This often leads mothers to think it isn't "rich" enough. Don't discontinue nursing for this reason, as that's the natural appearance of breast milk.

When to discontinue breast feedings

If your baby gets less than $\frac{1}{2}$ ounce of breast milk from you at a feeding, the milk isn't worth the trouble required to get it. The amount of milk Baby is receiving can be determined by weighing him before and after each feeding. Should this be consistently less than $\frac{1}{2}$ ounce after you've made every effort to increase your milk, the breast feedings may be abandoned and the bottle relied upon entirely. Get in touch with your doctor, however, as he may want to prescribe something to dry up your milk.

If Baby hiccups

If Baby swallows his food too fast, eats too much, or gets too much air, he may hiccup.

Usually this lasts only a few minutes and may be disregarded except to burp him.

If it persists, however, give him a few teaspoons of lukewarm boiled water.

Why burp the baby?

When tiny babies cry, they tend to swallow air. This also occurs frequently when they're eating. The swallowed air makes the baby uncomfortable and fussy, and takes up room in his stomach which should be reserved for food. After he has eaten, air may cause the milk to come up again, or make him wakeful.

How to burp him

Protect your clothing with a towel, diaper, or quilted pad when you bubble Baby, for when the air bubble comes up, some milk may come with it.

After Baby has nursed as much as he will from the breast or bottle, place him in one of the positions pictured on the opposite page and help him get rid of any air in his stomach.

An air bubble may also cause your baby to stop nursing halfway through a feeding. If it does, help him get rid of it.

Be sure to support Baby's wobbly little head if you hold him in the sitting position. Place your wrists on his back and cup your hands behind his head. Then gently rock him backward and forward.

After he gets the bubble up, continue the feeding. Burp him again when the feeding is finished. Otherwise an air bubble may make him fussy when he's laid in his crib.

Some babies need to be bubbled *before* a feeding as well as after. And other infants just don't burp at all. If yours is one of these, try to bubble him for a few minutes after each feeding, but don't worry if no air comes up.

After he's 5 or 6 months old, he'll be able to burp without help.

Formulas for bottle feeding

Cow's milk in some form or other is usually used for artificial feeding, for, properly modified, it has been found to be the most satisfactory substitute for human milk. Cow's milk in the following forms is suitable for infants:

1. *Boiled fresh milk.* Milk not too high in fat content (around $3\frac{1}{2}$ to 4 percent fat) is best. The milk should be boiled for three minutes before using (whether it has been

Good way to bubble a newborn baby is to lay him on his stomach on your lap, pat his back gently

Baby may like to be held against your shoulder, your hands firmly supporting his back and head

Baby may bubble best when held in sitting position on your lap, your hands supporting his back

pasteurized or not), to destroy harmful bacteria and to make it more digestible.

2. *Evaporated milk.* This is cow's milk which has been concentrated to one-half its original volume, sterilized, and sealed in airtight containers. The addition of water restores it to the consistency of ordinary milk. This milk, because of the treatment to which it is subjected, is a uniform, easily digested food which has been used with excellent success in infant feeding. For these reasons it has been coming into increasing favor with physicians.

Advantages of evaporated milk

Evaporated milk is more easily digested, uniform in quality, clean, and germfree than fresh milk. When the can isn't opened, it keeps indefinitely. Moreover, many allergic youngsters tolerate it better than fresh milk.

Evaporated milk has only one disadvantage, according to some medical authorities. The cream can't be removed. When there's any condition, therefore, such as severe diarrhea or eczema, in which it is desirable to remove cream before preparing the formula, fresh milk is sometimes more desirable.

It's believed now that a baby receiving evaporated milk is less likely to have eczema. If there is a tendency toward eczema, you may reduce it by boiling the unopened cans of milk in water for two hours. Some physicians, moreover, report that for cases of diarrhea, they have prescribed evaporated milk, without adding sweetening, with good results. Under all conditions, your doctor must be the judge of the course to follow.

These special qualities make evaporated milk particularly valuable for children when traveling or when refrigeration is inadequate.

Dried milk

This is milk from which practically all the water has been removed. It, also, is used with good results in infant feeding. Restore it to its orginal form by adding water in the proportion of 2 ounces to 1 level tablespoon of dried milk. Then modify according to the formula. Both whole and skimmed dried milk are obtainable. Use the whole milk, unless your doctor directs otherwise.

Canned dried milk will keep without refrigeration, but after the can is opened, it must be kept tightly covered and cold.

Fortified milk

Most evaporated milk is now fortified with 400 U.S.P. units of vitamin D. Most dairies have fortified fresh milk. If your baby is receiving fortified milk, it may not be necessary to give any additional vitamin D.

A formula if refrigeration fails

For certain conditions, doctors prescribe a lactic- or citric-acid formula in which sweet milk is soured by adding acid. This partially predigests the milk, and makes it possible to use a stronger milk mixture.

Such an acid formula made with evaporated milk has the advantage, especially valuable in an emergency period, of keeping 24 hours without refrigeration. The formula can be mixed, and the bottles kept standing in cold water. Citric- or lactic-acid formulas are given here and in following chapters. The acid formula is well tolerated by most babies.

Proprietary foods

In addition to the formulas using fresh, evaporated, or dried milk, there are many commercial baby foods. These consist of different varieties of carbohydrate (the element added to cow's milk to make it more nearly like mother's milk) and in some instances, of dried or concentrated milk. They're prepared by adding boiled water or milk, and are used widely. Many different formulas may be obtained in this dried, powdered, or concentrated form, including lactic-acid formulas, protein milk (for diarrhea), and formulas made without milk for hyperallergic babies.

Sweetenings generally used

To supply an infant's energy requirement, some form of carbohydrate is usually added. This is done in the form of a sweetening, though various kinds of cereal, such as barley, are used for certain conditions. Almost any of the sweetening agencies can be used in formulas—cane, beet, or brown sugar, milk sugar, honey, molasses, maple syrup—but most often employed are corn syrup and dextrin-maltose mixtures.

"Corn syrup" as used in the formulas in this book refers to commercially prepared table syrup. "Dextrin-maltose mixtures" mean commercial preparations of maltose and dextrin sugars in powdered form.

A good basic formula

A healthy, full-term infant does well on almost any one of many milk mixtures. The following formulas have been used successfully for thousands of babies. If your baby is checked regularly by a doctor, he will give you a formula for him. Use one of these only if you're unable to consult a doctor.

First formula using fresh milk

(one day's supply)

14 ounces whole milk
7 ounces water
2 tablespoons corn syrup or
4 level tablespoons dextrin maltose

How to prepare: see pages 70-73.

Baby at first will probably take about three ounces at a feeding, if he relies entirely upon the bottle. He'll take less if he gets some milk from you.

First formula using evaporated milk

(one day's supply)

7 ounces (1 small can) evaporated milk
14 ounces boiled water
2 tablespoons corn syrup or
4 level tablespoons dextrin maltose

How to prepare: see pages 70-73.

Citric- or lactic-acid formula

As the addition of citric or lactic acid makes cow's milk more easily digested, a considerably stronger formula can be given, and excellent nutritional results are secured. Babies receiving this formula, incidentally, vomit and spit up less than on sweet milk.

First formula using evaporated milk and lactic or citric acid

(one day's supply)

8 ounces evaporated milk
10 ounces water
½ teaspoon 25 percent solution citric acid
or 30 drops U.S.P. 85 percent lactic acid
2 tablespoons corn syrup or
4 tablespoons dextrin-maltose mixture

How to prepare an acid formula: Boil the water and sweetening together for 5 minutes; then chill. Add the acid to the water mixture when it is chilled; then very slowly pour into the milk (which must also be chilled), stirring all the time. Divide into as many bottles as there are feedings. Caution: With lactic acid especially, great care must be taken to add acid slowly drop by drop, stirring constantly. Milk must be very cold. Use no more acid than exact amount recommended, as an excess of acid can make Baby ill. Citric acid isn't as difficult to handle, as the formula is less likely to be spoiled if materials are not cold enough or acid is added too rapidly.

To warm for a feeding, place bottle in a pan of warm water. Acid formulas must not be heated rapidly or too hot. A baby relying upon the bottle alone will probably take around three ounces at a feeding.

If Baby is getting breast milk as well as the bottle, let him nurse first, and then take as much or as little from the bottle as he likes.

It's best not to give Baby, at a later feeding, any formula he has previously left in the bottle. Germs can multiply quickly in warm milk.

What kind of bottles and nipples?

Any type nursing bottle which can be scrubbed out thoroughly is satisfactory. The bottles should be heatproof, also. Disposable, plastic nursing bottles are now available, but each can be used only once. These bottles do not need to be sterilized before use. The nipples must be sterilized, however.

Any nipple that can be turned inside out, scrubbed, and boiled is likewise suitable.

Keep bottles and nipples germfree

As soon as Baby has taken a feeding, the bottle should be rinsed and filled with cold water until it's scrubbed with soapy water and brush and sterilized. One or two tablespoons of vinegar in the water will dissolve the lime deposit on bottles boiled in hard water.

Immediately after each use, clean the nipple thoroughly, for the butterfat in milk causes rubber to deteriorate. Turn the nipple inside out and wash with warm soapy water and a small brush. Rinse thoroughly. To make sure feeding holes of nipple are clear of milk particles, fill nipple with cold water. Then hold it between first and second fingers, with thumb over opening at base of nipple. Press with thumb, and water should squirt through

all feeding holes. To open any clogged feeding holes, shake salt down inside the wet nipple to form a paste. Then squeeze and roll nipple between fingers to force the paste through the feeding holes. Then rinse again.

Until you are ready to sterilize them, keep used nipples in a jar separate from those that are still sterile.

If you use corks, rubber stoppers, nipple shields, or caps, they must be washed and boiled each time before they're used.

If for any reason there's only one bottle and nipple available, these should be scrubbed and boiled each time before they're used.

Nipple holes must be right

Amateur parents often have difficulty making the right-size holes in nipples. Baby gets nothing but air for his efforts if the hole is too small. Or he may get tired before he gets enough milk and be uncomfortable from the air he has swallowed. If the hole is too large, the milk will come out too fast and cause him to choke or have indigestion. The milk should come out in large drops, one at a time, not run out in a stream.

Here's how to enlarge a too-small hole, or make a hole in nipples that have none:

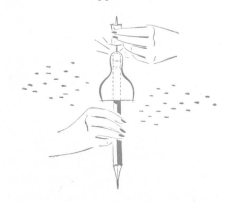

Turn nipple inside out over eraser end of a pencil. Insert blunt end of fine needle in a cork; heat the sharp point over flame. Stick needle into nipple; pull out quickly. Repeat if hole is still too small

The longer the hot needle is held against the nipple, the larger the hole will be. It's best, therefore, to enlarge it gradually, trying the nipple each time until the hole is just big enough and not too big. Sterilize the nipple before using.

Right care of Baby's bottles and nipples

When Baby finishes a feeding, throw away any formula that's left and immediately rinse out the bottle thoroughly under the cold-water faucet. Then fill the bottle with water and set it aside until next dishwashing time for proper washing with a stiff brush, soap, and hot water

With constant use and daily boiling, nipples soon deteriorate and collapse. Make them last as long as possible by taking care of them as shown here.

If you sterilize nipples and rubber shields in an open pan, wrap them in gauze or in a small white cloth sack so they'll sink. Add some salt to the water in which they're boiled to help keep the rubber from getting soft. (1 teaspoon of salt to a quart of water.)

Wait until the water is boiling before you drop the nipples and caps in. Then watch the clock—overboiling ruins the rubber. And don't let the pan boil dry, for this will scorch the nipples and make them worthless.

Once a day, boil for five minutes all of the utensils used in fixing Baby's formula. A sterilizer, pressure cooker or any large pan with a tight cover will do the job well. Bottle racks which fit inside the sterilizing pan are a great convenience for lifting articles out of the hot water

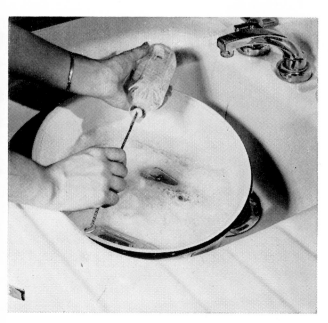

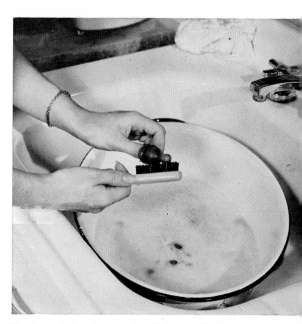

Proper washing for Baby's bottles means a vigorous scrubbing with a good bottle brush and lots of hot water and soap. Use a brush that reaches all corners of the bottle easily. Rinse the bottles out several times in hot water until there's no trace of soap left. Place in the bottle rack until time to sterilize them

Nipples and bottle caps should be scrubbed right after use. Turn nipples and caps inside out (if using rubber kind), and scrub with a brush in warm, soapy water. Force water through holes. Rinse well and store in dry, covered jar until sterilizing time

If you sterilize in an open pan, lay a cloth or wire rack on the bottom. Be sure water covers utensils while they're boiling. Don't let water boil dry, as glassware may break. Leave handle of tongs above water so you can reach it easily. Lift equipment out with tongs and place on sterile towel to dry, hollow pieces upside down

Boil nipples and rubber caps for 3 minutes only, in separate pan (not copper). Add teaspoonful of salt to water. Nipples shouldn't float. Lift out with tongs; drain on sterile towel. Keep nipples in covered, sterile jar, or put on bottles, and cap

Pour into sterile measuring pitch
required amount of hot boiled wate
Fill extra bottles with the remai
ing boiled water for drinking, and ca

◄ Let equipment drain in sterilizer a fe
minutes; then, with tongs, lift o
onto sterile towel. Turn bottles rig
side up. Funnel should rest in bott

How to prepare
a formula

Keep all the utensils for preparing Baby's formula separate from your household equipment, and scrupulously clean.

Sterilize all utensils you use by boiling for 5 minutes just before you prepare the formula, unless you're using terminal method. (See page 72.) If you use an open pan, be sure the water covers all articles. Two inches of water is enough if you're using a pan with a tight lid.

While the equipment is being sterilized, boil the water for the formula for 5 minutes. Keep it on the stove until you're ready for it as sweetening needs hot water to dissolve.

If you use the type nipples which are put on the bottles just before feeding time, be sure to store them in a sterile, covered jar until needed. Before putting the bottles of formula in the refrigerator, cover with screw caps, corks, disposable paper caps, or waxed paper.

Assemble all equipment before beginning. To prepare formula, you'll need: can of evaporated or bottle of fresh pasteurized milk; syrup or other sweetening; as much boiled water as needed in formula, plus some for drinking; glass measuring pitcher; measuring spoon; strainer; tongs; funnel; can opener; knife; all-metal, long-handled mixing spoon; nursing bottles, nipples, and caps.

Measure the syrup and add to water. If formula calls for dextrin maltose or other powdered sweetening, level spoon with back of knife. Stir well

Before puncturing the can, wash and scald the top thoroughly. Open with sterile can opener, and add enough milk to water and syrup to equal total amount of formula

Stir the formula so all ingredients are mixed thoroughly. Use a sterile, long-handled, metal mixing spoon. This formula requires no cooking

Place sterile strainer in funnel and divide formula into bottles according to amount needed for a feeding. Prepare a day's supply at one time

Steady bottle on table. Hold edge of the nipple with index finger of left hand. Grasp tab with right hand; pull nipple over bottle. Then cover with nipple cap

To prepare formula with fresh milk, wash the top of bottle and wipe dry. Shake bottle several times. Use fresh milk within 24 hours after delivery

Combine ingredients in pan and boil 5 minutes. Cool; remeasure in sterile graduate. Add enough boiled water to replace that lost by evaporation

Pour into sterile bottles; store in refrigerator until needed. To heat for feeding, stand bottle in a deep pan of hot water. Water should come up to the neck of the bottle

Turn off heat when bottle is in pan. Warm formula to body heat. Test by sprinkling a few drops on inside of wrist. Don't overheat acid formula

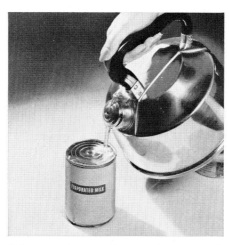

Pour required amount of water into measuring pitcher. Measure and add sweetening. Stir until dissolved. Hot water is needed for dextrin maltose

Before opening, scrub top of evaporated-milk can with hot soapsuds and rinse by pouring water over top. If using fresh milk, wash the bottle or carton under hot-water faucet

Punch 2 holes in can top to open. Shake fresh milk (except homogenized) to mix cream. Add to mixture up to amount of total formula. Stir

Another method—
terminal sterilization

Here's a new fast method of sterilizing Baby's formula and equipment all in one simple operation. The word "terminal" itself implies that the sterilization of the bottles and formula is the final step in the operation instead of the first.

The large pieces of equipment used in mixing the formula do not have to be sterilized before use as they must be in other methods. These items must, however, be washed perfectly clean with hot, soapy water and brush, and rinsed thoroughly.

The bottles, nipples, and nipple covers are not sterilized until after the formula has been mixed and bottled. The bottles, nipples, and covers should, of course, be scrupulously clean, the same as the mixing equipment.

Mix the formula with water just as it comes from the faucet and milk as it comes from bottle or can. Then pour into bottles, put nipples

and caps on loosely, and sterilize the bottled formula, either in a deep, covered pan or a pressure cooker.

This method is perfectly safe if you follow the directions here. However, if you live in a rural area and use well water or raw milk, either follow the conventional methods for preparing evaporated-milk or fresh-milk formulas given on the preceding pages, or preboil these two ingredients before preparing the formula if you want to adopt this "terminal" method.

Any tall pan, pail, or kettle may be used instead of a steam or pressure cooker as pictured here. Just be sure it's tall enough so the nipple covers will not touch the lid. If you use a pail, remove the handle and metal fasteners so the lid will fit down evenly. Lay a wire mesh rack or clean cloth in the bottom so the bottles will not touch the container.

Length of boiling time depends upon the

Pour formula through funnel into bottles in amounts needed for feedings. Also fill one or two bottles with cold tap water for drinking water

Place inverted nipples and caps on bottles. Or cover upright nipples with nipple shields. Caps or shields should be loose or tilted, or inside pressure from steam will break bottles

Place bottles on rack in sterilizer. Add water. Cover. If utensil is not the pressure-cooker type, boil 15 minutes in water up to milk level

With pressure sterilizer, follow manufacturer's directions. After sterilizing time is up, remove either type from heat. Open after 5 minutes

Then place bottles in pan of cold water for 10 minutes, or run cold water over them. To avoid scum, shake bottles frequently while cooling. Don't let water splash on nipple caps

After bottles cool, screw caps on tightly, or press covers down firmly over nipples. Shake each bottle again and then store in refrigerator

type of pan you're using. Follow the instructions recommended for your type cooker, or allow water in nonpressure containers to boil rapidly for 15 minutes.

Scum tends to form on any milk mixture that has been boiled. It will clog the holes in the nipple when Baby is nursing. You can avoid this by cooling the formula as quickly as possible after it has been sterilized. Stand the bottles in cold water and shake occasionally from side to side. If you use upright nipples and shields, stretch a small piece of sterile gauze over the top of the bottle before putting the nipple on. The gauze is left on when Baby nurses, and will strain the milk by keeping the scum inside the bottle.

Terminal sterilization is not practical if you are using disposable plastic bottles.

How to give a bottle feeding

Wash your hands thoroughly. Take formula from the refrigerator, shake to mix cream, and warm it to body heat in a pan of hot water. If a sweet-milk feeding is overheated, it can be cooled, and no harm is done. But take care not to overheat an acid formula, for the curd is likely to separate from the whey. If tested with a thermometer, the water in the pan should be from 98 to 105 degrees. Turn off heat under the pan when bottle is in the water. It's better to use a deep pan so that the nursing bottle is completely submerged up to the base of the nipple. If a shallow pan is used, shake the bottle frequently so the contents will heat evenly. You may find it more convenient to use an electric or chemical bottle-warmer, rather than a pan.

Remove nipple shield, or if you use nipples that are turned into the bottles during refrigeration, unscrew and turn nipple right side up.

If you do not put on the nipples (covered by nipple caps) when you bottle the formula, place nipple on the bottle now; always be careful not to touch either the end of nipple which goes into the baby's mouth or the bottle rim. See illustration, page 71.

Test temperature of milk by sprinkling a few drops on inside of wrist. It should feel warm, not hot. This is also a test for the size of the hole in the nipple. If milk is not warm, return bottle to hot water. If it's too hot, let it cool a little.

Before picking Baby up, put on a waterproof cover-all apron or have lap and shoulder protectors handy, so you won't be concerned about spit-ups and dampness.

If the room is cool, wrap the bottle in a clean diaper to keep the milk warm while Baby is nursing. And, unless the weather is very hot, keep a lightweight blanket loosely around Baby, so he won't become chilled during the feeding period. If he's wet or soiled, change him before the feeding. See that his shirt and diaper are not too tight when he's feeding.

Always hold Baby in your arms while feeding him. Assume a comfortable position in a comfortable chair. Hold him close to you so he feels the same security and warmth he'd have in nursing. Even visit with him a little while he's eating unless he is too ravenous for anything but food.

The nipple should be firm to encourage strenuous sucking. If the holes in the nipple are the proper size, it should take Baby about 20 minutes to finish a bottle, providing he sucks continuously.

Tip the bottle so that both nipple and neck of bottle are constantly filled with formula, so Baby will not suck air.

Let your baby decide how much he wants. When he has obviously had enough, it is unwise to make him take more.

After a feeding, help Baby get up any swallowed air (see page 64). He may need to be burped during the feeding. This should be done only at a real pause in his sucking.

After a feeding, place Baby in his crib on his right or left side.

What to do if Baby vomits

Spitting up, or regurgitation, is common and isn't significant as long as the weekly gain is made. It may be due to overfeeding. Try giving a little less milk. If Baby's head is raised a little by slipping a small pillow *under the mattress*, he'll probably spit up less in bed. The condition usually stops when a baby begins taking solid food.

Forceful, or projectile, vomiting of so large a part of the feedings that weight gain is impossible, is significant and may mean there's an obstruction at the outlet of the stomach. Your doctor should be notified at once.

Repeated or constant vomiting is another signal that something is wrong. It should be investigated by your doctor.

Bowel movements if Baby is breast fed

Constipation, like thumbsucking, is often a source of unnecessary worry to mothers.

The breast-fed baby is almost never constipated, but ordinarily has frequent stools during the first month or six weeks. When this is the case, the stools may be green and contain curds. (Green, because the bile hasn't had time to change from green to yellow, and curds because they haven't had time to pack together.) From five to six stools a day is normal during this period.

On the other hand, a baby may have only one stool in two or more days and still be perfectly healthy and all right. Doctors now make longer and longer the period the baby may be allowed to go before artificial aid is given. They assure us that there is seldom cause for alarm about the bowels of the breast-fed baby. Always consult your physician, however, if you suspect something may be wrong.

Bowel movements if Baby is bottle fed

Cow's-milk stools are more pasty than breast-milk stools. Normally there are from one to three daily—dry, pasty, and firm. A concentrated whole-milk mixture, such as the citric- or lactic-acid formula, will produce a large stool. A diluted mixture will give a small, yellow stool. The color becomes more brown when cereal is added to the diet. Beets and spinach may affect the color, too. As the food range increases, there may be more stools.

If Baby is constipated

As long as Baby's stools are soft and smooth, he isn't constipated no matter how far apart movements may be. But when the stools are so hard they're passed with straining and difficulty, your baby is constipated. Sometimes stools are so hard to pass there's blood on the outside. Blood-streaked stools should always be brought to your doctor's attention.

Constipation is often caused by a lack of water in the intestinal tract, due to Baby's sweating because of overdressing or overheating. The formula may be too strong in milk content, or may not have enough carbohydrate (sweetening). Check the milk content and add to the amount of sweetening. Offer Baby cool boiled water between feedings. Also, one or two teaspoons of prune juice or prune pulp may be given each day. Doctors advise that you be slow to use suppositories or enemas since Baby might learn to rely upon artificial stimulation.

Diarrhea? Call your doctor

If the baby's stools have been of the same consistency—whether soft and smooth, or firm and pasty, and then suddenly become loose, watery, frequent, greenish, or contain mucus, this may be an indication of diarrhea.

Baby may be receiving too large an amount of sweetening in his formula. Reduce the sweetening to see if this is the cause. If the condition continues, stop all food, including orange juice, give Baby plenty of cool boiled water to drink, and call your doctor at once. Diarrhea isn't a matter for home medication. (See Diarrhea, Diseases Chart, page 191.)

The danger of diarrhea lies in its rapid draining of the water from the tissues. Dehydration and acidosis may result. Hence the necessity for stopping the diarrhea and replacing the fluid that is lost. You may think he needs food, but withholding it will shorten the illness.

As the diarrhea lessens, you may offer skimmed milk, mixed with water in the proportions of his usual fresh-milk formula, boiled for five minutes and with no sweetening added. For an older baby, gradually add solid foods, beginning with a smooth nonlaxative cereal.

When to change diapers

Change diapers before and after a feeding, after a bowel movement, and whenever he seems to be uncomfortable because of a wet diaper. But don't disturb his sleep just to change him. Rest is more important. Baby won't be cold because of a wet diaper, if he's warm enough otherwise.

If he wakes and cries, change him, but check to see if there is some other reason for his crying. He may be too warm or too cold. Or a gas bubble may be bothering him.

All this doesn't mean that your baby should be allowed to go for long periods without changing. Prolonged stays in wet or soiled diapers may irritate his skin.

The buttocks and genital area must be thoroughly cleaned each time the diaper is changed. If the baby has only urinated, cleanse the skin by wiping with plenty of warm water and cotton. Dry thoroughly with more cotton or a soft towel. Then oil the area or apply lotion before diapering.

After a bowel movement, gently wipe off with soft toilet paper or tissues any feces that may be clinging to the skin. Then wash carefully with mild soap, warm water, and cotton. Rinse with clear, warm water. Dry thoroughly. Then apply oil or lotion. If you use powder, don't shake it around loosely in the air.

Care of diapers

Diapers should never be used twice without washing them in soapsuds, rinsing thoroughly in 4 changes of clean, hot water, and drying completely, preferably in the sun and air. Diapers dried in the sun need be boiled only twice weekly. If dried indoors, or if Baby has diaper rash or diarrhea, they should be boiled for 10 minutes every time they're washed.

Use a mild soap and no chemicals (soda, starch, or bluing). The water should be soft.

When you take them down from the line, smooth them carefully, fold, and put away.

How to diaper your baby

New materials and ways of folding make it possible to have just one size of diaper for the entire time your baby will wear them. Moreover, this can be made to fit him at every stage of his development. Some methods of diapering are the panel fold and the kite fold, shown below. These put the extra thickness in the middle where it's needed, while fitting Baby's dimensions quite comfortably.

As Baby expands, you will have to change from either of these folds, and adopt the triple fold for oblong diapers or a double fold for square diapers.

Besides the square and oblong diapers, there are fitted ones which fasten with tapes or gripper-type fasteners, and also several types of disposable ones which make trips and outings easier.

Also available are paper diaper liners. Placed between Baby's buttocks and the diaper to catch the bowel movements, they prevent hard-to-remove stains.

Waterproof outer diapers should be used only for outings or dress-up occasions. They may chafe Baby's skin if used continuously. And there is also a tendency not to change the diaper as often as necessary. These diapers should be made of a porous, washable material, or else be loose enough so they won't be airtight. Neither kind should bind.

1. Panel fold for oblong diaper. Bring right end over to about 8 inches from left end. Turn right end back upon itself to about 3 inches from fold. Now bring the left end over even with first fold on the extreme right

2. Kite fold for square diaper. Fold in two sides to make a long V. Turn down remaining flap, forming triangle. Bring point of V up to straight edge of flap. Makes thick center panel

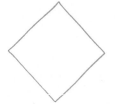 

3. Fold over one-third of end of square diaper. Then fold to three thicknesses. Extra thickness in front for boys, in back for girls if they lie on their backs. Fits the infant comfortably, but not adjustable as Baby grows

4. Fitted diapers are available or can be made. Double row of fasteners makes the diaper adjustable as Baby grows. Extra thickness is provided in the center where it's needed. This diaper can also be fastened with pins

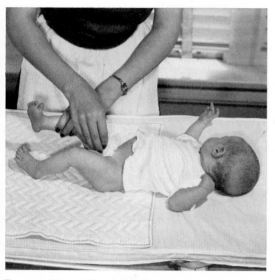

Remove diaper. If soiled, fold under as you unpin to hold bowel movement. Place pad under Baby's hips to catch moisture. Wash genitals and buttocks with cotton moistened in warm water. After bowel movement, wipe with soft tissue, wash with soap and water, rinse. Always wash from front to back. Pat dry with cotton or towel

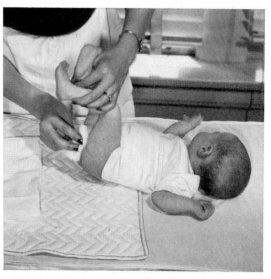

With your hand or a piece of cotton, apply oil or lotion to the genital area and buttocks, taking care to oil all folds and creases thoroughly. Powder lightly if you wish. Be careful not to shake powder around loosely in the air, or Baby may breathe it in. Have clean diaper at hand, folded to fit. Keep pins nearby, but out of Baby's reach

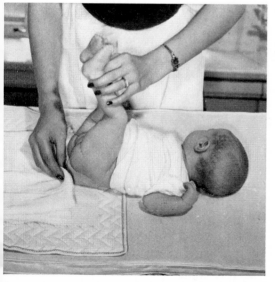

Grasp Baby's ankles between your thumb and middle finger, inserting your index finger between his ankles to keep from pressing them together. Gently raise Baby's legs and hips clear of the table, and slide folded diaper under him. Bring diaper up between legs, extra thickness in front for boys, in back for girls if they lie on back

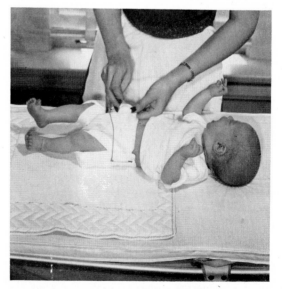

Pin diaper on each side, back overlapping front. Always keep your finger next to Baby when pinning to avoid pricking him. Shirt may be pinned at sides between front and back fold of diaper. Then smooth shirt down over diaper in front to keep Baby's tummy warm. May be pinned if you wish. Fold shirt up in back to keep dry

How to give an oil or sponge bath

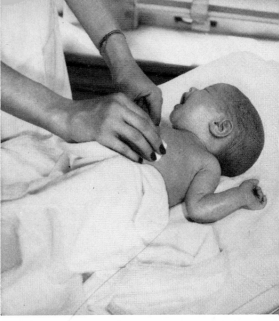

If your baby is very tiny and delicate, your doctor may suggest an oil bath for him. Or you may prefer oil to water if room is cold, or Baby's skin is irritated. Follow the same directions for an oil bath as shown here for a sponge bath, or work with Baby on a table

Until Baby's navel or circumcision is healed, and until you have fully regained your strength, you'll be giving him a sponge bath. Or, if your baby is particularly tiny and delicate, or has dry or irritated skin, your doctor may even recommend that you give him an oil bath for the first month or six weeks.

The procedure for both is the same, except that oil alone is used for an oil bath. Whichever kind you give your baby, know what you're going to do before you begin.

Many mothers find it simplest to bathe their babies before the midmorning feeding. But if it's more convenient for you just before his 6 p.m. feeding, do it then. Don't, however, give a bath just after a feeding.

Choose a warm room, preferably one that's sunny. Be sure there are no drafts in the room, and the temperature is from 75 to 80 degrees. Probably the most convenient place for you will be either the bathroom or kitchen, which are usually warm rooms and where the warm water is handy.

Get all equipment ready before you begin. You'll need: low table; chair; 1 or 2 pans of warm water; cake of mild soap in soap dish; cotton swabs; large pieces of cotton or soft washcloth; large bath towel to cover Baby; small towel with which to dry him; baby lotion or oil; powder, if you wish; nursing bottle of warm sterile water; diaper; safety pins; shirt; kimono or nightgown; and a bath apron

for you. Have a few toothpicks at hand to clean Baby's nails. Use the blunt tip. A bath thermometer is a convenience, but not a necessity.

Before you begin, scrub your hands and nails with hot, soapy water. Keep your nails short and round so you won't scratch Baby.

Fill pans with soft water that registers 95 to 100 degrees on the bath thermometer, or which feels comfortably warm to your elbow. If the water you use is hard, either boil it first and let cool, or add a water softener.

Sit down, with Baby in your lap, and you are ready to begin. (If you use a bath table, sit beside it on a stool of convenient height.) Proceed as in the photographs.

Give Baby a drink of water. Then open his mouth by pressing on his chin with your finger. Inspect his mouth, tongue, and gums to be sure they are clean and pink. The inside of his mouth should never be touched, though.

If Baby's finger- or toenails are long, they can be cut best when he's asleep. Use a sharp manicure scissors that has been wiped with alcohol, or boiled for a few minutes.

Pay special attention to the genital organs. If your baby is an uncircumcised boy, ask your doctor if he wants you to clean under the foreskin. He'll tell you how. For girls, separate the folds of the vulva, and clean. Always wash and wipe from the front toward the back in this area.

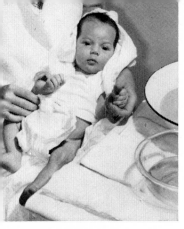
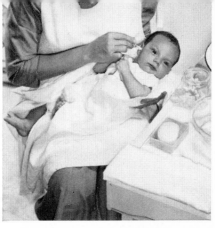
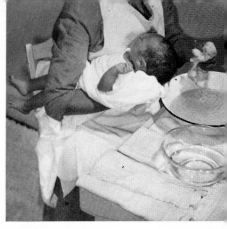

ssemble all supplies on a low table be-
de you. Sit on a low chair with Baby
big towel in your lap. Unpin diaper
it do not remove. Take the soiled
irt and diaper off as you go along

Give Baby a drink of sterile water to cleanse
mouth. Clean nose and ears, if needed, with
moistened swabs. Wash eyelids and face with
cotton or soft washcloth dipped in warm
water, working outward from corners of eyes

Shampoo scalp 3 times a week with
soapy water. Rinse well, supporting
Baby's head and back over basin with
your hand and arm. Pat head dry. If
scale forms, apply oil; leave on overnight

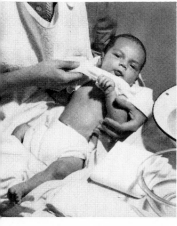
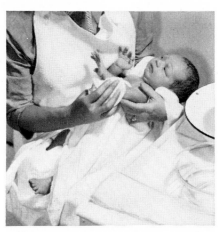
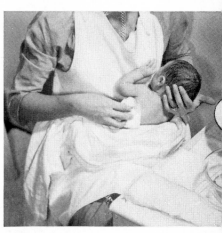

emove his shirt, keeping rest of Baby
vered as much as possible with the
g towel on your lap. Soap his chest,
ms and hands with a mild soap. Pay
ecial attention to folds in his skin

Rinse neck, chest, arms, and hands with
clean, warm water. Be sure to get all soap
out of creases, or his skin may chafe. Pat
dry with soft towel—never rub. Clean under
his nails with the blunt end of toothpick

Gently turn Baby over on right side to
reach his back and buttocks. Be sure to
support his head with your left hand.
With soft washcloth, soap and rinse his
back, then dry thoroughly with towel

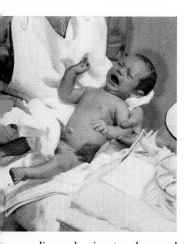
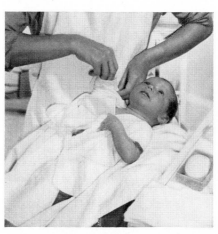
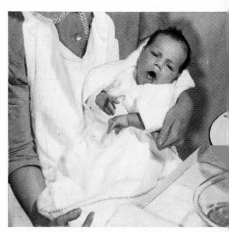

emove diaper, leaving towel around
aby. Wash and rinse abdomen, geni-
ls, legs, and feet. If navel is unhealed,
pe with alcohol on sterile cotton.
ver with sterile gauze and binder

Apply oil or lotion. Powder lightly if you
wish. Now put on Baby's clean clothes which
should be waiting, in order, on the far side
of table. Dress him right on your lap. Once
a week, weigh Baby before dressing him

All clean and sweet-smelling, Baby re-
minds you that it's time for his meal
and bed. Giving a sponge bath like
this is recommended during the early
weeks to save standing and bending

How to give a tub bath

By the time Baby's navel and circumcision have healed, he's ready to graduate from a sponge to a tub bath, unless your doctor advises otherwise. Use the same arrangements as for the sponge baths, except to substitute a small tub or bath table for the basin or pan.

The folding canvas bath table is convenient, but any pan or tub that's large enough and which can be kept clean easily will do.

The first few times you give Baby a tub bath, use no more than 3 inches of water in the tub so he will become accustomed to the water gradually.

Leave Baby in his shirt and diaper, covered by a towel or cotton blanket, while you wash and dry his face and head. Remove the shirt first, then the diaper, when you're ready to soap those areas. When he's all soaped, he goes into the tub to be rinsed. Work quickly on soaping, so lather doesn't dry on his skin.

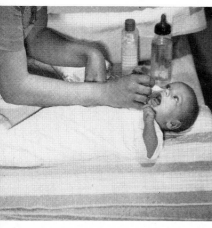

4 With cotton swabs rolled to a point, moistened in water, gently clean ears, nostrils, and the creases around ears and nose. Use a clean swab for each part. Don't poke in nostrils or inner ear

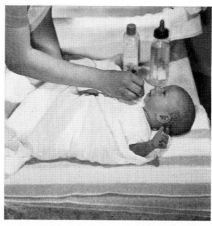

5 Next wash Baby's face with soft washcloth or cotton and clean, warm water. Pat dry. Moisten cotton with clear water and wash eyelids, not eyes. Work outward from inner corner. Use fresh cotton for each eyelid

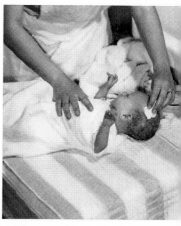

6 Baby's hair needs a shampoo about 3 times a week. Use clear water other times. First, soap his scalp well with a mild, neutral soap, using your hand, a piece of clean cotton, or a washcloth

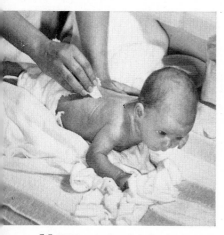

10 With your hand under his armpit, thumb clasping his arm, turn Baby over on his stomach to soap his back. Handle him carefully; he's slippery. Loosen diaper and soap buttocks, too

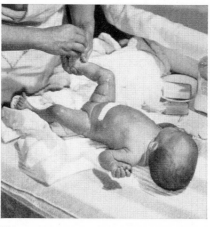

11 Remove diaper and soap abdomen, groin, legs, and feet. Wash carefully genital folds, and between toes. (Adhesive strip on Baby shown here is precaution against hernia. Your doctor will advise you if it is needed)

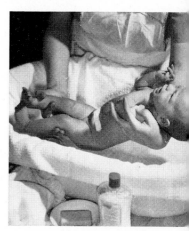

12 With your left arm supporting Baby's head and shoulders, fingers firmly clasping left arm near shoulder, right hand grasping legs, forefinger between ankles, lower him into the tub

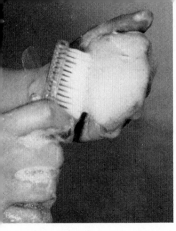

Before you begin Baby's bath, scrub your hands and fingernails with warm, soapy water and a brush. Put on clean apron. Have all supplies that you'll need laid out within reach on table

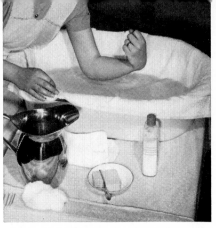

2 Line tub with clean towel and pour in 2 to 3 inches of water. Temperature of water should be from 88 to 105 degrees, or feel comfortably warm to your elbow. Keep a pitcher of hot water handy to warm the bath water

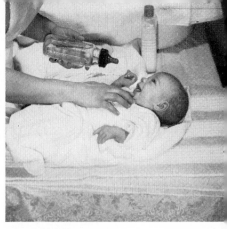

3 Lift Baby onto clean towel on table. Give him a drink of sterile water to cleanse his mouth. Inspect the inside of his mouth, gums, and tongue, but be careful not to touch inside his mouth

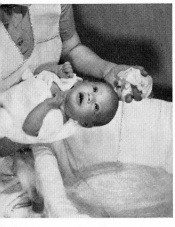

Hold Baby's head over the tub and rinse his scalp thoroughly with washcloth. Support his back and hips with your arm, your hand supporting his head, his legs tucked under your arm

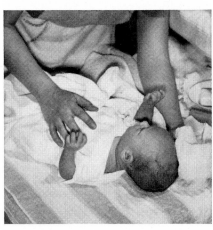

8 Lay Baby back on the table and dry his scalp thoroughly. Rub head gently with a soft absorbent towel. After bath is finished, you may oil his scalp lightly with baby or olive oil if you wish, then brush hair in place

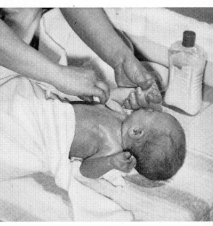

9 Remove shirt, and with your hand, cotton, or extra washcloth, soap Baby's chest, arms, and hands, especially folds in neck, under arms, and hands. Keep him covered up as much as possible

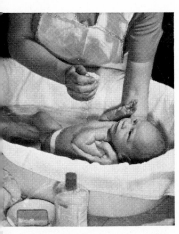

3 Keep firm grasp of his arm with one hand, supporting his back and head. Rinse with washcloth in other hand. Lift Baby back on table, cover with towel, and pat dry. Apply oil or lotion

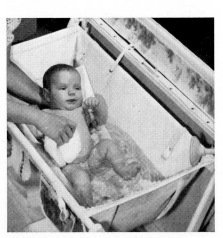

14 If you're using folding table tub, have warm water ready in tub. Hold Baby securely when raising top, after soaping him. If tub has hammock and spray, soap and rinse in tub. Test spray temperature carefully

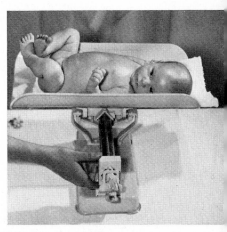

15 Bathtime is weighing time. Once a week before dressing, place him on scales. Weigh pad separately and deduct from total. Record weight. Report any unusual change to doctor

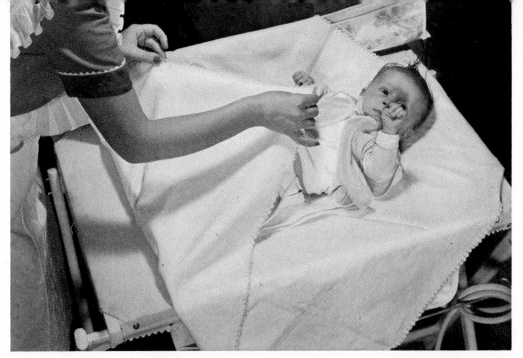

Dressed in diaper, shirt, and sacque, baby is folded and pinned envelope-style in outing-flannel square, on which has been laid 12x18-inch moistureproof sheeting and pad. He is snug, warm, yet free to kick

Dress your baby the easy way

His clothes should be simple and
carefully chosen for his comfort

Get Baby's clothes on him as easily and quickly as possible. Handle him gently and be careful not to jerk or twist a tiny arm or leg. Always reach through a sleeve for his hand.

When you get out the bath articles, lay Baby's clean clothes on a handy chair or table, arranged in the order in which you'll put them on him.

Use garments made of washable materials, most of which need no ironing. They should slip on and off freely and quickly, and should never interfere with his exercising. If your house is cold and you have to put more clothes on Baby, be sure to leave them loose enough so he'll be comfortable and free to move.

In warm weather and hot climates, your baby need wear only his shirt and diaper. If the weather is very hot, he can appear in a diaper alone.

At night your baby wears a nightgown over his shirt and diaper. After he's 6 months old, nightgown and diaper alone are sufficient.

The nightgown is long, opens part way in front or back, and has drawstrings in the bottom hem and cuffs so his toes and fingers will stay warm.

During early infancy you may use short sacques and nightgowns, and wrap Baby in outing-flannel squares or cotton blankets. Spread the blanket on a table diamondwise. Lay Baby on it with his head near upper point. Fold lower point up over his feet and stomach, then lap the side points over it, envelope-fashion. Fasten with safety pins.

Frequently this is enough covering for Baby even in bed, if your house is warm. Another blanket may be placed over him if additional cover is needed.

A small waterproof pad inside the wrapping blanket will keep it from getting wet.

One dainty dress and petticoat are sufficient for dress-up occasions. Don't have it too long, and don't starch it or it may scratch Baby's tender skin. Booties may also be worn.

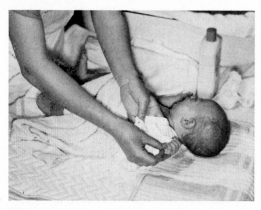

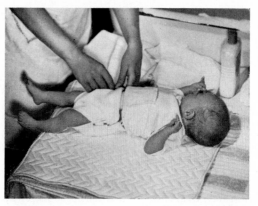

Baby's shirt goes on one arm at a time. Put your fingers up sleeve, grasp his fist, and guide it through. Sleeveless closed shirt is pulled over his feet. Roll Baby to opposite side and smooth shirt under his back

Fasten the shirt, then fold it up in back so it doesn't reach below hipline. Put the diaper on and pin it, taking care it isn't too snug or too loose. Smooth shirt down over diaper in front to keep tummy warm

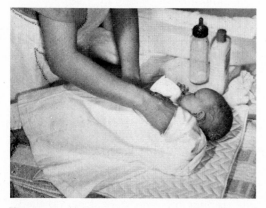

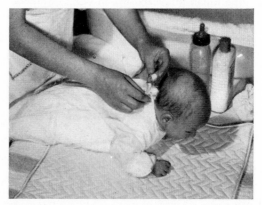

Kimono or nightgown goes on next. Long-sleeved shirt and kimono may go on together. Place shirt sleeve inside kimono sleeve and gather them together in one hand. Reach through for Baby's arm.

Many mothers prefer to tie kimonos in back, so Baby's hands don't catch in ribbon or tape ties. Spread lower back of the kimono open to keep it dry. Front opening is equally satisfactory if you like it

Baby's "company dress" is put on over his head, unless it opens all the way down front or back. Petticoat is slipped up over his feet and buttoned at the shoulders. Booties are worn for dress occasions if you wish

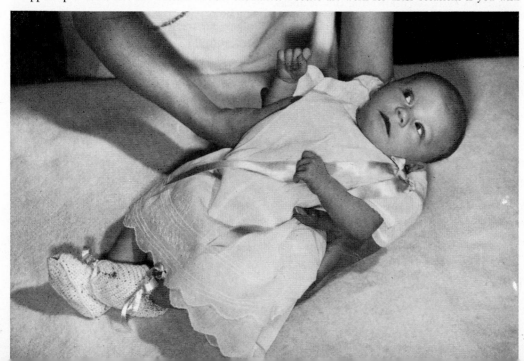

Handling soiled diapers

In some convenient place, you'll want a covered 2-gallon diaper pail, half-filled with water in which 2 tablespoons of borax has been dissolved. Immediately after changing Baby, rinse the diaper in clear water and drop into this pail.

Soiled diapers require special treatment. Shake or scrape the contents off into the toilet. Flush it; then rinse stained places in the clean water which refills the toilet.

(The rim and bowl of your toilet must be kept scrupulously clean and disinfected frequently so that no germs from other persons using it can be picked up on Baby's diapers.) Drop the diaper into the pail. Rub out stains before washing with the rest of the diapers.

If the diapers get a strong ammonia smell, boil them each time after using. Add about 8 tablespoons of boric acid to a gallon of water for the last rinse, or use one of the diaper rash preventive rinses which have been approved by medical authorities.

Diaper rash

This condition, which can make your baby extremely uncomfortable, results either from ammonia formed by the action of bacteria on urine-soaked skin, diapers, and bedclothes, or from acids in diarrheal stools.

If the irritation is caused by diarrhea, it is usually confined to the area touched by the stools and clears up rapidly when the diarrhea is controlled.

An ammonia rash is more widespread than a diarrhea rash, often affecting the buttocks, groin, and lower abdomen.

The bacteria that causes urine to decompose and form ammonia is present in the intestinal tract of many infants and remains in diapers, clothing, pads, and sheets, unless they are boiled after each use.

If your baby shows any indications of diaper rash, adopt these measures immediately.

1. Boil all diapers, shirts, nightgowns, kimonos, crib sheets, and absorbent pads for 10 minutes every time they're washed. Change waterproof sheets and pads several times a day. If these can't be boiled, wash them with soap and water, rinse, and dry in the sun, if possible.

2. Add boric acid powder to the last rinse water (8 tablespoons to a gallon of water), and sprinkle boric acid powder inside each diaper before it is put on Baby.

3. Change diapers as soon as they are wet or soiled, even during Baby's sleep, unless this disturbs him so much that he can't go back to sleep afterward.

4. Clean Baby's skin thoroughly at each diaper changing. If the skin irritation is severe, clean with oil instead of soap and water.

5. Apply zinc ointment to the whole area. This gives a heavy, protective covering to the skin so that subsequent wetting or soiling will not further irritate the rash.

6. Expose Baby's buttocks to the air for several hours each day. Remove his diaper, wash and dry the skin, but don't apply any ointment. Put several diapers, an absorbent pad, and a waterproof pad under him. Let him lie like this, in his shirt and a short sacque, for an hour or so several times a day in a warm room. Change the diapers under him if they become wet or soiled. Remove his diaper whenever he's taking a sunbath, too, being careful, of course, that this area (or any other part of his body) doesn't get sunburned.

If your baby has a tendency to diaper rash, continue to boil at least his diapers daily, and rinse and powder the diapers with boric acid, even after the condition clears up.

Airings start at three weeks

For the first few weeks of his life, the best place for Baby is a well-ventilated room, without drafts, and with an even temperature, day and night, between 70 and 75 degrees. This can be reduced to 60 degrees, but no lower, after he reaches 8 pounds in weight.

When he weighs 8 pounds or more, he may be taken outdoors for airings if the sun is shining, and it's not windy. The temperature of the spot where his carriage is placed should be at least 65 degrees. Except in summer, the middle of the day is the best time. After he weighs 10 pounds, he can be outside any nice day when the temperature is above freezing. As he gets a little older, he can even spend an hour or two in below-freezing temperature, if his carriage is in a sunny, sheltered place. Be sure to protect his eyes from the sun, though.

Airings are very good for Baby, but don't

place him outside in wind, dampness, or extremely cold weather. In winter, apply oil or lotion to his face and hands before he goes out, and wipe off immediately any drooling or moisture from his nose. Dress him in warm outer clothes and cover his hands and ears, but not his face.

Occasionally, when you just can't get out, Baby can have an airing indoors near an opened, sunny window. Be sure he's warm enough and close other windows and any doors in the room so there'll be no drafts.

When your baby cries

Crying is the only way Baby can tell you he's uncomfortable or hungry.

Soon you'll learn to distinguish the hunger cry, which simply means that it's getting toward dinnertime; the fretting of a tired, sleepy baby who needs to be let alone so he can go to sleep; and the cry of pain or discomfort.

It's always best to investigate thoroughly and be sure he's as comfortable as you can make him. Try "bubbling" him. Sometimes all the air is not brought up after feeding. If it's just a short time after a feeding, offer him a bottle of cool boiled water. He may be too warm. If he's perspiring, take off some of his covers or clothes. In hot weather, give him a cooling sponge-off.

He may be cold. If he is, his flesh will feel cold to your touch. Put on more clothes or covers and place a small hot-water bottle filled with warm water at his feet.

He may be wet or have a soiled diaper. Investigate and make him comfortable. If he has a skin irritation, bring it to your doctor's attention and get relief for him.

Perhaps his position in the bed is uncomfortable. He may have lain too long on one side, slid down toward the foot, or become tangled in the bedclothes. He may even have a pin sticking him!

He may be ill. The symptoms of common baby illnesses are described in this chapter. Others are covered in the Diseases Chart (pages 190–197).

If he seems to be hungry, nurse him or let him have his bottle. If he wakes regularly, crying from hunger, make a 24-hour check of the amount of milk he's getting from you (see page 64). If he's formula fed, ask your doctor about increasing the amount of the formula.

If there doesn't seem to be any reason for Baby's crying, he may just want to be held for a few minutes and comforted. You may do

this long enough to quiet him, but, for the most part, in these early months, your baby is better off by himself once he has been made comfortable. He needs to sleep the greater part of the day and can do this best in his bed. See that he gets plenty of snuggling and loving when you nurse or feed him. Or set aside a special period, perhaps just before his evening feeding, as a loving-and-playtime.

Thumbsucking

Sooner or later during these early weeks you're going to find your baby with his thumb in his mouth. There was a time when a mother would have beamed and said, "A baby that sucks his thumb is a good baby."

But some 20 years ago, thumbsucking among babies came into much ill-repute. It was held responsible for crooked teeth and other complications. Parents tried to eliminate the habit with various mechanical aids. They even resorted to mild torture, with the result that their child sucked his thumb even harder than previously.

Sucking is a means of satisfying hunger. The baby who sucks his thumb may not be getting enough food. Or he may have another type of hunger—he may be getting insufficient affection. Using mechanical restraints or bitter-tasting applications on his fingers won't correct either of those basic needs. For an older child who *wants* to stop the habit, one of the bitter-tasing products sold for this purpose may serve as a reminder when he puts his fingers in his mouth.

The important thing is to remove the underlying cause of the thumbsucking—whether it's the need for more food or more love.

It's believed that babies have an instinctive need to do a certain amount of sucking. Breast-feeding probably satisfies this need better than bottle-feeding because Baby has to work harder to extract milk from the breast.

If your baby is formula fed, take care not to have the nipple holes so large that he gets the milk without effort.

Be sure your baby is well nourished, comfortable, and happy. Then dismiss thumbsucking from your mind. It's probable that he'll stop, and you won't realize for some time that the once-feared habit has taken care of itself. He may continue to suck his thumb at times when he's tired or sleepy. Thumbsucking in such circumstances simply means that he needs to go to bed.

If, however, your baby isn't making the

weight gain that he should, cries a great deal, usually seems unhappy, and falls upon his thumb as if he would chew it off, ask your doctor to examine him and his diet to see what may be wrong.

Don't call attention to the thumbsucking as such. Just remember that if a baby or small child sucks his thumb constantly during his waking hours, he's either hungry, uncomfortable, or lacks something else to do.

There is still a great deal of disagreement among doctors and dentists about the results of this habit on a child's teeth.

Baby needs his sleep

When he first comes home from the hospital, Baby will sleep most of the time when he's not being fed or bathed. Gradually he'll sleep less and perhaps, according to a pattern of his own, for babies differ in the amount of sleep they need.

Some babies, from birth on, seem to sleep only fitfully and have long periods of wakeful-

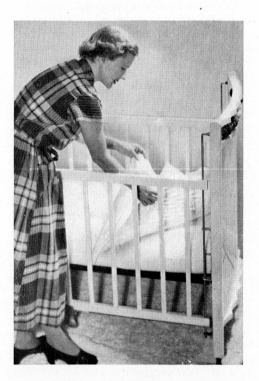

Baby's mattress should be firm. If not moisture-proof, cover with a waterproof sheet, large enough to tuck well under mattress. Over the mattress and cover go a soft, absorbent pad and cotton sheet

ness. This need not cause any alarm, and he should be allowed to rest even though awake.

In the section on arrangements for Baby before he arrives, the right sort of sleeping provisions were described. Be sure he has a comfortable bed, and if at all possible, a room to himself, even if it's only a well-ventilated cubbyhole. Put him in his bed with the door closed and lights out. This way he'll get all the sleep he needs, to grow and develop good nerves.

At this age, Baby can't move himself, so you'll have to shift his sleeping position from time to time, from back to one side, and then to the other. Just after a feeding, lay him on his side. He'll be less likely to spit up. To keep him on his side, roll up a blanket and prop it against his back.

Don't waken him to show him to people. There's no harm, though, in letting relatives or friends slip in for a look while he's sleeping, provided they don't disturb him.

No more clockwork babies

Doctors nowadays agree that a strict on the-hour schedule isn't good for Baby. They believe that allowing a hungry baby to cry for any length of time just because it isn't time for a feeding disturbs his nervous system.

So, have a schedule for your sake as well as Baby's, but keep it *elastic*. Let common sense and consideration for Baby's needs be your guide.

If your baby wakes ahead of schedule, crying and gnawing at his fists, feed him. Adults often get hungry and eat before their next scheduled mealtime, so why shouldn't Baby? And don't worry that he'll be set in bad habits.

Occasionally, when he wakes up like this, he may not want the full amount of formula. Allow him his freedom of choice and let him take as much as he wants. Next time he may sleep right through until time for his bottle. If he does, his schedule is probably all right. The reason for his waking early before may have been that he hadn't taken all of his previous feeding, or may have spit up a lot of it.

However, if Baby continues to cry ahead of time and is always hungry, try increasing the amount of formula or shortening the length of time between bottles.

A schedule to fit your baby

Baby will quickly establish his own schedule, which will be the one best suited to his own intestinal rhythm. This is called the "self-demand" schedule, which many doctors now recommend for Baby's first few weeks.

So, let Baby have a hand in determining his schedule. Take things easy for the first week or two after you get Baby home, and get the feel of things. Find out when he seems to want to eat and sleep, and take this into account. At the same time, though, guard against letting him be disturbed, for this will throw both you and Baby off the track. For the first week after you're home, keep a record of the times he sleeps, eats, and so forth. A chart for this purpose is provided on page 219.

A schedule of a sort, of course, has already been established at the hospital. When you get home, it's possible that the change and added responsibilities which land on your shoulders may interfere with your milk supply. After you find the time when he seems ready to eat with appetite, that will become his feeding schedule.

Most newborn babies sleep the greater part of the time, except when being fed, changed, or bathed. There are a few, however, who seem to be awake much of the day. This is no cause for concern, but such a baby should be allowed to rest quietly without being disturbed, even though he's awake.

It's usually convenient to bathe him before the midmorning feeding, and Baby usually needs a bath after the night's sleep. Never bathe him after a feeding. He's ready to sleep then. But the bath hour can be changed if a later time is more convenient.

By the time he's 3 or 4 weeks old, you'll have found the best time from Baby's standpoint for the various operations of his day. That is his schedule. There's no need to follow to the letter any particular time for any one operation. His day may begin at 6 a.m., 7 a.m., or 8 a.m., according to his ideas and your convenience.

But when you've worked out a satisfactory routine, follow it consistently every day. Not to the minute necessarily, but within 15 minutes, for instance. Baby will be better and happier, and he won't wear himself out crying. If an occasion arises, however, which you think is important enough to justify some rearranging, do it. Let common sense guide you.

After you've had a chance to learn how smoothly things go when you follow a planned day, you'll be in a better position to decide whether or not something is important enough to disrupt it!

Take Dad's convenience into account, though. Arrange it so that he can have some of the pleasure of taking care of his baby.

Here's a suggested schedule. Revise it, and all the other daily routines given in this book, according to your baby's rhythm and your household convenience.

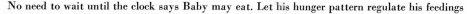

No need to wait until the clock says Baby may eat. Let his hunger pattern regulate his feedings

At two weeks your baby's day may go like this

6:00 a.m. Nursing (or bottle feeding) 10 to 12 minutes at first, but increasing as your nipples toughen and Baby gets stronger. After the feeding, make bed and Baby dry and clean; then put him back to bed.

9:30 a.m. Bath.

10:00 a.m. Nursing or bottle feeding.

10:30 a.m. to 2:00 p.m. Nap in his own room, with door shut and window open. Temperature between 70 and 75 degrees if Baby weighs less than 8 pounds, not lower than 60 degrees after he reaches this weight.

2:00 p.m. Nursing or bottle feeding.

3:00 p.m. to 4:00 p.m. Airing, out of doors after 3 weeks of age when weather isn't stormy or too cold. Otherwise, in the bedroom.

5:00 p.m. to 6:00 p.m. Exercise period. Fun for all! Put Baby on your big bed with all his clothing but the diaper removed. Place a large thick pad over the bed to protect it. The room temperature should be 75 degrees. Let Baby kick freely. It's a fine idea to massage his back and hold him during the last half hour of this period. Visit with him, love him, carry him about the house. This will rest him for the night. Don't bounce or throw him around, however. That comes under the head of overstimulation and interferes with the sleep and digestion of most babies.

6:00 p.m. Nursing or bottle feeding. Put on his nightgown, and return him to bed in a room by himself with the door closed, lights out, and window open. Room temperature should be the same as given above.

10:00 p.m. Nursing or bottle feeding.

2:00 a.m. Nursing or bottle feeding if Baby wakens. Don't wake him for it. This feeding is usually eliminated when he's 6 to 7 weeks old.

Time for vitamins C and D

Cow's milk, while it is the most nearly complete food for babies—except for mother's milk—is lacking in vitamins C and D. It's also lacking in iron and copper, two minerals which Baby has to have for health.

Baby comes into the world with enough copper and iron stored up to last him for some time, but if he's formula-fed, he needs vitamins C and D added almost from the first. This is why they're now introduced in some form as early as the second or third week.

Human milk contains vitamin C in ample amount, especially if the mother is getting vitamin C in proper amount in her own diet. But the breast-fed baby *does* need vitamin D.

In the section "Before Baby Comes" the reasons why vitamins C and D are so important are given (page 26).

Starting vitamin D

Cod-liver oil. Cod- and other fish-liver oils contain both vitamins D and A. If your doctor recommends cod-liver oil, a pure, unflavored variety is best. Be sure the label states that it contains at least 85 U.S.P. units of vitamin D to the gram.

Since the taste and feel of the cod-liver oil will be new to Baby, start with a few drops on the end of a teaspoon. The best time to give the oil is when Baby is undressed on the bath table, and you have your bath apron on, as cod-liver oils or concentrates make hard-to-remove stains on clothing. It's a good idea to have several disposable tissues spread on Baby's chest. (Fish-oil stains can be removed with carbon tetrachloride, followed by soap-and-water washing.)

When you've poured the oil into the spoon, place the bottle of cod-liver oil on a table where it can't be knocked over. Then raise Baby to a semi-reclining position against your arm. Slip the spoon gently over the tip of his tongue and let him suck off the oil, if he will. If he doesn't try to suck it in, trickle it gently into the back of his mouth. Stop immediately if he chokes or coughs, or he may gasp some of the oil into his lungs.

Increase the amount each time until, in a few days, he's taking a teaspoonful each day. The amount may be divided and given twice a day if he has difficulty taking the full teaspoonful at one time. Keep cod-liver oil and vitamin D concentrates in the refrigerator.

Concentrated fish-liver oils. Many doctors have been prescribing fish-oil concentrates. A smaller amount of concentrate is required to do the job, and because it's easier to give, it can be started earlier. Babies usually spit up less concentrate than cod-liver oil.

A handy way to give vitamin D concentrate at first is from a medicine dropper, gently pressing open the baby's mouth. Since a few drops of concentrate amply supply Baby's requirement of vitamin D, the full amount can be given from the start. When Baby gets big enough to recline against your arm, a teaspoon containing the oil or concentrate can be pressed against his lips. He'll probably suck it in—and will have learned to accept food from a spoon. Or insert it through a corner of his mouth. Even in the summer months, doctors now advise a teaspoon of cod-liver oil, or a few drops of concentrate, every day to insure good bone formation.

Dispersible vitamin D. Many dispersible varieties of vitamin D are now on the market, and your doctor may prescribe one of these. Some are in solution, some in dry form. The use of a dispersible variety permits very early giving of vitamin D without risk of the baby breathing oil into his lungs. It is put into the formula, and is more effective than vitamin D in an oily concentrate.

Fortified milk. Fortified milk has 400 U.S.P. units of vitamin D added to the quart (in the case of fresh milk). In evaporated milk, 400 units of vitamin D are contained in the amount of milk which, when combined with an equal amount of water, will make 1 quart. If this type of milk is given, less cod- or fish-liver oil or concentrate is needed.

Know your units

Vitamin-rich foods are now assayed in standard units. It's not enough just to give a certain amount of cod-liver oil or concentrate. You also need to know the number of units of vitamin D in the brand you're using. To insure superior skeletal development, at least 400 I. U. (International Units) of vitamin D must be provided every day. Many pediatricians recommend 800 units a day for safety. The potency in units per ounce should be stated on the label of any bottle of cod-liver oil or concentrate.

Around 400 units of vitamin D are contained in 1 teaspoon of U.S.P. cod-liver oil, 3 drops of viosterol, 4 drops of percomorphum, and in 1 quart of fortified milk. It's a common failing not to give enough fish-liver oil from a standpoint of unitage, and to give too much concentrate. Read the unitage on the brand you're using, and govern the dose accordingly.

Starting vitamin C

After Baby has been taking vitamin D a few days, begin vitamin C. Offer him an ounce of strained orange juice diluted with an ounce of water that has been boiled and cooled to body heat. (Never heat juice or add hot water to it, as this destroys vitamin C.) The juice may be offered in a 4-ounce nursing bottle. Increase the amount of orange juice 1 teaspoon every few days, omitting that much water, until at 1 month Baby's getting 2 ounces of undiluted orange juice a day. Sweetened lemon juice may also be used. Prepare any juice just before giving it, as vitamin C is lost on exposure to air.

Tomato juice is a good source of vitamin C, and may be used to advantage a little later on. But twice as much tomato juice as orange juice is required for the same amount of vitamin C; hence it isn't so practical with the tiny baby, who may have difficulty taking enough tomato juice to supply his vitamin C needs.

There is a trend today toward prescribing ascorbic acid during the early months of infancy instead of giving orange juice. By giving vitamin C in this form, many cases of orange-juice allergy are avoided.

So, if your baby can take neither orange juice nor tomato juice, ask your doctor about vitamin C (ascorbic acid) tablets. The tablets can be given in his formula, but as vitamin C is destroyed by heat, must not be boiled with the formula or heated in the bottle. Add the tablet just before Baby is fed.

Vitamin B₁

Vitamin B_1 is coming more into the limelight in the feeding of infants because there is a direct connection between energy metabolism and the requirement of thiamin (vitamin B_1). Your baby is an energetic little fellow and needs his thiamin. Both the breast-fed and the artificially fed baby get only the minimum requirement of vitamin B_1 in their food until whole-grain cereals and other B_1-rich foods are added to the diet. Therefore, many doctors now add vitamin B_1 in the form of thiamin-chloride tablets, dissolved in Baby's milk. Ask your doctor about this.

Vitamin A

At this age, your baby's need for vitamin A is supplied in his milk and orange juice. Cod-liver oil and some concentrates also supply vitamin A, as well as vitamin D.

Your doctor may suggest that you add egg yolk to the formula. Egg white, like orange juice, often causes an allergy, and for that reason, only the yolk is given to the infant until he's about a year old.

To prepare the egg yolk, separate the yolk from the white. Add 2 or 3 tablespoons of cold boiled water to the yolk and mix well. To this add an equal amount of hot feeding and mix well. Then strain the egg mixture into the remainder of hot feeding, stirring constantly. Place over the fire and bring just to the boiling point. Don't boil the formula after the egg has been added to it.

Other vitamins

Baby's vitamin needs, other than those just described, are supplied by his food, except for vitamin K, which must sometimes be given to the newborn baby. Your obstetrician takes care of that whenever it's necessary.

Formula changes

By the time your baby is 1 month old, he will have a slightly different formula.

The formula for this age, using fresh milk, is as follows:

Fresh-milk formula for baby one month old

(one day's supply)

16 ounces whole milk
8 ounces water
2½ tablespoons corn syrup or
5 tablespoons dextrin-maltose mixture

How to prepare: Follow the directions given on pages 70 through 73.

Evaporated-milk formula for baby one month old

(one day's supply)

8 ounces evaporated milk
16 ounces boiled water
2½ tablespoons corn syrup or
5 tablespoons dextrin-maltose mixture

How to prepare: Follow the directions as given on pages 70 through 73.

(Please remember that these formulas are for the perfectly normal and flourishing baby, and are suggested if you're unable to consult a doctor. If your baby is smaller or weaker, isn't making his gains, or in other ways not doing as he should, make every effort to have a doctor examine him at once.)

A word about worrying

Some mothers worry themselves sick when their babies really are doing beautifully.

But let's say that the doctor has found your baby perfect in every respect—a fine, healthy fellow. Then what's your role?

Given loving care, warmth, and proper food, your healthy baby will continue to be all right. You can always reason that as long as he's happy, eating his food, and making his gains, there can't be anything much the matter with him.

He may skip a meal, have small appetite for it, or even lose it without anything serious being wrong. For such mild upsets, you can afford to wait until the next meal or two before you start worrying. If Baby takes his next meal voraciously (as he probably will) and keeps it down, be assured all's well. It isn't necessary to bother your busy doctor. And don't bother a perfectly well baby by taking his temperature every few hours.

Infant illnesses need doctor's care

There are, however, conditions which need your doctor's attention at once. Listed below are the more common conditions which could —not necessarily will—lead to something serious unless you take steps in time.

Babies are believed to be born with a certain immunity to the so-called children's diseases. This cannot be counted upon, however, and the greatest care should be taken to protect your baby from infection. No one with a cold or runny nose should be permitted in the same room with him. If you have a cold, wear a gauze mask over your nose and mouth when you care for him. Better still, turn his care over to someone else until you're well.

If Baby refuses food several times in succession or vomits it, seems unduly listless, develops a cold, or cries as though in pain, take his temperature rectally. There's a special rectal thermometer for this purpose that has a large, round bulb. You should have one. Shake the thermometer down until it registers not more than 96 degrees; then grease the bulb with petroleum jelly or cold cream. Hold Baby flat on your lap or bath table, either face up or face down. Spreading the baby's buttocks apart with thumb and finger, insert the thermometer one-third its length

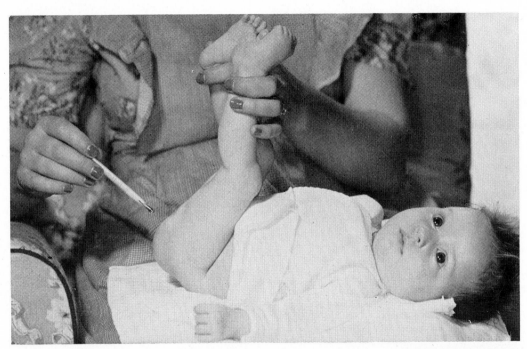

If your baby seems ill, take his temperature rectally and report it to your doctor when you phone him. Use special rectal thermometer that has a large, round bulb for this purpose. Grease end with petroleum jelly

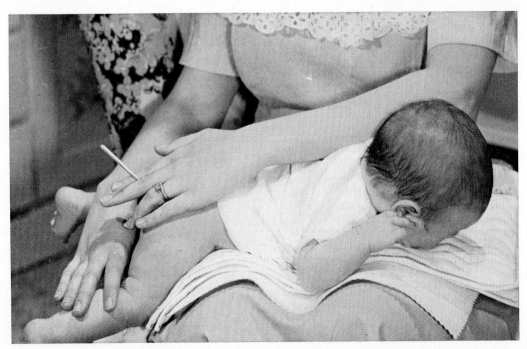

Hold Baby on lap in either of the positions shown, or on table. Holding thermometer loosely, insert it into anus, leave for 2 minutes, clean, and read. Rectal temperatures are about a degree higher than those by mouth

into the anus. (See pictures on page 91.) Leave for two minutes, holding it all the while. Then clean the thermometer with a piece of toilet paper and read what it says.

Rectal temperatures are normally about one degree higher than those taken by mouth, so if the reading is one degree above the line for normal on your thermometer, Baby's temperature is as it should be.

When you're through, wash the thermometer thoroughly with soap and warm water—hot water will break it.

When your describe Baby's symptoms to your doctor over the telephone, it will be helpful to him to have this temperature reading.

If Baby shows any sign of illness, keep him quiet in his own bed and away from family or visitors until the doctor can see him or advise you what to do.

The common cold

You pay attention to the common cold, for instance, because a number of serious diseases start this way. The great majority of times, though, it's a cold and nothing more. But get in touch with your doctor. Isolate Baby in a room that's well ventilated, but with a temperature of 70 or 72 degrees. Let him have all the lukewarm boiled water he wants. A cold sometimes interferes with appetite, so Baby may take less food. Don't press it on him.

Keep a supply of tissue for cleaning his nose. If crusts form, you may try to work them loose with cotton swabs, rolled to a point and dipped in sterile water.

Don't give a laxative unless your doctor advises it.

Bronchitis and pneumonia

If your baby has had a head cold for several days, and then develops a persistent cough, either with or without vomiting and fever, consult your physician immediately. It may be only a mild case of bronchitis, but since there's a possibility of pneumonia, prompt medical attention is necessary. Modern drugs will quickly clear up either condition.

Croup

Croup often comes on suddenly in the night when the baby seemed perfectly well when put to bed. Its symptoms are a barking cough, hoarseness, and rapid breathing. Telephone your doctor, and while you're waiting for him, get moisture into the air in Baby's room. The most satisfactory device for doing this is an electric vaporizer. If you haven't one, an electric bottle-warmer will serve the purpose. Fill it with boiling water and keep the water hot by turning on the electricity.

If you've neither, a kettle boiling on an electric plate will make steam, but you must be extremely careful that Baby doesn't burn or scald himself. Set the kettle so far from his bed that he can't possibly hit or pull it over, and the bedclothes can't come in contact with it. All these things have caused serious accidents. It's a good rule, indeed, not to leave Baby alone in the room under any circumstances when you're steaming him.

Never put a vessel of hot water in Baby's crib!

If you haven't a way of keeping water at the boiling point in Baby's room, take his bed into the bathroom or kitchen and turn on the hot water there. Or warm his room to about 80 degrees and hang up several big bath towels, wrung out of hot water. Several such towels placed over a warm radiator will provide steam.

When Baby's coughing and heavy breathing stop, take all the damp cloths away. Give him dry garments and bedclothes, and let him go to sleep.

Keep his room warm and the air moist for several days.

Colic

This is a condition that's distressing to Baby and to you. Yet, surprisingly, it doesn't seem to interfere with his development. The colicky baby usually thrives as well as, and often better than, babies who are not bothered with this infant illness.

Colic is nearly always associated with gas in the intestinal tract.

Baby will cry hard, clench his fists, get red in the face, draw up his legs and then straighten them out. His stomach may be hard, his hands cold.

Lift him over your shoulder, and pat him a few times on the back to release the gas. Then put him to bed lying on his stomach with a wrapped hot-water bottle under his abdomen. Rub his back. He may get relief face down on your lap. If he doesn't seem to get relief, telephone your doctor and describe the condition.

If the attack is extremely severe, a warm enema may be given, although this should not be done routinely.

A bulb-shaped rubber ear syringe with a soft rubber tip is the best equipment for giving a baby an enema. Prepare a solution of $\frac{1}{2}$ teaspoon of baking soda to 4 ounces of lukewarm water. Place a rubber sheet on a bed and lay Baby on it, on his side. Have the enema solution ready, together with petroleum jelly or cold cream, a small potty, and some tissue right at hand on a table. Completely fill the syringe bulb, by inserting the tip in the solution and squeezing the bulb. Then grease the tip with petroleum jelly or cold cream and gently insert it an inch or so into Baby's rectum. Do not push it in. Squeeze lightly on the bulb to slowly expel the water into the rectum.

When you've emptied the syringe, remove the tip from the rectum and press Baby's buttocks together for a few moments to allow the water to soften the bowel movement. You may not be able to do this, though, as the movement may come with explosive force. Have the potty ready to catch it. If the water comes gushing out without any bowel movement, you may try another enema in 15 or 20 minutes.

Tension and fatigue may play a part in colic, since many babies have colic spells at a certain time each day—often in the evening. For this reason, it doesn't seem to be any fault in Baby's food that's causing it, as the rest of his meals cause no distress. Your doctor may prescribe a mild sedative to be added to the feeding that usually precedes a spell, or given in his bottle of water, as breast-fed babies are just as prone to colic as those who are receiving a formula.

The colicky baby should be kept in a quiet room and handled gently. He needs his loving just as usual, but no exciting play.

You should be calm yourself, and not worry. Anxious, nervous parents seem to transmit their tenseness to their baby. Hold your baby in your arms during a spell of colic, if that seems to relieve him. But if he cries just as hard anyway, it's best to leave him in bed and try to make him comfortable there. Otherwise, he may develop a fondness for being held and walked in the wee, small hours, and you can expect that to last long after his colic has disappeared.

For that's the fortunate thing about colic—it does disappear. Even the most severe case of colic seldom continues after 3 months. Chances are it takes Baby's nervous system that long to adjust to his new world.

Another condition is similar to colic but does not have periodic severe attacks. Instead, it seems to be a form of indigestion. The baby is restless, fretful, or crying most of the day and frequently passes gas. A change in formula may benefit this baby. The acid formulas given in this book may help. They may be weakened for the time by adding 2 or 3 ounces more cool boiled water than called for in the formula.

If your baby has indigestion or is losing weight or fails to gain, consult your doctor immediately.

Some babies cry or fret almost constantly the first few months for no apparent reason. Here again, it's believed it is just a nervous tension which soon disappears.

Convulsions

The commonest cause of convulsions in infants and young children is the high fever associated with the onset of an infection, such as a cold or a sore throat. The baby's eyes become fixed or roll upward, and his whole body twitches convulsively. Attacks are usually of short duration, but sometimes may be prolonged. Rarely do convulsions occur after the first day of fever.

Convulsions which occur in the absence of a fever are likely to be of a more serious nature and call for immediate medical care.

Call your doctor at once. Then prepare a warm bath (105°) and put Baby in it for from five to ten minutes. Dry him well, put him in his crib, and give him an enema. Then darken his room and keep him quiet until the doctor comes. A convulsion is terrifying to parents, but a baby rarely, if ever, dies because of one.

Bath to reduce fever

If your doctor advises a sponge-off to reduce fever, follow the general plan given for the first sponge baths on page 78. The temperature of the room should be from 78 to 80 degrees with drafts carefully exluded. Lay Baby on one large bath towel and have a second at hand. On his forehead place a cloth, wrung out of cool water. Sponge each part of his body several times. Dry him with the second towel. If the room is cool, keep Baby covered with the second towel.

After you've sponged the front of his body, take the cloth from his forehead, turn him over, and sponge his back, using a fresh washcloth. Dry him well, put on fresh garments, and get him back to bed quickly.

Typical day for baby one to two months old

6:00 a.m. Nurse 20 minutes on one breast, or 15 minutes on one and 5 on the other. Or give as much of the bottle feeding as Baby will take in 20 minutes. If he wants more, give an additional ounce or two. Baby then sleeps.

9:15 a.m. Undress him for his bath. Give cod-liver oil, or vitamin D concentrate according to your doctor's orders. Follow this with 2 ounces of orange juice.

9:30 a.m. Bath.

10:00 a.m. Nursing or bottle feeding, same as above.

10:30 a.m. to 2:00 p.m. Nap in a room by himself, with the door shut and window open. The temperature should not be below 60 degrees.

2:00 p.m. Nursing or bottle feeding.

3:00 p.m. to 4:00 p.m. Airing outdoors, if weather is suitable. If not, in bedroom.

5:00 p.m. to 6:00 p.m. Exercise period.

6:00 p.m. Nursing or bottle. Into his nightgown and to bed. Temperature not lower than 60 degrees.

10:00 p.m. Nursing or bottle.

2:00 a.m. Feeding only if Baby awakens.

Chapter II

Your baby from
two to three months

Development

Between the ages of 2 and 3 months your baby may:

...follow a moving person with his eyes.

...stare at a bright object.

...lift chest a short distance when placed on his abdomen.

...lay awake for longer periods at a time.

...kick feet or push with legs in bath.

Physical development

Your baby's weight gain now should be at least 2 pounds over his weight at birth. The probabilities are it will be between 3 and 4 pounds, as babies generally gain from 6 to 8 ounces a week during the first three months. However, some gain less, and others more.

Feedings

There should be no more than five milk feedings daily by this time. If your baby still requires the 2 a.m. feeding, he probably isn't receiving enough during the day. Many pediatricians omit the 10 p.m. feeding if Baby is gaining well and takes a sufficient quantity in 4 bottles. However, if a fifth bottle is necessary, it is better to wait until Baby wakes up.

Formula using fresh milk

(one day's supply)

20 ounces whole milk
10 ounces water
3 tablespoons corn syrup or
6 tablespoons dextrin-maltose mixture
How to prepare: See pages 70-73.

Formula using evaporated milk

(one day's supply)

10 ounces evaporated milk
20 ounces boiled water
3 tablespoons corn syrup or
6 tablespoons dextrin-maltose mixture
How to prepare: See pages 70-73.

Tub bath's the thing

By this time your baby should be ready for a tub bath. In fact, it's all right at any time

Although sleeping and eating are still Baby's main interests, he now begins to take notice of his surroundings after the navel is completely healed. See pages 80-81 for "How to Give a Tub Bath."

The bath table should still be used for convenience in undressing and dressing Baby.

Care of the scalp

If a crust called "cradle cap" forms on the scalp, wash his hair daily, soaping and rinsing it well. Soften the crust on scalp with an application of oil at night.

Frequently, a crust forms because Mother is afraid to touch the "soft spot" on top of Baby's head. There is no danger from touching this spot. It should, of course, be handled gently as should all the rest of Baby's body.

Early bowel training not advisable

Most doctors suggest that bowel training wait until the baby can sit up strongly, around 8 or 9 months, or later. Some authorities believe that trying to train too early may antagonize Baby and make him resist acceptable toilet habits long after he's really ready to learn. (See page 123.)

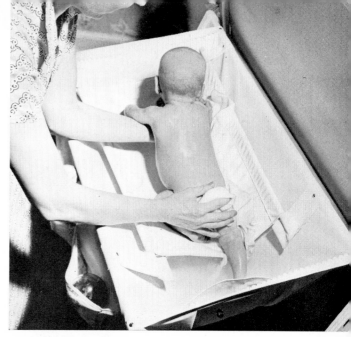

If you have a bath table equipped with a hammock, you can turn Baby stomach down to wash his back. Lowering the foot end of the adjustable hammock permits Baby to wiggle and squirm around in the water

Or, Baby can be raised up as shown to have his back washed and rinsed either on the hammock or in a tub. Be sure to support his wobbly head and his back with one hand while you wield the washcloth with the other

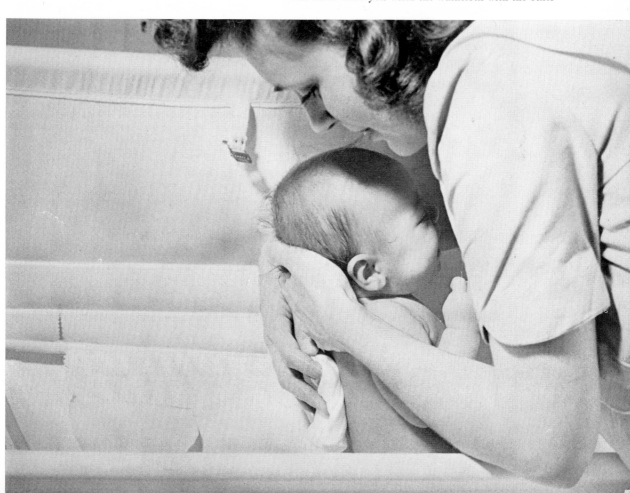

Sunbaths

When the weather's suitable, Baby may be exposed to the direct rays of the sun after he reaches 10 pounds in weight. His sunbaths may be given outdoors or by a window, opened to allow the ultraviolet rays to reach him. Begin by placing Baby on his stomach and back for two minutes in each position. Then increase one mintue a day up to 20 minutes front and back. When Baby's on his back in the sun, shield his eyes. Don't let his skin become sunburned. Use plenty of lotion so his skin won't become dry.

"Suitable weather" will have to be inter-preted by your own good judgment. Even in many localities with severe winters, a baby can be uncovered to the sun on a south porch, protected from the wind, around the last of March, and be well tanned by late April. The warmth of Baby's flesh can be your criterion as to his comfort. If he feels warm to the touch, he's all right, even though the day may seem chilly to you.

Baby shouldn't be exposed to the direct rays of a hot midsummer sun. The ultraviolet rays permeate the outdoor atmosphere, and he'll get the benefit of them on a porch or in the shade. Never expose him directly to sun which feels unduly warm to you.

In suitable weather, Baby can take his sunbaths outdoors as soon as he weighs 10 pounds. Buggy is good for spring and fall sunning. It may be too warm in summer, as top, sides, and pad retain heat

Toddler can get plenty of sun in his playpen in the yard. In the summer when heat is intense, do not put his pen in the direct sunlight. Even in the shade, he'll absorb vitamin D from reflected light

Canvas table or playpen allows air to circulate when Baby gets his sunbath. A peaked cap shades his eyes. Start outdoors with 5 minutes, and gradually increase his period in the sun to 30 or 40 minutes daily

In winter, Baby's hands, legs, and feet may be exposed to the sun's rays at an open south window in a warm room with no drafts. Keep upper part of his body covered. Two minutes in sun is enough at first

Care during hot weather

During hot weather keep your house cool and well ventilated. Clothe Baby lightly so that his skin will not be irritated. He may wear only a loose diaper or may go naked. Put him to bed in very light clothes. On the hottest nights a diaper and a lightweight band are enough. For covering, use a sheet which should be pinned loosely enough to allow him to turn freely if he so wishes. The room should be made as cool as possible. An electric fan may be used, but see that the current of air does not blow toward Baby. Always avoid drafts.

During the day give several tepid baths.

Do not expose Baby to the hot sun for too long a period. On very hot days give the sun-baths before 10 a.m. and after 4 p.m. Don't allow him to become sunburned.

For Baby's protection, be sure to keep the flies out of the house, as they carry disease.

Remember that during very hot weather your infant will not want or need as much food as he usually takes. Offer cool boiled water every hour when he's awake.

Daily routine changes

A normal 2-months-old baby's rhythm of eating and sleeping will call for four feedings within the 12 hours of the day. Use common sense and convenience in mapping out a routine for Baby's day.

Baby will now have his airings and his social contacts, for he'll be sleeping less. It is suggested, however, that you don't take him away from home, except to the doctor, before the third month. After that, an occasional social visit within the waking time on the schedule will be a good thing. But give him three months of quiet and regularity to grow on!

Sleeping on his face

At 2 or 2½ months, or as soon as he's able to lift his head when on his abdomen, Baby may be taught to sleep on his face. There are several advantages to this position: 1. You avoid flattening the back of his head and wearing the hair off. (Neither of these conditions is serious, and both later correct themselves.) 2. The covers stay in place better. 3. Baby can lift himself on his hands and arms and exercise his arms and back just as soon as he feels the inclination.

Sleeping on his face must begin within the first months of his life, because as soon as he's able to turn himself, he'll roll onto his back. Don't begin, however, until Baby's strong enough to lift his head and turn it in order to breathe easily. Choose a time when he's very sleepy. Put him on his face, speak soothingly to him, and leave him. He'll probably cry the first time or two, but will quickly become accustomed to the new way and will like it.

Sleeping on his face is good for Baby. Start when he lifts his head up strongly. Soon he'll like it

Sleeping bags are a help

Many mothers have found some kind of sleeping bag very helpful. If Baby's in a sleeping bag, he can't get uncovered, and after a time, going into the bag becomes his signal to go to sleep. The familiarity of his bag is a help, too, when he's in a strange place or situation. There are several varieties of these bags in stores, or you may make your own. Such a bag should be long so his feet won't get cramped—should not bind around the neck or confine Baby too much. And be sure there is no way he can get tangled up in it.

Summer sleeping bags may be made from unbleached muslin.

Either before or after Baby has become ac-

customed to sleeping on his face—don't try more than one new experience at a time—put him in the sleeping bag for his long nap.

Sleeping bags are a great help in keeping Baby covered. You can use them any time after second month

Discipline begins at birth

What is discipline? To the Romans, who gave us the word, it meant learning. Just when and how the idea of punishment got mixed up with it is uncertain, but forget that for the time being and center upon the learning angle.

When does discipline, in the sense of learning, begin? It starts when your baby's born, and he begins learning things about this world he has come into.

He has learned that all his needs and legitimate wants receive attention. When his stomach contractions begin to get interesting, his dinner always appears. When he requires attention, he receives it. He feels the love in your voice and hands.

What a lot he knows already, this baby only 2 months old! Your job is to continue to train and teach him in the future as you've done these past 2 months.

It isn't necessary that you follow the advice in this book to the letter. No baby so far born into the world was quite like your baby. Some of the suggestions will work perfectly, but others will have to be altered a bit to fit you, your home conditions, and your baby's individuality.

But be consistent in following the ways that you adopt.

Much latitude is allowed as to when you should begin some new phase of training.

Try to look at things through your baby's eyes. What a strange, perplexing world this is into which he has come! How much he has to learn! How much is expected of him!

So be gentle and patient. The tense way in which some parents go at teaching a new skill often defeats their purpose. A punishing attitude on your part will bring out all the power of resistance your baby possesses. On the other hand, he'll enter happily into a learning situation which you've made as pleasant as possible.

Your baby and his doctor

By now, both you and your baby have had that 6-weeks' checkup that was mentioned earlier. Good doctors are always busy men, but, keep in mind that if your baby gets sick, or things don't go as they should, *he wants to know it.*

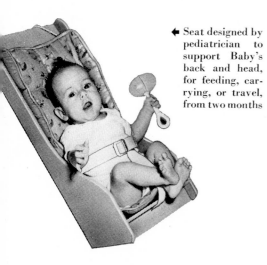

← Seat designed by pediatrician to support Baby's back and head, for feeding, carrying, or travel, from two months

Baby should mainly be a stay-at-home, but there are ➤ times when you'll have to take him along. A well-padded basket is the handiest way to do this, and can serve as his bed if he must nap or sleep away from home

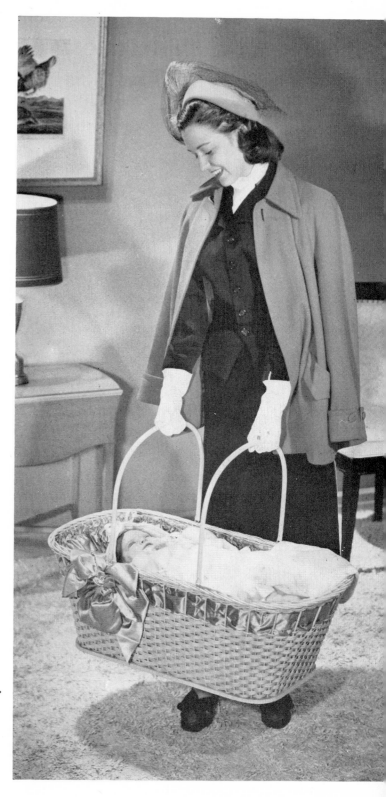

To give Baby his bottle, hold him reclining on your arm. Keep bottle tipped so milk fills the nipple

Typical day for baby two to three months old

6:00 a.m. to 7:00 a.m. Feeding. Back in his bassinet. He may or may not nap.

9:00 a. m. Fish-liver oil or concentrate as prescribed. Two ounces of orange juice.

9:30 a.m. Bath, followed by feeding.

10:30 a.m. Sunbath on the porch or before an open window. Then Baby sleeps, either on the porch or indoors, depending upon the weather. In hot weather, sunbath should be before 10:00 a.m. Change bath period to ½ hour earlier.

1:30 p.m. to 2:00 p.m. Feeding. Will probably nap after this.

4:00 p.m. Outdoors on the porch, in bassinet, or in buggy.

5:00 p.m. Undress for night, followed by exercise on big bed.

5:30 p.m. Can be held or carried about house.

6:00 p.m. Feeding, followed by bed.

Night feeding, if he wakes and cries for it.

Baby sleeps less as he gets older. This is to be expected. But opportunity should be given a baby of this age to get a nap before his bath, after the midmorning feeding, and after the early afternoon feeding.

Chapter III

Your baby from
three to four months

Development

Between 3 and 4 months your baby may:

. . . begin to grasp toy in hand.
. . . raise himself up by his arms.

. . . coo and gurgle with pleasure.
. . . roll from his back to his side.
. . . be quieted by a voice or music.
. . . begin to play with his hands.

. . . turn his head freely to watch activities and things around him.
. . . smile and respond to friendly overtures.
. . . hold his head erect.

Formula using fresh milk

(one day's supply)

24 ounces whole milk
8 ounces water
3 tablespoons corn syrup or
6 tablespoons dextrin-maltose mixture
How to prepare: See pages 70 through 73.

Formula using evaporated milk

(one day's supply)

13 ounces evaporated milk (1 can)
19 ounces boiled water
3 tablespoons corn syrup or
6 tablespoons dextrin-maltose mixture
How to prepare: See pages 70 through 73. If your baby is on a citric- or lactic-acid formula, continue to use the one on page 66.

A perfectly healthy, normal baby who does nicely on fresh or evaporated milk can be fed the above formulas. But remember, it's always best to have your doctor prescribe the formula most suited to your baby.

He'll need a bed

Baby will soon outgrow his bassinet; so now is the time to shop for a regular baby bed. Select one that's at least large enough for a 4- or 5-year-old child, so it will last as long as a baby bed is needed, and there'll be plenty of room for him to stretch and exercise. There are some models that can be converted later into single beds.

You may continue to use the bassinet for his waking hours, or for short naps. But he'll need a bed for long naps. A bassinet is fine for airings on the porch or under a tree after he's outgrown it as a bed.

He may start rolling

At three months, Baby's muscles are growing much stronger and larger, and he'll be able to twist and squirm about quite freely. Never leave him alone on his bath table or your big bed where he can roll off. And when you hold him in your lap, don't restrict his movements, but do be sure he can't wiggle away from you.

Give Baby a playpen

It's time now to get Baby a playpen so he can take part of his exercise on the floor. A good schedule for his exercise periods is from 8 to 9 a.m. and from 5 to 6 p.m. If he becomes accustomed to the pen at this early age, he'll not object to being put in it later.

There are several types on the market. One model has a platform raised a few inches above the floor. This places Baby above floor drafts indoors, and above damp or cold ground outdoors. A collapsible type is also very convenient for moving in and out of doors. You can also buy thick, nonabsorbent, washable pads for his pen. Put the playpen in a spot where it's out of drafts and where you can keep an eye on Baby. Place a pad, or heavy comforter, folded, on the floor of the pen. Over this, lay a rubber or waterproof sheet (if the pad isn't waterproof), and a clean muslin sheet on top.

He should have toys

When Baby begins reaching for things and trying to grasp them, it's time to place one or two toys within his reach—a rattle, or a bright-colored knitted doll which he can easily hold. Hang toys on strings to the sides of his playpen, so he can hit at them whenever he wants to. However, an allergic baby shouldn't have stuffed or wool toys. Don't hang bright objects above him in his crib for any long period, as they may excite him too much. The rattle and doll may be placed within his reach, and he'll play with them or not as he likes.

Leaving Baby with strangers

There may be one drawback to Baby's ready recognition of familiar faces—he may object to being left with strangers. Be very careful in your choice of a person to be left in charge while you're gone. Don't, however, make the mistake of yielding to Baby's whims if he decides you shouldn't leave him at all.

Have the person who'll take your place come in before you leave to become acquainted with things and, if possible, perform some operation for Baby while you're still there. Then when it's time, go; don't sneak out.

Guard Baby against disease

By now your baby is well started in life, but he'll need uninterrupted good health to continue growing at the pace he has set for himself. As your baby's parents, therefore, you're obligated to see that he does not contract any preventable illnesses in the future. Complications or aftereffects of the common contagious diseases are often much more frequent and severe with an infant than an older youngster, because of his size. Do everything you can now to protect him.

Program of immunization

Here are listed the ages at which the normal baby or youngster may be immunized against the various preventable diseases, and the circumstances under which immunization is advisable. Acquaint yourself with the immunization programs, but your doctor will decide when and what ones to give your baby.

Smallpox. Babies may be vaccinated against smallpox at any time after birth, but the routine procedure is to have your child vaccinated between 3 and 12 months. Usually it's around 6 months. Your youngster will need to be revaccinated at 6 and 12 years of age, or any time after he's exposed to the disease.

Diphtheria. Most babies are immunized against diphtheria before the ninth month, usually between 6 and 9 months. Multiple vaccines are now being used to obtain simultaneous immunization against diphtheria, tetanus, and whooping cough. If your doctor uses these three toxoids combined, he may start the immunization at 3 months of age. Approximately 6 months after immunization and before 2 years, the Schick test will be given to determine whether or not your child is immune to diphtheria. If the test is positive, your doctor will reimmunize him. The Schick test should be repeated when your child is 5 or 6 years old to be sure immunity persists. If the test is positive, reimmunization is necessary.

Whooping cough. Vaccination against whooping cough, or pertussis, may be begun as early as 3 months. A repeat or "booster" shot should be given from 12 to 18 months after the first vaccination, and again at 5 years, or just before your child enters school.

Scarlet fever. Inoculations against this disease may be given when your youngster is about 18 months old. Although scarlet fever toxin protects your youngster against the rash, the other values of the shots are uncertain. They do not protect against the streptococcic infection itself. If there should be an epidemic of any severity, be sure to have your child vaccinated. The chief usefulness of scarlet fever toxin is for epidemics in nursing homes, sanitariums, orphanages, or wherever children are in a group. If your child is immunized, have your doctor give him the Dick test before he enters school, to see if he is immune to the disease. If the reaction is positive, a booster shot is given at that time.

Tetanus. Vaccinations for tetanus may be given any time after 9 months, but the reactions are not so severe if given between 2 and 6 years. If the multiple vaccine protecting against whooping cough and diphtheria as well as tetanus is used, it will probably be given much earlier. One year after the original injections, your doctor will probably give your child a booster shot. If your youngster is exposed to tetanus infection—through a deep puncture wound from an object which has been in the dirt—tell your doctor if he has had the tetanus toxoid inoculation. He will then give further toxoid, instead of tetanus antitoxin.

Typhoid. Children may be vaccinated against typhoid fever at any time after 2 years if there's an epidemic, or if they're going to travel where the water or food supply may be contaminated. Immunity can be maintained by booster shots each year, if the need for typhoid protection exists.

Guard against infectious adults

Sometimes children contract diseases, such as syphilis and tuberculosis, from adult members of the household who may be infected and not be aware of it. As protection to children, parents and relatives, or anyone else living in the home, should have periodic physical examinations.

Orange juice in a cup

Between 3 and 4 months is a good time to begin offering Baby his orange juice from a cup. Then when it's time for weaning, he'll be less apt to rebel when offered his milk from a cup.

Use a small cup or glass that fits Baby's mouth easily. At first, be content if he takes

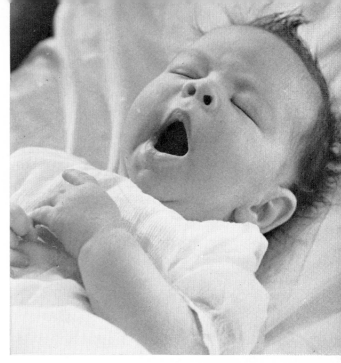

A good immunization program keeps your child healthy

only one swallow at a feeding. He's catching on to what is expected of him, and with regular practice, will soon be able to take all of his orange juice this way.

Begin solid foods

A healthy, normal infant could probably tolerate strained foods in small amounts almost from birth. The tendency now is to start them earlier than in the past, most doctors recommending them by the third month. With your doctor's consent, there's no harm in beginning earlier still to accustom Baby to new tastes and feeding methods.

If your baby is growing like a weed and completely digests everything he eats, begin now to introduce solid foods into his diet gradually. If the weather is hot, though, and the new foods upset Baby, drop them and wait a few weeks.

You may start with cereal

Cereal is ordinarily given first since it is a bland food which Baby can digest easily. Just be sure to use an enriched variety so your baby will get the extra vitamins it provides.

You have a wide range of cereals to choose from. Special precooked baby cereals are available on the market, and all you have to do is mix them with warm formula, milk, or water, and they're ready for use.

Then there are the cooked, canned cereals prepared by baby food companies. Some of

To feed solids, hold Baby half-reclining on your arm

these are cooked in milk, and all are ready to serve after being warmed.

A third possibility are the cereals your family eats. Directions for preparing these for Baby are on the containers. Be sure, however, to use a whole-grain or fortified variety. Cook the length of time prescribed for Baby. Then dilute his portion with water or some of his formula until it's the consistency of thin gruel.

All of these cereals, prepared according to the directions for baby feeding on the container, are all right for a normal, healthy baby. The only ones not to give are ready-to-serve varieties such as wheat flakes, rice puffs, etc.

When your doctor says you can begin solid foods, ask him what cereals he'd prefer to have you start with.

Give Baby a teaspoonful at first, and work up to 2 or 3 tablespoonfuls just before the 10 a.m. feeding. In introducing new foods, give one at a time and let an interval of several days elapse, before trying another. Then if Baby is upset, you can easily find the cause.

Some begin with fruit

Which solid food you offer Baby first depends upon your doctor and your baby. Doctors advise introducing fruit between 3 and 6 months, and some prefer to start Baby on fruit instead of cereal if he seems to dislike cereals.

Good fruits to start on are strained applesauce or ripe banana (one with brown spots on the skin and tan-colored pulp). Mash the banana with a fork and thin it with a little formula until it's the consistency of whipped cream.

If you use home-prepared fruits instead of those commercially prepared for Baby, be sure to run them through a fine sieve.

A little later, gradually alternate these first fruits with strained apricots, prunes, pears, pineapple, and the various commercial mixtures prepared for Baby. Prunes or prune juice is given if a laxative is needed, but use them very cautiously, as they tend to cause cramps or loose bowels.

Start with a teaspoonful of applesauce or banana the first day at the beginning or end of either the 10 a.m. or 6 p.m. feeding. As soon as Baby shows you he likes it, increase the amount a teaspoonful each day until he's taking a half can of fruit or a whole banana, if it agrees with him.

If you start with fruit, then add the cereal about 3 weeks later. Just be sure he's used to one food before you begin another.

May get egg yolk

Your baby may begin to get hard-cooked egg yolk after he's taking cereal. Since he may be allergic to egg, don't feed it to him until your doctor gives you the go-ahead signal.

Start with ½ teaspoonful and gradually work up to the whole egg yolk. Mash the yolk with a fork and mix with a small amount of formula, so Baby can swallow it more easily. If he doesn't like the consistency, mix it with his cereal. Stop feeding the egg immediately if Baby develops a rash or vomits.

To prepare the egg yolk for Baby, wash the egg carefully in clear water. Break the shell in half and separate yolk and white. (Slip yolk from one shell to the other to allow white to drain off entirely.) Place the yolk in a custard cup and set cup in a pan of boiling water for 2 to 3 minutes.

How to offer a new food

Whether you give your baby his solid food before or after his milk will depend entirely on him. You'll just have to experiment to find out which time he prefers. Some babies must have their milk first when they're particularly hungry, and will accept solids at the end of their meal. Others will take the solids only at the beginning, since they're too full after drinking their milk. Offer your baby the solid food first. If he rebels or spits it out, then give him his milk and try again at the end of the meal. Increase the amount of a new food a little at each offering until Baby is taking the full amount.

It's very important not to become upset if Baby refuses the food. Eating foods of this consistency is a new experience for him, and at first he may spit them out because he doesn't like the feel of the food in his mouth. Never coax or force a food down your baby, but repeat the same food the next day. If there are some varieties he doesn't like, drop them for the time being. Baby may change his mind in a month and accept them.

The best way to feed Baby is to hold him in a semisitting position, with his head cradled on your arm. Place a very small amount of the food on a teaspoon, or after-dinner coffee spoon, and place the food far back on Baby's tongue, so he can't spit it out.

Schedule for baby three to four months old

6:00 a.m. or 7:00 a.m. Breast or bottle feeding.
Play or sleep in crib or bassinet.
9:00 a.m. Two ounces orange juice or 4 ounces of tomato juice, if you prefer.
Vitamin concentrate or 1 teaspoon cod-liver oil, as prescribed by your doctor.
Bath. Undress Baby and let him play and kick on big bed for a few minutes before his bath.
10:00 a.m. One-half tablespoon cereal. Gradually increase amount to 2 or 3 tablespoons.
Hard-cooked egg yolk may be mixed with cereal.
Breast or bottle feeding.
10:30 a.m. to 2:00 p.m. Sunbath and long nap out of doors if weather permits. Drink of water.
2:00 p.m. Breast or bottle feeding.
2:20 p.m. to 5:15 p.m. Nap. Sunbath unless weather is too hot. Drink of water after nap. Play.
5:15 p.m. Undress for night. Play period on big bed before being dressed in night-clothes.
6:00 p.m. One-half tablespoon strained fruit. Gradually increase to $\frac{1}{2}$ can.
Breast or bottle feeding.
6:20 p.m. Bed in well-ventilated room.
10:00 p.m. Breast or bottle feeding.
The 10 p.m. feeding is sometimes omitted if Baby is sleeping soundly and has taken at least 7 ounces at a feeding. However, the breast-fed baby should get this feeding.

Chapter IV

Your baby from four to five months

Development

Between 4 and 5 months your baby may:

. . . laugh out loud.
. . . hold his head steady when carried.
. . . splash with his hand when in his bathtub.

. . . hold his toys.
. . . raise his hands when lifted.
. . . make a noise when he hears a voice.

. . . reach for objects.
. . . turn his head to visually follow objects removed from his sight.

. . . lift head and shoulders and roll over.
. . . play with his own hands.

. . . lift himself by hands or forearms when lying on stomach.

If your baby is on a fresh- or evaporated-milk formula, use the same formula as given on page 103, for a baby of 3 months.

How to prepare: Directions on pages 70–73.

Your baby will probably take from 6 to 8 ounces at a feeding. You may increase the milk in the formula 1 ounce each week.

Formula using citric or lactic acid with evaporated milk

(one day's supply)

3 tablespoons corn syrup
1 teaspoon 25 percent solution citric acid or ½ teaspoon U. S. P. 85 percent lactic acid. Enough boiled water, cooled, to make 1 pint
13 ounces evaporated milk, chilled.

How to prepare: Method of preparation is given on page 67. Do not overheat the formula when warming the bottle at feeding time.

He'll like a ball

Now, too, a soft rubber or woolly ball may be added to Baby's toys. When you place him in the playpen for exercise, give him a rattle, soft doll, and the ball. Then leave him alone except for necessary care.

Don't rush new activities

You'll probably notice now when you hold your baby that he is beginning to push with his toes. This doesn't mean that he wants to stand up, so don't rush him. It's simply his way of exercising muscles that he'll use later in pulling himself up.

After a while, too, he'll begin sitting up. Let him accomplish this task at his own speed, and don't prop him up with a pillow until he can sit steadily by himself. There's a chance that he might slump and sit there for a long period, thereby weakening his back muscles. This doesn't mean that you can't sit him in your lap or pull him up to a sitting position, but be sure to keep his back straight whenever you do. A better practice, however, is to put Baby in his playpen and let him sit and stand whenever he gets ready.

Teeth on the way

Your baby may get his first tooth soon, although the average baby gets his between the sixth and eighth months. There are wide variations in the ages at which first teeth come through, and there's no need to worry if your baby is late in getting his. Occasionally, a baby will be over a year before he has any. If your baby gets his supply of milk and cod-liver oil or concentrate, and plenty of sunshine, fresh air, exercise, and rest, his teeth will take care of themselves.

There's little discomfort attached to teething for the normal baby of good habits and nutrition. You'll probably not even know what's happening until the teeth appear, although he may be slightly fussy. A teething ring can be tied to Baby's bassinet, so he can chew on it, but be sure to boil it frequently.

Time for vegetables

Now is the time to add vegetables or vegetable soup to Baby's diet if he's taking his fruit and cereal well. Your doctor may have started him on vegetables before this. You can buy strained vegetables prepared especially for Baby, or those you prepare at home are good if you mash them through a sieve after cooking and before adding seasonings.

Tomatoes, spinach, kale, lettuce, chard, collards, green beans, carrots, beets, peas, asparagus, squash, and celery may be used, or any of them combined.

In starting, offer a teaspoon of the warmed vegetable at Baby's 2 p.m. feeding. Increase the amount until he's taking 2 or 3 ounces. Cover and store the unused portion of a can or jar of vegetables *in the refrigerator*. Don't use any that has stood for more than 24 hours.

You'll probably find that Baby dislikes the flavors of some of the vegetables. Don't force him to take any he doesn't like. In a month's time, offer the disliked foods again. He may take them then.

Other foods

Instead of fruit, you can occasionally substitute a simple custard or rennet-custard dessert. Fruits are a more valuable food than custard, however. Custards may be a bigger help later if Baby refuses to drink milk.

Your doctor may now suggest giving one of the strained meats or meat soups commercially prepared for young babies. These are very good for Baby and may be substituted for his cereal or vegetable several times a week.

Build good eating habits

Now is the time when your baby will build his food habits for years to come. He can learn now to take and like almost any healthful food that's presented to him. Your own calm reassuring manner is an important factor in introducing new foods. Baby's acceptance of each strange eating experience may be slow since almost all babies resent changes. Be content if he merely tastes the new food at first.

Never force a feeding of any food.

If your baby becomes slightly ill or develops a cold, he'll probably not want to eat as usual. At such times, allow him to eat only what he'll take willingly.

Schedule for baby four to five months old

6:00 a.m. or 7:00 a.m. Breast or bottle feeding.

8:00 a.m. to 9 a.m. Exercise on floor or big bed.

9:00 a.m. One teaspoon cod-liver oil, or the amount of vitamin concentrate prescribed by your doctor. Two to 3 ounces of orange juice, or twice as much tomato juice.

9:30 a.m. Bath.

10:00 a.m. Cereal.

Egg yolk, cooked in custard cup for 2 to 3 minutes. May be mixed with the cereal if Baby refuses it alone.

Breast or bottle feeding.

10:30 a.m. to 2:00 p.m. Sunbath and long nap, outside if weather permits. Drink of water after nap.

2:00 p.m. Two to 3 ounces strained vegetable or vegetable soup, starting with 1 teaspoon and increasing gradually.

Breast or bottle feeding.

2:20 p.m. to 4:30 p.m. Out of doors if weather permits. In sun part of time unless it's very hot. Nap. Drink of water after nap.

4:30 to 5:45 p.m. On floor or in playpen.

5:45 p.m. Undress for night.

6:00 p.m. One tablespoon custard or puréed fruit, or cereal. Breast or bottle feeding.

6:20 p.m. Bed.

10:00 p.m. Breast or bottle feeding.

Chapter V

Your baby from
five to six months

Development

Between the ages of five and six months your baby may:

. . . roll from his back to his stomach.
. . . turn his head at the sound of a hand bell, or voice.

. . . sit up with some propping.
. . . object noisily when an object is taken away from him.

. . . recover rattle if it falls within easy reach.
. . . reach for paper.

. . . cough artificially and know he's cute.
. . . drool—a sign that salivary glands are beginning to function.
. . . play in bath water.

Formula using fresh milk

(one day's supply)

24 to 26 ounces whole milk
6 to 8 ounces boiled water
3 tablespoons corn syrup or
6 tablespoons dextrin-maltose mixture

How to prepare: Follow the method as given on pages 70 through 73. If using the terminal method of sterilization, water need not be boiled.

Formula using evaporated milk

(one day's supply)

13 ounces (1 large can) evaporated milk
17 ounces boiled water
3 tablespoons corn syrup or
6 tablespoons dextrin-maltose mixture

How to prepare: Method described on pages 70 through 73. The citric or lactic acid-evaporated milk formula is the same as for the baby of 4 months, on page 108. Seven to 8 ounces are usually taken for a feeding at this age.

Your baby probably has doubled his birth weight by now, although there's no cause for worry if he hasn't. You needn't be concerned at all as long as he makes a steady gain. From now on, however, you can expect his rate of growth to slow down considerably.

Schedule for baby five to six months old

If Baby's bottle fed, he's probably emptying his bottle at each feeding. He may also be given considerably more orange juice. The amounts of solid foods may be increased gradually.

6:00 a.m. or 7:00 a.m. Breast feeding or bottle. Left alone in crib to sleep or play.

8:00 a.m. to 9:00 a.m. One hour's exercise on floor.

9:00 a.m. Concentrate as prescribed by your doctor, or 1 teaspoon cod-liver oil. Two to 3 ounces orange juice or more, or twice as much tomato juice. Plays undressed on bed a few minutes before bath.

9:30 a.m. Bath.

10:00 a.m. One to 2 tablespoons cereal fed with spoon. This amount means cereal as it is mixed and ready for Baby, not in dry form. Hard-cooked egg yolk may be added to cereal, or given at night if you prefer. Breast or bottle feeding. (Part of formula may be fed with cereal.)

10:30 a.m. to 2 p.m. Sunbath for a few minutes if the weather permits. In summertime, move sunbath period up before 10 a.m., or after 2 p.m. Nap on porch, if possible, or in his bedroom with windows raised. Drink of water when he awakens. Play.

2:00 p.m. One-half to 1 tablespoon strained carrots, spinach, string beans, green peas, asparagus tips, beets, or squash. Feed with spoon. Nursing or 7 to 8 ounces of formula.

2:30 p.m. to 5:00 p.m. Outdoors if weather permits, in sun part of the time, except on very hot days. Short nap. Drink of water when he awakens. Play.

5:00 p.m. to 5:45 p.m. Undress for night. Plays quietly on bed or floor for a few minutes before dressing in night clothes.

5:45 p.m. One to 2 tablespoons mashed ripe banana or puréed prunes, apples, apricots, or peaches. Nursing or 8 ounces of formula.

6:00 p.m. Bed in room by himself, with door closed and window open.

10:00 p.m. Breast or 8 ounces of formula, if needed.

Chapter VI

Your baby from six to eight months

Development

Between 6 and 8 months your baby may:

. . . sit momentarily without support.
. . . bang spoon or pat table in play.

. . . be more active with a little help.
. . . discriminate between a stranger and a familiar person.
. . . pick a cube or block up off the table, or hold a cube in each hand.

. . . show his temper if things don't suit him.
. . . reach for objects he sees.

. . . show pleasure by cooing or crowing.
. . . get a tooth—maybe two—in the middle of his lower jaw.

From now on you'll find this lusty little chap of yours a force to be considered in family affairs. Six months represents completion of half that all-important first year during which your child grows and develops faster than at any other time. His progress mentally and physically will amaze and delight you.

Formula using citric or lactic acid with evaporated milk

(one day's supply)

3 tablespoons corn syrup
1 teaspoon 25 percent citric-acid solution, or
½ teaspoon U.S.P. 85 percent lactic acid
Enough boiled water, cooled, to make 1 pint
16 ounces evaporated milk

All materials should be cold. Mix first three items together and pour slowly into evaporated milk, stirring constantly. No cooking is required. Do not overheat when warming the bottle before feeding.

Formulas using whole and evaporated milk

You can use the same evaporated and whole milk formulas for your baby at 6 months as given on page 110.

It's fun helping Baby learn

From now on the emphasis shifts. Definite training duties are now added.

If you've followed the suggestions thus far, your baby has probably established habits of eating what's set before him, sleeping well, and amusing himself. Each month or two from now on will bring some new phase of training to build upon this foundation.

If you deal with each phase of learning at the proper time, you'll be astonished to see how easy training is. Psychologists who have studied babies and small children for years in the Normal Child Development Clinic at Columbia University say that there is a "critical time" in a child's life for learning each different habit and skill. Many parents have found from experience, too, that at a certain age, a child seems to be willing to tackle a new learning situation. This doesn't mean that he can't learn them later, but it will be harder for him, and harder for you to teach him, too.

Children indicate by signs when they're ready for a new type of learning. For instance, your baby will be ready for bladder training when he notices the puddle he has made on the floor or listens to the sound in the stool. To attempt to teach control before he has any idea of what it's about would be futile. But to delay training too long after he has exhibited interest makes it harder for him to learn.

Children differ in the age at which their muscles and nervous systems have developed sufficiently to permit a certain type of learning. It is better to rely upon such signs as those described above, rather than upon chronological age, to determine when it's time to start new training.

As his mother, you'll soon become adept in detecting these signs if you're on the lookout for them. Study your baby, work with him, and play with him. When he shows he's ready for a next step in training, start to work!

Always remember to keep this training easy and fun. Expect Baby to fail many times before he masters a skill. He isn't failing deliberately; he simply has to learn, as you have had to learn something new to you. Crossness and punishments don't help when Baby doesn't understand, or isn't ready yet to grasp the lesson. Know your own baby; then be gentle but firm in working out the things necessary for his development.

The times at which Baby might be ready for training are suggested in this book, so you can be on the lookout and prepared to provide the training indicated. If your baby isn't quite ready for the training suggested at a certain age, let him take his time. If he beats the gun, sneak a look into the pages ahead and help him along.

The period approaching right now is that of "sitting up," when your baby is going to be ready for a whole series of new experiences and a certain amount of independence. Independence is something you'll want to build for all you're worth; so get any equipment your baby will soon be needing to develop his new abilities.

A safe chair for sitting alone

When your baby of his own accord pulls himself to a strong sitting position, he's ready to leave your lap and arms, and sit alone for play and eating times.

A popular arrangement is a low chair set in Baby's special table. Plenty of room for eating or play

To make this comfortable for Baby, you'll need a safe chair in which he can eat his meals. A high chair should have a wide, sturdy base with safeguards to prevent Baby from tipping it over. The high chair which has a base that swings up to become a table and low chair for the older baby is very practical. If you already have a high chair, you can lower it by sawing off the legs. To avoid bad eating habits, Baby will be better off during the entire preschool period if he has his principal meals, or at least the main part of them, alone and before the family eats. At least, give him his meals alone during his first two years.

When Baby grows too active for his high chair, it can be lowered by sawing off legs

A low chair should have a tray or table which will serve the double purpose of keeping Baby in and giving him something to eat or play on. There are several kinds on the market, and you can choose the type most

Canvas seat with wide overshoulder strap
saves Mother from strain, leaves hands free

convenient for you and comfortable for Baby.

Don't hurry the sitting process. Baby will do this himself as soon as he's ready.

Offer formula in a cup

It's a good idea now to give a formula-fed baby some of his milk from a cup occasionally.

(A small cup over which his mouth fits easily is good, and one with a lip is best of all.) There'll be considerable spilling and leakage at first. Put a long, moistureproof bib on Baby and hold a towel under the cup while he's learning.

In the beginning, Baby will take only a swallow, and you must remember to take it slow and easy. He'll probably be a little suspicious of the cup at first, even though he's accustomed to taking water or orange juice this way. Too, he's used to his milk coming from a bottle. It'll be quite a few months yet before he's ready to give up his bottle altogether. If cup feedings are introduced in this way, however, he will be less likely to balk at milk from a cup when he's ready to be weaned entirely.

Many mothers find about this time that their breast milk is beginning to diminish in quantity. If this happens (you'll know by Baby's failure to gain), offer the formula for your baby's age in a cup after each nursing.

Baby can now drink his formula from a cup. Take it slow, as he'll probably accept only a swallow at first

(See formulas on page 112.) Let him take as much or as little as he wants. As your milk gets less and less, you may give more and more of the cup feeding.

Don't start giving your breast-fed baby a bottle now. He's able to drink from a cup, and you'll save yourself much bother by using it, if complementary feedings are needed.

He gets a social life

It's good for Baby to see some outside people, but his eating and sleeping schedule should on no account be disturbed. He can go visiting occasionally between 3 o'clock and bedtime. Visitors may play with him quietly during that period. He shouldn't be tossed, tickled, spoken to loudly, or made to laugh hard. These things are overstimulating, and most babies pay for them with crying spells. It's nice for Baby to join the family circle while eating his zwieback and for a time before the evening meal, but he shouldn't be overhandled or excited.

As Baby widens his contacts, shield him from people with colds or other infections. They might also give him children's and other diseases. Don't ever let anyone with an infection near your baby.

Graduates to overalls

Now that Baby's entering a more active phase, there'll be some changes in his wardrobe. The shirt and diaper remain his basic dress, but when Baby is on the floor and outdoors, little overalls or coveralls should take the place of dresses or kimonos.

Too, if he's outgrowing his nightgowns, he's ready for sleeping garments with legs and feet.

In warm weather, a sleeveless cotton shirt or sunsuit, and a diaper are quite enough. A diaper alone may even be sufficient. In cooler or cold weather, a sweater or coat, cap, mittens, and leggings may be needed in addition to the coveralls. Make him as comfortable as possible. Clothe him as lightly or as warmly as is necessary for this purpose. A well-nourished baby is more likely to suffer from too much clothing rather than too little. Here you will have to use your own judgment and check indoor and outside temperatures.

These garments may be made of lightweight cotton or flannelette, and should be loose and roomy. It's a good idea to have several changes.

Now that Baby's doing so many things, he may wear overalls or coveralls for his playtimes

Playtimes are scheduled

Your baby should now be put in his playpen both indoors and out (the same pen can be used) for regular playtimes with his toys—rattle, cloth or knitted doll, and a soft ball. A porch is ideal for his outdoor play, or in warm weather, the pen can be put on the grass. Be sure it's in the shade if the weather is hot. Part of Baby's waking hours may be spent on your own bed if it's barricaded so he won't fall off. He's very active now and needs more space. The big bed and the playpen outdoors will make Baby's waking time pass pleasantly and with a minimum of trouble for you.

How to handle fears

Baby's big enough now to be a member of the family, and to be around everyday-living processes which may frighten him at first. The noise of the vacuum sweeper, the radio next door, or the swirling of bath water down the drain may bring forth sudden screams from him.

Although you can head off many frightening experiences before they happen, these are things he'll have to get used to. Instead of shielding him from contact with them entirely, show him by your cheerful matter-of-fact handling of the situation that there's nothing to be afraid of.

Pick him up in your arms and hold him while you show him how the vacuum works. Or watch with him the water running out of the tub, and laugh about it as though it were fun. Make your manner extremely reassuring, but not comforting, for no hurt is involved.

If your child has been badly frightened by any sudden, loud noise, such as thunder, pick him up and talk to him gently. Let him feel your physical strength and protection. Once you're sure he feels calm and safe again, start him off on a new line of interest. However, stay at his side until a storm is over. After a while, he'll realize that the thunder and lightning aren't going to hurt him, and he'll conquer the fear himself. Remember, he'll soon learn to take frightening experiences in his stride if he knows you are near.

He's learning to understand speech

Your baby's bubbling, gurgling, and cooing sounds are all part of his learning to talk. At the same time, he is detecting differences in the tone of your voice. He can tell whether it's cross, comforting, or approving.

At this age, he babbles sociably and even surprises you with inflections and intonations that resemble adults' speech—even to the rising inflection of a question. About this time, too, he begins to understand and recognize some of the words you say to him.

By the time he's a year old, he'll understand a good many words, even though he can't say them. This is known as his "passive vocabulary," and it will always be made up of more words than his active vocabulary, or the words he uses in everyday speech. Since he's picking up the words you say, it's doubly important that you talk to him a lot in short, simple sentences, and pronounce your words correctly and distinctly.

He'll sleep less

About now, many mothers become alarmed because they feel their children aren't sleeping enough. It's quite natural, however, for your baby to sleep less during the daytime. Many babies take only a short nap between breakfast and bathtime, and may stay awake for the entire interval between their afternoon nap and bedtime.

Keep to his night schedule as before, with 12 hours in bed, and continue the afternoon nap until your youngster enters school. If he spends the full time in bed, you may leave it to him how much of it he sleeps.

On the other hand, let him sleep as much as he wants to. Babies differ in the amount of sleep they need just as in the amount of food required. If Baby gets fussy and irritable, or sleepy at any time, put him in his bed for a nap. Close the door of his room, so he may sleep if he likes.

Night wakefulness may be hunger

If your breast-fed baby begins waking and crying at night, or crying a great deal in the daytime, he may be hungry. As was said before, it's rather common at this time for your milk to drop off in quantity.

His weight gain may have dropped off, and it's a good idea to weigh him, with diaper on, before and after each feeding for a 24-hour period to see how much milk he's getting from you. If it's much less than 32 ounces in a 24-hour period, consult your doctor about starting milk in a cup, if you haven't already. (See page 114.)

If your baby needs more food, by all means give it to him. But if he's getting plenty and gaining regularly, follow the suggestions given above for sleeping.

Tips to make eating go well

Feed Baby before the family mealtime in his chair at his own little table. After that he may, if you like, join the family circle by playing in his pen while the family eats. Don't give him food from the table.

It's a good idea to handle the evening meal in the same way, with Baby going to bed immediately after his supper and before the family eats. This will be convenient for you, as well as very good for Baby.

Introduce any new food at the beginning of the meal when your baby is hungry. Give only a little at first, increasing the amount gradually until the required amount is taken. If Baby shows a disinclination for a particular food, try to get him to take a small amount, but do not make an issue of it. Urging will only make him balky.

If he spits out the food several times or just won't try it at all, give up on it for a few days or a week. He may feel differently about it later. If you try to force it down him now, he may develop a permanent dislike for that particular food. And any unpleasantness at mealtime may lead to resistance to all foods.

Usually, it's advisable to give his milk last, after the solid foods have been taken. With some babies, however, milk is the least-liked food. When this is the case, offer the milk first. Sometimes it's difficult to strike a balance between milk and solid foods. You don't want Baby to get into the habit of filling up on milk at the expense of other needed foods, yet milk remains the principal food in his diet and will for some time to come.

First, try offering the various solid foods at the beginning of the meal as has been suggested. After he's taken a reasonable amount, offer the milk. One time he may refuse the milk altogether, then at the next meal drink two cups. As long as his daily intake of milk, including what is used in cooking for him, is approximately a quart, there's no need to be concerned. But if he consistently refuses milk, begin offering it at the first of the meal before the solid foods.

Use as much milk as you can in preparing his food—through desserts made with milk such as custards, rennet mixtures, creamed vegetables, cream soups, cereals cooked in milk, and milk toast. His milk intake can be increased still more by using evaporated milk (diluted very little or not at all) instead of fresh milk for cooking. Most babies like the taste of evaporated milk. And if it's used full strength, Baby is really getting twice as much milk as he would from the same amount of fresh milk.

It should be possible in this way to get the equivalent of a pint of milk into his cooked dishes, on cereal, etc. Most children will drink at least two cups in a day, and this amount is quite satisfactory if he's getting the rest of his milk in his food.

If your baby stubbornly refuses to take any milk over a period of several days, talk it over with your doctor.

If Baby refuses food he has been in the habit of accepting, take it away from that meal without fuss or emotion. If he has good eating habits otherwise, and refuses most of a meal, it may be a sign of indisposition, and the best treatment is to let him go without until he's ready to eat again. Should this continue for more than a meal or two, especially if he has fever and appears ill, call your doctor. If there is nothing or apparently very little the matter with him, he'll probably make up for his fast at the next meal.

New foods on his menu

Don't force your baby to eat. This may result in real mealtime antagonism. And you should introduce new foods only when Baby is feeling well and happy.

At the half-year mark, your up-and-coming eater should have stewed fruit once a day, in addition to a simple dessert made with gelatine or milk.

Now he can be introduced to vegetable, liver, lamb, or beef soups, or those with a cream base; potatoes; and butter or margarine.

Study the schedule on page 118, and give your baby, in rotation, all the foods allowed him at this age to accustom him to a constantly widening range. When he's getting several familiar dishes at a meal, it's a good idea to alternate in feeding them. That is, give a spoonful of vegetable, then one of dessert, and then back to the vegetable. Babies who eat their full helping of one food first and then clean up the next food are inclined to continue the habit. No great harm is done, but this can be avoided by going from one dish to another during the early training period.

Three meals a day

Babies nowadays are getting accustomed to foods earlier all the time, and occasionally a small prodigy is ready for three meals a day when he's 10 weeks old.

It's true that most babies are not ready at that age, but they do make amazing progress on formulas and diet schedules that are well suited to their needs. Many babies are fully ready at 6 months for the momentous change to three meals, and some big babies are ready sooner than that.

Your baby may have begun to lose all interest in his 10 a.m. and 2 p.m. feedings, even though he's making his weight gains and is all right in every way. If that's the case with your baby, ask your doctor about cutting the four meals a day he's been having to three. If he approves the change, combine the 10 a.m. and 2 p.m. feedings into one dinner at noon or 11:30—it's a good idea to use the earlier time for a while, so he won't get too hungry.

You'll see as you study the schedule that there is no actual change, just a rearrangement. Baby will have the same foods, but it has been found that many babies eat better from now on if their solid foods are spaced more widely.

Keep on giving Baby his meals alone, before the rest of the family eats. Place him in his low chair when he eats.

Be content with a small taste of a new or disliked food. When he's taken it, give him one he likes very much, and let him have as much of it as he wants. This might be his nursing or bottle.

Let two or three days pass before offering a disliked food again. If he has a chance to get used to it gradually, he'll soon accept it readily.

Your baby under 1 year needs every day:

Vitamin A—a minimum of 1,500 I. U. (International Units):

1 quart of milk provides about . . . 1,500-2,100 I. U.

2 tablespoons spinach . . . 2,600-5,400 I. U.

2 tablespoons carrots . . . . 470-850 I. U.

1 teaspoon of cod-liver oil . . . 1,200-2,000 I. U.

Vitamin B₁ (thiamin)—a minimum of .4 milligrams or 400 micrograms:

1 quart of milk (whole) supplies . . . 360 micrograms

1 portion (3 tablespoons) banana . . . 50-100 micrograms

1 portion (3 tablespoons) tomato . . . 30-52 micrograms

1 portion (3 tablespoons) oatmeal . . . 52-116 micrograms

Vitamin C (ascorbic acid)—a minimum of 30 milligrams:

1 ounce fresh orange juice yields . . . 15 milligrams

4 ounces fresh lime juice . . . . . . 38-120 milligrams

4 ounces fresh lemon juice . . . . . . 52-60 milligrams

4 ounces fresh grapefruit juice . . . . . 38-41 milligrams

4 ounces tomato juice . . . . 21-29 milligrams

Vitamin G (riboflavin)—a minimum of .6 milligrams or 600 micrograms:

1 portion (2.7 ounces) of liver provides . . . 1,386-2,002 micrograms

1 portion (3 tablespoons) beet tops . . . 156 micrograms

1 egg yields . . . . . . 151-227 micrograms

1 quart of milk . . . . 1,872-2,304 micrograms

Vitamin D—a minimum of 400 I. U.:

1 teaspoon U.S.P. cod-liver oil contains about . . . 400 I. U.

3 drops of viosterol . . . . 400 I. U.
1 quart fortified milk . . . . . . 400 I. U.

Niacin or nicotinic acid is required in varying amounts and will be adequately supplied by the foods and milk in a well-balanced diet.

Schedule for baby six to eight months old—four meals a day

6:00 a.m. or 7:00 a.m. Nursing or 8 ounces of formula.

8:00 a.m. Nap in bedroom with window open.

9:00 a.m. Concentrate or 1 teaspoon cod-liver oil. Two to 3 ounces orange juice in a cup, or twice as much tomato juice.

9:30 a.m. Bath.

10:00 a.m. Two to 3 tablespoons cereal with 1 or 2 ounces warm formula or boiled milk. No sugar. Egg yolk, partially cooked or hard-cooked and then grated. Nursing or bottle.

10:30 a.m. Nap in bedroom, window open.

2:00 p.m. Two tablespoons coarsely sieved vegetable—carrots, spinach, beets, green beans, asparagus tips, fresh peas, or squash. May be creamed, in vegetable water, or in meat broth.
Liver soup, beef soup, or vegetable soup. Zwieback with butter or margarine or arrowroot cooky.
Custard, rennet custard, rennet-custard dessert, or plain gelatine dessert.
Nursing or bottle feeding. May take only a half bottle at this meal.

2:30 p. m. Outdoors in pen, either on porch or in yard.

5:00 p. m. On big bed to exercise.

5:30 p. m. to 5:45 p. m. Held, or carried about house.

5:45 p. m. One to 3 tablespoons custard or cottage cheese. One to 2 tablespoons strained, stewed fruit—prunes, apricots, pineapple, pears, peaches, apples, baked apple, or applesauce. Nursing or bottle feeding.

6:00 p. m. Bed.

Schedule for baby six to eight months old—three meals a day

7:00 a.m. to 7:30 a.m. Breakfast. Two to 4 tablespoons cereal served with formula or boiled milk. No sugar. Enriched cereals or those made from whole grain are preferable. Milk toast or sieved ripe banana may be substituted occasionally. Egg yolk, partially cooked or hard-cooked and grated.

Slice of toast or zwieback with butter. Nursing or bottle feeding.

8:00 a.m. Nap in bedroom with window open or play in pen.

9:30 a.m. Two to 4 ounces of orange juice in a cup.

Concentrate or 1 teaspoon cod-liver oil.

9:30 to 11:00 a.m. Nap. Bath following nap.

11:30 a.m. to 12:00 N. Dinner: Two to 3 tablespoons coarsely sieved vegetable—carrots, spinach, string beans, green peas, tomatoes, asparagus tips, beets, or squash.

Liver soup, beef soup, or vegetable soup. Zwieback or arrowroot cooky.

Two to 3 tablespoons dessert—cornstarch pudding, custard, rennet custard, or gelatine.

Nursing or bottle feeding.

1:00 p.m. to 3:00 p.m. Nap.

3:00 p.m. Four to 8 ounces milk. Zwieback, graham cracker, or arrowroot cooky.

5:30 p.m. Supper: Two to 3 tablespoons boiled or baked custard or cottage cheese.

One to 3 tablespoons stewed fruit—prunes, pears, peaches, apple, pineapple, applesauce, baked apple, or apricots.

6:00 p.m. Bed.

Chapter VII

Your baby from eight to twelve months

Development

Between the ages of 8 and 12 months your baby may:

. . . sit up strongly with no support.
. . . play with his image in a mirror.

. . . creep and pull himself up. He may even walk, but don't hurry him.
. . . wave bye-bye.

. . . pick up large and small objects in his hands and examine them carefully.

. . . understand many things you say to him.
. . . cooperate in rhythmic nursery games.

. . . make sounds, such as da-da and ma-ma. He may say several words.

. . . have two teeth and cut four more.
. . . show an interest in throwing things.

When he starts to creep

For some time you've been placing Baby in his playpen both inside and outdoors for his regular play periods. Besides getting him used to amusing himself, this has given him full opportunity to develop his muscles, which he couldn't have done if he had been kept in a bed or buggy all the time. Around the seventh or eighth month, he'll be able to pull himself over the floor, and soon make good speed. Babies creep in various ways; some sitting up, some on all fours, and some on their knees. The method doesn't matter—any one serves the purpose and gets him where he wants to go.

Whenever he can be watched, let Baby creep about the house. This gives him more freedom and helps his mental development. He'll need to be protected, of course, from falls which might injure him, but if a hands-off policy is followed as far as possible, he'll soon learn to keep his balance and pause at the top of flights of steps.

Clothes for creeping

The shirt and diaper remain his basic dress, but when Baby creeps, he'll need something over his knees, if he hasn't had it before. The preferred garment nowadays for this period is the overall or coverall, mentioned in Chapter VI. These are roomy enough to make diaper-changing fast and easy, and can be bought ready-made in many styles. You'll need several pairs, for the creeping stage is perhaps the dirtiest and messiest of all. But what a happy one for Baby! For the first time, he can explore under his own power some of the interesting things in this marvelous world into which he has come.

Eliminate home hazards

As soon as Baby reaches the place where he can move at will, go over your house and clear out anything on which he might hurt himself.

Any poisons or medicines that you must keep should be locked up far beyond his reach. This applies to cleaning materials, dyes, cosmetic preparations, hair oils and tonics, cough drops, aspirins, or other remedies of any kind. Don't ever allow Baby to play with a full or empty can of talcum powder, since the powder, if inhaled, can cause severe inflammation of the lungs.

Watch out for boiling liquids, hot coffeepots, and buckets of scrub water. If you have a single-pipe register in the floor which gets very hot (it's much better not to have this kind where there's a baby around), fence it off with the playpen during your baby's period of creeping.

Danger ahead for your household treasures! They need protection when the pulling-up stage comes

Keep all instruments with sharp points or ragged edges out of Baby's reach. Dry beans and peas should be stowed away high because they swell and cause real trouble if Baby sticks them up a nostril or into an ear. Small objects such as coins, marbles, corn, jacks, and seeds should always be kept from Baby.

While Baby is still so young, it's better to wash his shoes off than to use shoe cleaner on them, since he's apt to put them in his mouth.

Toys aid creeping

Soft, washable toys which Baby can grasp are still best for him at this age. Knitted or rubber dolls and animals are easily kept clean, and he can't hurt himself on them. Balls of various kinds—soft-rubber which can be grasped readily; woolly balls; bright-colored balls—will help in the first stages of creeping by giving Baby an incentive to go after them.

Soft balls, rattles, rag dolls, and stuffed animals are toys which aid the mental growth of tiny tots

Give your baby a chance to explore

Any time after about the ninth month, Baby may start pulling himself to his feet, holding to furniture, or to the sides of his pen. Don't hurry or urge him, though. When Baby's muscles are strong enough for this type of exercise, he will begin it.

And now you'll be confronted with your first great problem of management. As soon as your baby reaches this stage, objects on tables are within his reach; and you can depend on it, he'll reach for them. Baby's curiosity, however, is proof of his alertness and growing independence.

During this phase of your baby's growth, clear out of the house or yard anything on which he might get hurt. Put all breakables out of his reach. Then give your baby a chance to explore.

Some of your housework can be combined with baby-watching. You can dust the floor or furniture, or make beds while Baby roams around the room. He'll probably investigate the contents of the wastebasket, tug at bedclothes, or play with the shoes in the closet, but he won't be doing a bit of harm. Do make sure, however, before you turn him loose, that all hazards are removed from the room, especially the kitchen, if you let him play there while you're working. And to prevent falls and other accidents, disconnect the lamps in the living room and wind their cords around the bases. Whenever the weather permits, take your small chores outside, so you can let him wander about the yard while you work.

All these precautions aren't giving in too much to Baby. He needs to handle and investigate everything he can in order to learn.

Give him a playroom

Before your little fellow reaches the place where he's getting everywhere, he should be given a playroom, or play corner in a family room, where he can touch anything he likes. This should be on the first floor where he'll be near you as you go about your work. An older child would be content to play alone upstairs, but your youngster at this age is still too young.

Confine Baby in his playroom for regular play periods. A little gate or his playpen across the doorway will keep him safe and still not give him the sense of being shut in that a closed door would. If he's given this room where he can have perfect freedom, Baby will obey the rules of the rest of the house with good grace.

His playroom may be anything from a cubby hole or breakfast room to a large, luxuriously furnished nursery. Your circumstances

Baby's playroom should have low shelves for toys

must, therefore, dictate the furnishings. The room shouldn't have a polished floor on which Baby might slip, or a nice rug which would have to be protected. The ideal floor-covering is linoleum, for it provides a safe footing, a good surface for play activities, and is easily cleaned.

The playroom should have an open cupboard or set of shelves (made from boxes, if you like) where Baby's toys can be placed in orderly fashion, within his reach. These are the essential furnishings of a playroom. Add to them as your purse and desires dictate. Any furniture you buy, such as small tables and chairs, should be strong and durable.

Baby needs companionship

Continue his play periods by putting Baby in his playpen, either indoors or out, depend-

ing on the weather. He'll be interested in his toys, and in kicking, stretching, and investigating his toes. It's best for his development to let him have these periods of self-activity without interruption. After a while, however, he may tire of his own company and fuss for companionship. Go to him then. Sometimes, if you give him something new to play with, he may be happy for another hour. If he's still dissatisfied, give him the attention he needs, or play with him for a while.

He joins the family circle

In addition to the lesson of amusing himself, Baby also needs social contacts. He can have these in his journeys of exploration about the house, and there should be a period each day when he joins in family activities. Whenever strangers come to visit you, give him every chance to get used to them.

If you take him with you when you do your marketing, he'll soon become accustomed to unfamiliar surroundings. And at times along the way, stop whenever he wants to watch other children at play.

Beginning to talk

By 11 or 12 months, your baby will probably say a real word and show you that he knows what it means. Sometimes his first word may go unnoticed for a while because it doesn't sound like the word he is trying to imitate. But, after he has used a certain sound several times to indicate a certain thing, you'll catch on.

Because babyish first words are so appealing, you'll be tempted to repeat them back to your youngster. Don't do it. Many mothers and fathers make this mistake. It definitely doesn't help your baby learn to talk. He

He needs regular periods in his playpen outdoors

thinks he is imitating the way you talk. If you reverse yourself now and adopt his way of saying things, you'll really mix him up.

Don't try to make him change the way he pronounces words. Just be sure you say the words he uses clearly and correctly each time you use them.

Your baby may stop adding words to his vocabulary for a while after his first two or three are understood. There may be a definite lag, too, while he is learning to walk. But he'll make up for lost ground after he has become an accomplished walker. In the meantime, you can help him add to his unspoken vocabulary if you talk to him in short, simple words, sing nursery songs, and recite jingling rhymes. Don't talk too fast, though, and keep your sentences short.

Of course, your baby will have other models besides you. He'll copy the speech of anyone who is around him a lot. Keep this in mind when hiring a servant or baby-sitter. Relatives and friends are more difficult to control, but you can ask them not to talk baby talk to your youngster, and to avoid slang expressions as much as possible.

Baby's in the big tub

Your baby is getting big indeed, for now he can take his bath in the big tub. He'll love this, and how he'll splash! Place a towel or mat in the bottom of the tub so he won't slip. Continue to test the water with a bath thermometer or your elbow as you did with his own tub. Let him play awhile with celluloid fish or other water toys, then give him a regular bath. Remember, though, that he's still a baby, and never leave him alone in the tub. Too many things might happen.

You'll probably find the bath table convenient for dressing and undressing Baby as

At any time after he's able to sit up strongly, Baby may have his bath in the family bathtub

long as you can keep him on it. When he gets too lively, however, you'll have to put this handy object away and graduate to a bigger table, your bed, or a pad on the floor.

Don't break his sleep routine

As Baby gets older, he'll sleep less during the day. His night sleep of 6 p.m. to 6 or 7 a.m. should be religiously observed for years to come. His nap times will shift (see schedule at the end of this chapter). But for his long afternoon nap, Baby should be put in his own room, with the window opened and the door closed, and left there for the full period. If he cries hard, attend to his needs, but leave him for his full nap time. Don't begin now, or ever, the practice of staying with Baby until he goes to sleep. See that he's comfortable, then leave his room, and close the door behind you.

He starts to walk

Once Baby tries to pull himself up and stand, let him practice at his own speed. Some babies may not even try until they're over a year, while occasionally one will stand at seven months. Just be sure to give him plenty of opportunities to use his newly found power whenever he chooses to.

If your baby stands until he's tired and then begins to cry, let him down easily. Chances are he just hasn't figured out for himself how to sit down yet.

After he gains confidence in his standing ability, Baby will begin to take a few tentative steps, still holding on to the furniture or playpen rail. Don't urge him at this point. Let him take his time, and sometime between the twelfth and fifteenth months, he'll probably take out on his own.

Toilet training may begin

If you wish, you may start placing Baby on a toilet seat or "potty" chair now, although many parents put off all training until the baby is fifteen or sixteen months old and better able to understand the purpose of a toilet seat.

The toilet seat should have arms, a back, and a strap to hold him in. This may be placed over the toilet in the bathroom or have it's own pan so it can be used anywhere. Some models have folding steps, an aid to self-help when Baby gets big enough to walk and climb.

Accustom Baby to new toilet habits gradually. Let child examine the toilet seat before being placed on it. Stay close by the first few times Baby's put on the seat. After that, fasten strap and leave for a while

Observe for a week the times at which he has bowel movements. Usually, at least one comes fairly regularly after the morning meal.

Choose a day to begin training when Baby is feeling particularly well and happy. (Never start a new phase of training when he's fussy or tired or not quite himself.) Place the toilet seat with the footrest slightly extended and

the strap loosened. Sit down in front of it with Baby and help him get acquainted with it. When the usual time for the movement comes, lift Baby on; but don't fasten the strap for the first few times; and don't leave him. Sit with him, making an occasional cheerful comment and holding his hand, until he's relaxed and feels at ease on the training seat.

Indicate what is wanted. A grunt is usually the best understood sign. If the movement occurs, act pleased so he'll understand he has done what was expected of him. Leave him on the toilet seat long enough for the bowel to be evacuated. If nothing happens after five minutes, take him off without showing any disappointment, and don't put him on again until the next day at the same time.

It's extremely important to keep the toilet-training experience a happy, easy one. It may take a long time for your baby to get the idea, and it will probably be some time after that before he has sufficient nervous and muscular control to prevent accidents. Never scold, punish, or hurry him.

After he is having one movement on the toilet a reasonable part of the time, you may start trying to catch other movements during the day if he has them. Put Baby on the toilet seat a minute or so before the movements usually occur.

Praise accomplishment and ignore failures. Don't be angry or discouraged at a soiled diaper. You'll have these for a long time yet.

If Baby's bowel movements are not regular, he may indicate by a certain sign that he is about to have one. Some babies become quiet just before a movement. They may appear to be listening to something. Others may grunt once or twice.

When your baby does make such a signal, lift him calmly and carry him to the toilet. Don't grab him up and make a scene about getting him on the toilet in time.

After Baby becomes used to the seat, you may strap him in and go out of the room, leaving him alone. Move the toilet paper and all breakable objects out of his reach. You can look in occasionally to see how he's doing. Five minutes at a time is long enough for him to stay on the seat, unless he's evacuating. Longer might produce antagonism. He should never be made to feel that he is being forced to remain on the seat against his will.

After Baby seems to have caught the idea and has kept clean for some time, a new food or a new posture, such as crawling or walking, may change the time of his movement. It's not uncommon at all for a supposedly trained youngster to start having a movement during the night, or early in the morning before you get him up, or at unpredictable times during the day.

This can often be controlled by manipulating the laxative foods in Baby's diet. To control a too-early movement, try giving stewed fruit in the morning rather than the evening.

At certain ages, your baby may rebel against being placed on the toilet seat, even though for some time past he has accepted it and had his bowel movements there. Stop the training immediately at any sign that your baby has taken a dislike to it. Wait a month or so before trying again.

Praise has its place

Your child probably shouldn't be praised extravagantly for every small act of the day. Either it will make him a terrible egotist, or praise will lose its meaning. Too, you want him to conform to good habits as a matter of course.

Nevertheless, when your baby or child does perform creditably, don't hesitate to tell him so. When you first put him on the toilet, for instance, he has no idea what you want. The occurrence of the movement is pure accident. But when you show him you're pleased, it helps him get the idea of what the toilet session is about.

Praise, in the beginning at least, is what everyone works for. When a certain course brings the approval of others, efforts are made to continue in that direction. Your praise of Baby when he succeeds helps him know that he did what you wanted, and encourages him to do it that way the next time. Just be careful not to carry praise to the place where it's ridiculous.

What if your baby fails or disappoints you? The less attention called to this fact the better, for small youngsters love drama and are apt to repeat the undesirable conduct just to hear you sound off.

Not in toilet training alone, but in all future training situations, you'll find it's a good rule to praise successful accomplishment and to pass over failures. The youngster who gets recognition and satisfaction from doing the right thing has little temptation to make a practice of doing the wrong.

Time to think about weaning

After your baby is about 9 months old, breast milk is no longer adequate for his needs. Somewhere about this time, therefore, your breast-fed baby should be weaned. At this age, your baby can drink from a cup; so there is no need to wean him from breast to bottle. Follow the same procedure as for teaching the bottle baby to drink from a cup.

In hot weather, a diaper is enough clothing. Place Baby's crib, stripped of covers, in front of (but not too close to) an open window. An electric fan helps, but be sure it's out of reach and directed away from Baby

Baby's own inclination is your guide in weaning and don't worry if he's slow to change over. Don't measure your baby's readiness by the time some other baby was completely weaned. Some formula-fed babies don't lose their liking for milk from a bottle until they're 18 months or older.

What time of the year you start the weaning process won't matter as long as your baby is well. Doctors used to warn against weaning Baby in hot weather, but with good selection of food and proper refrigeration, weaning can be done at this season as safely as any other time. However, don't wean a sick baby at any time, unless your doctor advises it.

The milk you'll use

When you decide the time for weaning has come, select the kind of milk you want to give your baby. Your choice will be guided somewhat by the circumstances in your community. As has been said before, evaporated milk has various advantages which make it especially valuable in a period of emergency. It keeps indefinitely when the cans aren't opened and is always clean and germfree. Too, it's considered more allergenic because of the heat process it goes through. Moreover, babies and children like its taste, and it agrees almost universally with them.

To wean your baby from the breast to evaporated milk, dilute the milk with a slightly larger amount of boiled water. For this age, 17 ounces of boiled water to 15 of evaporated milk is a good ratio. Gradually use less water and more milk, until by the tenth month, your baby is getting 16 ounces of evaporated milk to 16 ounces of boiled water, or about the consistency of whole milk. Your child can continue on evaporated milk, both for drinking and cooking purposes, as long as you wish. If the fresh milk supply is reliable, however, it's a good idea to teach him to take fresh milk at least by the time he starts to school, for in social contacts that's the milk he will be given for drinking.

It's a good idea to consult your doctor about the amount of vitamin D your baby is getting if you change to evaporated milk that is fortified with vitamin D. If your baby is taking cod-liver oil, or concentrate, and fortified milk, he may be getting too much vitamin D. Research studies have found that if they get over 1,500 units of vitamin D daily they lose their appetites after a while.

If you want to wean your baby to fresh milk, and there's a good, reliable supply of it available, boil the milk until your youngster is about 2 years old if it is not pasteurized. Baby may be able to take the boiled fresh milk undiluted from the start, but if he has a digestive disturbance of any kind, add several ounces of boiled water. Gradually use less and less water until he's taking the milk full strength.

Many babies take evaporated milk better than fresh; so it's a good idea to wean to evaporated milk from the breast, even though you change to fresh milk later.

Don't put any sweetening in the cup feedings you offer your baby during the time you're weaning him.

Until your baby is at least a year old, the milk as it comes from the refrigerator should be warmed to room temperature. Many mothers find it better to wait until their baby is at least 2 years of age or older before offering ice-cold milk.

Weaning your breast-fed baby

Begin by offering at each meal a cup of diluted (see preceding section) but unsweetened evaporated milk, or boiled fresh milk, until Baby becomes accustomed to the taste. For this purpose it is permissible to offer the cup before the breast feeding. After he takes his first taste, he may have the breast. Next time let him have more of the cup feeding.

Carry the cup and breast feedings along together until Baby accepts the cup nicely. Then drop out the midday breast feeding. The next week omit the morning breast feeding, and the following week the evening, substituting the cup of milk. At the end of a month, Baby will be completely weaned without annoyance to anyone.

Care of breasts

If your breasts cause discomfort as the feedings are eliminated, a tight binder around them will give you relief. You can decrease your milk supply quickly by cutting down on your food and liquids. Get back to your regular amount of both. A mild laxative, which reduces bodily fluids, will also help. It's a good practice to discuss this matter with your physician; he may prescribe something to dry up your breast milk.

Weaning your bottle baby

If your baby has been on an evaporated milk formula, it's not necessary to change. Gradually reduce the sweetening and dilute the milk in the ratio of 17 ounces of boiled water to 15 of evaporated milk. If you wean your baby to fresh milk, offer it boiled and cooled, full strength or slightly diluted, but without any sweetening. Substitute the cup for one bottle feeding, then another, as was suggested for weaning from breast feedings.

It's important to Baby's wholesome development that you take him from the breast or bottle at the right time. Otherwise, he'll be retarded in an important phase of his growth and will continue in an infantile habit which he should discard. The longer the breast or bottle is continued after the ninth month, the harder it is to wean Baby.

It's not at all uncommon for Baby to seem to lose interest in milk around weaning time, if he hasn't done so before. If this occurs, follow the suggestions given in Chapter VI to make sure that he will get his milk ration any-

128

way. Use all you can in cooking; remember that undiluted evaporated milk gives Baby double nutrition for the amount he takes. One cup more than equals two of fresh milk.

Begin chopped food

Between 10 and 12 months (depending upon what your doctor says), start introducing chopped foods in the same gradual way you did solids. Baby will accept chopped foods more readily at this age. Later he may reject any "lumps." The makers of strained baby foods also have a line of chopped ones in many appetizing combinations. Or you may chop, or mash with a fork, the fruits and vegetables you're serving the family. Take Baby's portion out before seasoning to adult tastes, for he requires only about half as much salt and sugar and should have no spices at all.

Add a small amount of a chopped food to a serving of strained, preferably a strained food which your baby particularly likes. Gradually increase the chopped food, until Baby's taking his whole serving in this form. Then do the same with another food.

Until he's about 3 years old, chop or grind the meat you give your youngster. Or buy the excellently prepared diced meats for juniors which are on the market in several varieties suitable at this age. In this form, he'll eat it better, and you'll avoid the danger of having a chunk of meat breathed into his windpipe. After you quit straining his cereal, take special pains to make it smooth.

Schedule for baby eight to twelve months old

7:00 a.m. or 7:30 a.m. Breakfast: Two to 4 tablespoons whole-grain or enriched cereal. Serve with milk or thin cream, no sugar. Milk toast or ripe banana may be substituted.
Egg, poached or soft-cooked. (Give this for supper if you'd rather.)
Fruit sauce if desired.
Slice of toast or zwieback, with butter, if Baby wants it.
Diluted evaporated or boiled milk, in cup, with a lip if possible, until Baby becomes adept at drinking. Refill to get 8 ounces.
After breakfast: On toilet seat for bowel movement, with door closed. Leave him alone, but not for more than 5 minutes unless he's evacuating. Afterward he can return to his bed, or visit with members of the family from his playpen or the floor.
9:30 a.m. Three to 4 ounces orange juice, or as much as he likes. Vitamin concentrate, or one teaspoon of cod-liver oil.
9:30 a.m. to 11:00 a.m. Nap. It may be out of doors, with Baby's face and eyes shielded from the sun, or in his room with the window open and the door closed.
11:00 a.m. Bath.
11:30 a.m. to 12:00 N. Dinner: One-half to 1 can of strained vegetable, liver, beef-and-liver, or chicken soup.
One to 2 tablespoons diced bacon, diced beef, minced chicken, chicken or calf's liver, or strained lamb, pork, or veal.
Four to 6 tablespoons of strained or chopped vegetable, such as carrots, potatoes, spinach, mixed greens, green beans, peas, beets, squash, cauliflower, asparagus tips, or stewed tomatoes.
Two to 4 tablespoons of one of the following: applesauce, baked apple, prune, apricot, peach, or pear pulp; scraped raw apple, or ripe banana. Cornstarch pudding, custard, rennet custard, flavored gelatine, tapioca, or rice pudding may be given instead of fruit.
One-half slice dry bread with butter.
Milk, 4 to 6 ounces as desired.
1:00 p.m. to 3:00 p.m. Nap, outdoors again or in his own room, according to the weather.
3:00 p.m. Milk, 4 to 6 ounces.
Zwieback, graham cracker, or arrowroot cooky.
3:30 p.m. to 5:00 p.m. In his pen, with his soft toys. Either outdoors or in.
5:00 p.m. Clean him up, then play with him or let him creep about the house.
5:30 p.m. to 6:00 p.m. Cereal or soup.
Dry bread; graham or soda crackers with butter.
Egg, if none was given at breakfast.
One-half to 1 tablespoon scraped or ground beef or cottage cheese if not given at preceding meal.
Vegetables chosen from above list.
One to 2 tablespoons or more of the fruits or puddings listed for dinner.
Eight to 12 ounces of milk.
6:00 to 7:00 p.m. Bed.
Allow no other foods than those listed. Baby may schedule his morning nap a bit differently than on this outline.

Chapter VIII

Your baby from twelve
to fifteen months

Development

Between the ages of 12 and 15 months, your baby may:

. . . walk with help.
. . . lower himself from a standing to sitting position.

. . . hold a crayon to make a stroke.
. . . repeat his actions if laughed at.

. . . hold a cup to drink from.
. . . say two words.
. . . stop when spoken to.

Your youngster has probably trebled his birth weight during his first year and gained about nine inches in height. There are large differences in the rates at which children grow, however, and your baby may vary considerably from the averages given above.

His first birthday should find him with good habits of eating, sleeping, and playing.

Continue to have your physician give him regular physical examinations, including a check of his feet and legs.

His first shoes

If Baby's feet and legs are normal, his first shoes should have soft, pliable soles. They should be designed to give him plenty of toe room. If the weather's warm, Baby can go barefoot.

What to expect

Your youngster is entering upon a year of great mental and emotional development. In contrast, his physical growth will slow down, and his appetite will slacken. His food preferences may change. He is moving out of the baby stage, and during the next 12 months, he'll learn to walk well by himself, begin to talk, have fair control of his bowels (although there will still be accidents), and his bladder control will develop sufficiently so that daytime training will be successful a good part of the time.

He may be going through a period of shyness with strangers, but this will soon pass.

Independence develops

And sometime during this next year, your baby will discover that he has a mind of his own, and he will want to exercise it. He'll resist your efforts to get him to do things, and his "no" will become almost automatic.

He'll become more and more energetic, and in his urge to explore, will be "into everything." He'll want to touch and handle everything he sees. Sometimes, for his own welfare, you'll have to hold him back. Your common sense must be your guide, however, since this is his way of familiarizing himself with the world about him.

What kind of discipline?

This period can be very exasperating, and you may be tempted to bear down on him. You may feel that his balkiness shows lack of respect for you and that his busyness and destructiveness are deliberate naughtiness. However, the drive for independent thought and action is so important that it's cause for rejoicing rather than dismay. It's a sign that your youngster is growing up normally from an emotional standpoint. If you make every situation as pleasant as you can, and interfere with your child's actions only when absolutely necessary, he may never develop habits of behavior which are annoying to you.

Encourage him to think for himself and to become increasingly self-confident and

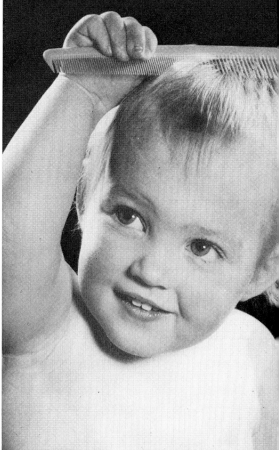

Imitating your actions is your youngster's way o showing you he or she is growing up. Build self-con fidence and encourage independence at all times

Taking off his shoes is your youngster's way o showing you he's ready to learn to dress himself Give him every opportunity to learn a new skil

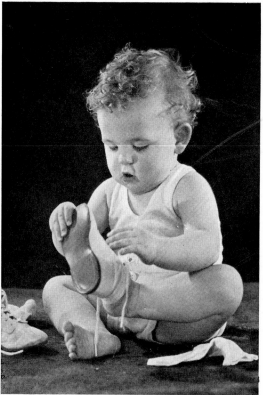

independent. At the same time, protect him from his own lack of experience. When common sense dictates, you'll have to put your foot down. Avoid demanding too much of him for his age, and be consistent in what he may and may not do. If you let him do something one day, you can't expect him to understand why you try to stop him from doing it again. But if he is sure of your love and faith in him, he'll be able to take limitation when it's necessary to protect or help him.

Follow regular daily routine

Keep to the daily routine that you have established. The child who seems naughty is very often tired, hungry, or overstimulated.

With the first year past, it may not seem so important that Baby have his meals and go to bed at regular times. You may feel that a few slip-ups won't matter. But don't be tempted. Baby is happily adjusted to a regular routine now, which is good for him as well as you. It is much easier to maintain regularity than to regain it, once it is relaxed.

Keep up the routine you've already established so that each necessary function of Baby's day is performed regularly and as a matter of course. Thus, if every morning you dress him after the morning bowel movement and brush his hair and teeth, the brushing becomes as natural to him as breathing. If you're haphazard about these matters, or about mealtimes and bedtime, they often become a contest of wills that ends in some form of punishment before he gives in.

The unspoiled, unabused child is anxious to do what you want him to do, as soon as he understands what this is. The whole attitude of the young child is of wonder at the world, of a desire to be one with it. He imitates you. If you do a thing twice a certain way, he wants to continue to do it that way. Your greatest allies in training are his desire to do what you want and his imitativeness, provided you yourself use them in the right way.

Parents who keep in close touch with a child can teach him the right way to do each new thing before he has a chance to fall into a wrong way. Sometimes this is easy. Sometimes it's more difficult, but it's always easier than overcoming a bad habit. Continue an orderly routine throughout the first two years, and you'll be rewarded by an excellent set of habits and a cooperative attitude.

Punishment has little place in this scheme of discipline. Provide Baby with places to play, indoors and outdoors, where he can "let go" without colliding with adult requirements. And at the times when he does run counter to grown-up ways, find out what's causing him to act as he does. Be patient and understanding of his need for independence.

He still needs you

Along with this desire to express himself as an independent person, there'll be noticeable dependence on you at times. He'll run back from things he's doing to make sure you're right where he left you. He may start to cry when you go out of his sight. This may seem babyish and to belie his drive for independence. Instead, it means that he's checking up on his security. He wants to be free, but he also wants to be sure that you're standing by. After he has reassured himself on this point, he goes back to his new-found independence.

This doesn't mean that you can't ever leave him alone for short periods in his playpen or fenced play yard. Or that you can't go out occasionally and leave him in the care of someone else. But when he calls you in the midst of his play, or comes running to you, or whimpers at signs that you are going out, give him the reassurance he needs.

Is he ready for bladder training?

There's no magic formula for bladder or bowel training. Your baby won't be successful with his toilet training until he's physically ready for it. Maybe not even then if you have set him against it by unreasonable demands.

Chances are your baby may be 15 months old before he can remain dry for as long as 2 hours at a time. Until then, his bladder won't have developed enough to hold on that long. With some babies, of course, this development comes earlier. An occasional girl baby may be able to hold her urine for 2 hours at 10 months. But other babies, boys especially, may have to urinate much oftener until they're nearly 2 years old.

It does no harm to place your baby on the toilet before he reaches the 2-hour stage, especially if he wakes dry in the morning or after a nap. Put him on before and after meals, and at bedtime, too, if you wish. That way you'll get your baby accustomed to the toilet seat gradually, but you should understand

When you start bladder training, discard diapers for training panties. Put two-piece suits on boys

that any luck is just that at this age and it won't happen every time.

Training won't come all at once

A few minutes on the toilet seat is enough. If you praise your baby for any success, it will help him learn what he's there for. But no frowns if you fail to hit every time.

Don't get impatient about wet diapers or wet training pants. When Baby passes his first birthday, it's only natural for you to start hoping that he will soon graduate from diaper days. But it'll be good for your morale, and Baby's, if you remind yourself, better a wet baby than an unhappy one.

Even after your baby can remain dry 2 or 3 hours, he still may lack the muscular control to hold his urine even a second longer, once his bladder becomes full. It takes time for him to develop this control. And, he must learn how to let you know when he has to go. Bladder training, like bowel training, is a product of both physical and mental development. It can't be expected all at once.

When Baby can remain dry for 2 hours, he should be taken to the bathroom at 2-hour intervals, in addition to the before-and-after-nap-and-meal routine. Take him first thing in the morning, even though he wakes up wet. He may be ready to go anyway.

Keep toileting casual

Toileting should be casual. Don't give your baby a chance to debate whether he wants to go. Take him by the hand and lead him to the bathroom with the announcement that it's toilet time. If nothing happens after a few minutes on the toilet seat, remove him just as casually. It doesn't do much good to urge him just because he's on the toilet. The best way to teach him the word you have chosen is when he has successfully voided at the toilet. Then he learns what you mean.

Training pants

Gradually, you will have more and more success in catching him dry at 2-hour periods and getting him to cooperate as soon as he is put on the toilet. When this regularity begins, substitute training pants for diapers. This change is often very effective. Some authorities think it is because the baby has been accustomed to wetting his diapers, whereas the training pants represent a step forward in his growth. Others believe bulky diapers stimulate more frequent urination.

He'll start telling you

Soon your baby will acquire some sense of responsibility and tip you off to his needs. He may start by telling you *after* he has wet pants. His timing may be a little off, but it shows he is associating the signal word with the act. It also shows that he realizes he should have voided on the toilet, and probably indicates that he is beginning to prefer his pants dry.

Other signs of readiness

You may notice other signs of increasing awareness: interest in the puddle if he has an accident, listening to the sound when he urinates in the toilet, and tugging at his pants when he wants to go.

Three essentials in toilet training

After several months, the three essentials—control, recognition of the feeling of fullness, and knowing the word to tell you—will start clicking together. The whole process will be helped along if Baby is allowed to observe other members of the family in the bathroom.

It will still be your responsibility to get him to the toilet when his bladder is full. He's not likely to try to go by himself until he's about 2 years old. (See "Self-help and Night Dryness," page 146.)

May want less food

Continue to feed your child by himself. It's usually a good idea to give his cup of milk after solid food has been eaten—unless milk is the least-liked food. If your child refuses milk or takes very little, add as much to his food as you can by cooking the cereal in milk, creaming soups and vegetables, and giving him milk desserts every day. Children often go through phases of refusing milk, then come back to it with renewed zest.

At this age, your youngster is easing off in the rapidity of his growth, and so he may not be as hungry as when he was gaining from a pound to two pounds every month. Try to keep up his food balance by planning his meals so that each day he will have fruits, vegetables, milk, whole-grain cereals or bread, meat or eggs. His appetite will vary, so let him decide how much food he wants.

Energy producers

Sugars, cereals, fats

The energy-producing foods are *sugars, cereals,* and *fats.* Syrups or sugars are used in the formula, and again in desserts. The whole-wheat cereals, and the new enriched ones, are often chosen as a first solid food because they're easily digested and your baby needs the vitamin B_1 they contain. Butter is needed both as a fat and as a source of vitamin A.

It's the burning or oxidation of these products in the body which produces the heat needed for growth, development, and bodily activity.

Body builders

Milk, eggs, cheese, meat, fish

The body-building foods are *milk, eggs, cheese, meat,* and *fish.* They provide the materials for growth and physical development, and also repair wear and tear upon body tissues. You mustn't shortchange Baby on building materials!

Body protectors

Fruits, vegetables, fish-liver oils, vitamin concentrates

Body protection is furnished by *fruits, vegetables, fish-liver oils,* and *vitamin concentrates.* They contain vitamins and minerals which act as regulators of the body and growth processes, keep everything going as it should, and protect your child from sickness.

Food likes may vary

About this time, in addition to having a smaller appetite than formerly, your baby's food likes may become unpredictable. A food that's a favorite one week may be rejected the following week. And he may go all out for a certain food for days at a time, never seeming to get enough of it and not wanting much else. Then when his craving for that particular food has been satisfied, he'll lose interest in it for a while.

He may go from one such food "binge" to another. You'll worry that he isn't getting a balanced diet, but such preferences don't last long at a time and, apparently, they do no harm.

Dr. Clara M. Davis, now on the staff of Children's Memorial Hospital in Chicago, took children so young they could just finger-feed themselves and set several dishes of suitable foods before them. After a few tentative tastes, the babies frequently selected one food, ate the entire serving, and signified they wanted more of it—ignoring the other foods on their tray. At every meal, they were permitted to eat as much as they wanted of any one food.

But over her period of observation, Doctor Davis found that the children's preferences included all the elements they needed. And, what's more, they gained and developed as well as children eating so-called balanced meals.

All of us have known cravings for certain foods. When such cravings are appeased, they pass quickly. But at the time it seems to us, at least, that an instinctive need is driving us to the food desired.

It's the same way with your child. It doesn't hurt once in a while if you allow him to eat more of one wholesome food and pass up another if he seems to crave the preferred item. About the only sweets you give him when he's little are gelatine, custards, and sometimes ice cream, so you don't have to worry about his going on a sweets orgy. And, to avoid catering to his whims, you can rotate foods so that his favorite one does not appear too frequently.

As Doctor Davis and others point out, your baby has more food sense than you might expect. So, if he's healthy, be content when he is satisfied at mealtimes, and rest assured he's getting the nutritional elements he needs.

If he loses weight or fails to gain over a reasonable period of time, then it's a case for your doctor. If your baby really needs more food, nagging won't help out a bit.

Why diet is so important

If there's a long-time deficiency of any one of the three food groups shown on the preceding page, or an excess of one at the expense of the other two, your child is bound to suffer. The consequences may not be apparent for some time and may be delayed because the body has material in reserve. But they'll turn up eventually. If you want your child to be above average in health and growth, you must provide him with protective foods to make him so.

That's why it's desirable to teach your baby in the very beginning to take the whole range of foods allowed him. The only reason for dropping any food entirely would be an allergic condition, which your doctor finds is due to that particular food.

As pointed out, his food likes will vary at times. He'll want more of one food and less, or none, of another. You may safely let him have his fill of the other he seems to crave as long as his interest in it lasts.

He'll probably switch over to some other preference in a short time.

The favored food isn't likely to be served at more than one meal in a day, so he'll balance out his diet all right with foods from the other meals. If milk is his favorite food, that's fine, even though it is taken at every meal every day. Milk is the most nutritionally complete food he could have, lacking only vitamins C and D. He'll get vitamin C from orange or tomato juice (or ascorbic acid tablets), and his vitamin D from fish-liver oil or concentrate, or from milk or cereal that's fortified with vitamin D. If he drinks a quart of fortified milk a day, no vitamin D supplement is necessary. Too great an intake of vitamin D over the required amount has been found to cause lack of appetite.

Niacin or nicotinic acid will also be adequately supplied if his diet is balanced.

However, don't allow him to take just milk. He needs other foods for fuel and roughage. So if he likes milk best, it's a good idea to offer it after he's eaten some solid foods.

On the other hand, if he loses his taste for milk at times, you should try to work at least a pint of it a day into his meals in soups, creamed vegetables, custards, or cereals, etc., because he needs the calcium milk supplies.

If the milk dislike is so pronounced that he won't even take foods mixed with milk, you should try to find what's causing it. Then consult your doctor about giving him calcium tablets.

A balanced diet is simply one that contains all the groups of food your youngster needs, and in such proportions that the energy-producing, body-building, and body-protecting ones balance each other. You can be sure he's getting this balance in this diet.

1. Milk—boiled or pasteurized. One pint (minimum) to 1 quart (maximum). Butter—3 teaspoons daily.

2. Green or yellow vegetable. Portion: ½ to 1 cup. It's best to give two vegetables daily. They may be divided between dinner and supper.

3. Egg—1 to 2 daily. The yolk is more valuable than the white. May be given at any of the meals.

4. Cooked fruit. Portion: ½ to 1 cup daily. May be given at any of the meals or for lunch in the midafternoon.

5. Meat, poultry, or fish. Portion: 2 tablespoons daily. Usually should be given at lunchtime.

6. Cod-liver oil or vitamin concentrate. One to 2 teaspoons of the oil or the amount of concentrate prescribed by your doctor. Should be given daily from November to May. Smaller doses may be given during the summer months.

7. Orange, tomato, or grapefruit juice. One-half cup or more.

8. A serving of whole-grain, fortified, or enriched cereal, or 1 to 3 slices whole-wheat or enriched bread.

The above foods provide the protein, minerals, and vitamins necessary for satisfactory nutrition and growth. Make sure that your boy or girl gets them.

A word of caution is needed in regard to cereals, bread, and potatoes. These are valuable foods. But be careful not to let your youngster fill up on them and leave out some of the things listed above.

He can eat all these

So far, the range of foods has been rather limited, and confined mostly to foods that the majority of children naturally seem to like.

But now it widens out. Here's the list of foods you can give your youngster after he's 1 year old. It'll probably be some time, though, before he develops a taste for strong-flavored foods such as broccoli, Brussels sprouts, asparagus, and cauliflower.

List of suitable foods for child of one year to eighteen months

Dairy products and eggs

Milk	Eggs
Cream	Cottage cheese
Butter	Cream cheese
Buttermilk	

Vegetables—chopped or mashed

Carrots	Lima beans
String beans	Squash
Green peas	Beets
Tomatoes	Parsnips
Asparagus	Brussels sprouts
Cauliflower	Broccoli
Stewed celery	Swiss chard
Cabbage	Lettuce
Turnips	Onions
Spinach	Sweet potatoes

Meats—ground, chopped, or diced

Chicken	Liver (chicken, calf, beef, or pig)
Turkey	Fish—white, nonoily, all bones removed
Lamb chop	Any of the meats and soups commercially prepared for babies
Roast pork	
Crisp bacon	
Beef broth	
Roast beef	
Roast lamb	

All meats should be lean and well-cooked.

Fruits

Orange juice	Stewed pears
Grapefruit juice	Stewed apricots
Orange (sliced)	Stewed plums
Ripe apple, scraped	Stewed prunes
Applesauce	Cooked raisins (seedless)
Baked apple	Baked banana
Ripe banana	
Stewed peaches	

Stewed fruits should be mashed, the skins chopped into particles, and all stones removed.

Cereals

All cooked, canned, or specially prepared infants' varieties.

Miscellaneous

White potatoes	Sponge cake
Macaroni	Jelly

Spaghetti
Whole-wheat bread
Whole-wheat muffins
Corn bread
Crackers
Graham crackers
Zwieback
Arrowroot cookies
Plain cookies

Custard
Rennet custard
Rennet-custard dessert
Unflavored gelatine
Cornstarch pudding
Tapioca pudding
Rice pudding
Prune whip

It looks as though he's practically grown up, doesn't it? This list doesn't mean that you must start now, this minute, giving your youngster all the foods mentioned. But sometime during the next 6 to 12 months, do give him a chance to taste and to like each one. The child who eats everything set before him is a pearl without price in the home, a pleasure to take visiting, and far better fitted to meet life than the finicky eater.

How to cook vegetables for small children

Vegetables are often the least-liked foods. The following cooking hints have proved helpful to mothers.

Small children don't like strong tastes, and they do like crispness and color. They require only about half as much sugar or salt as adults, and should not have spices or strong seasonings. So to have your youngster like the new vegetable you're cooking for him, use half as much salt as for your own taste, and just enough water to keep the vegetable from burning. Cook it fast, and just long enough to be tender and yet to retain some crispness. Pressure cookers do this job efficiently, but a well-covered saucepan works well, too.

Exceptions are strong vegetables such as onions, cabbage, cauliflower. Use more water and cook them in open vessels. It's more important at first to have your child like the vegetable than to save vitamins. That comes later, of course. Children like even onions—one of the least popular—when they're precooked three times, and very strong vegetables go down better when cooked in milk. (Don't serve the milk with the vegetable though.)

Many youngsters like certain vegetables raw better than cooked. After your child gets to be about 2 years old, you can cater liberally to this fancy. At present, however, there's danger of his getting slivers or chunks of food in his windpipe. An excellent food rule for the mother with children under 2 years to follow is "No food that won't melt." That bars raw vegetables for the time being.

Foods should be easy to eat

Most fruits should be cooked and chopped for the preschool child till he's about 3 years old. Exceptions which may be served raw are oranges, bananas, very ripe apples, and occasionally, peaches and apricots.

Keep your tapioca and rice puddings thin and creamy. Bits of chopped apple, pineapple, peaches, or raisins make them more interesting, and fruit bits in the bottom of the cereal make eating fun for your child.

Liver or salmon loaf should be made very moist—baking in a pan of water helps. If the skins of apples are tough, pare before baking. Most youngsters like canned peas and spinach better than fresh, and canned peaches and apricots better than dried. They like frozen squash, at the same time refusing it cooked fresh. Try yellow sweet potatoes, baked whole with no seasoning.

Youngsters usually like the flavor of evaporated milk, and this can be used freely, both in cooking and for drinking. Evaporated milk has all the qualities of fresh milk, and in many localities is cheaper.

Offer new foods this way

And now for presenting a new food to Baby. Choose a time when he's happy and all's well with him. Offer it at the beginning of the meal when he's hungriest. Just a taste is sufficient at first, but do try to get him to take that amount. No one can learn to like a food unless he tastes it. After the taste, allow him to fill up on foods he especially likes. Never offer more than one new or disliked food at a meal.

The thing to work for at this stage is to have your child like all good, wholesome foods, and look forward to mealtime as a happy experience. When you achieve that, you've given him something of incalculable value.

He shouldn't eat these

Do not give your child of 12 to 18 months the following foods:

Cocoa
Tea
Coffee
Hot fresh breads
  and rolls
Griddle cakes
Ready-to-serve
  cereals

Radishes
Condiments
Spices
Nuts
Popcorn
Pastries
Chocolate
  pudding

Sweet cakes	Angel cake
Fried foods	Ice cream
Gravies	Sherbet
Sausage	Candy
Salt fish	Berries or melon
Corned beef	Figs
Dried beef	Dates
Eggplant	Rhubarb
Green corn	Fresh fruits, except
Cucumbers	those mentioned on
	page 135

Enough teeth to brush?

Between 12 and 14 months, your child will probably cut six more teeth. You can begin brushing them now, if you like. Get a tiny, soft brush for the purpose and begin by letting Baby see you brush your own teeth. Be very gentle about tooth-brushing and don't force the issue. Wait until your tot wants it done—as he will from seeing you.

A drink of water after a meal will remove food particles from his gums and teeth.

Schedule until bladder training begins

Until you start bladder training, continue the same schedule you have been using, except that you may add new foods from the allowed list. At any time now, your child may be expected to stop sleeping in the morning at the 9:30 to 11:00 period. When this happens, drop out the morning nap and let him spend this time in his playpen.

When bladder training has begun

Keep in mind that your baby may not be ready for bladder training before the fifteenth or eighteenth month. If he has exhibited some of the signs of being ready for it, however, his daily routine may go something like the one suggested below. (Choose vegetables, fruits, and meats from the list of allowed foods.)

7:00 a.m. Arises, to toilet at once to urinate. Into bathrobe for breakfast.

Breakfast:

Two to 4 tablespoons any cooked or canned or prepared baby cereal. Serve with milk or thin cream, no sugar. Milk toast or sieved ripe banana may be substituted occasionally.

Egg, poached, or soft-cooked. (May be given for supper instead.)
One to 2 tablespoons fruit sauce. (If he has fruit sauce for supper, this isn't essential, unless there's a tendency toward constipation.)
Boiled or pasteurized milk, or diluted evaporated milk, 8 ounces, or as much as he'll take.

7:30 a.m. On toilet for bowel movement. Leave him not more than 5 minutes, unless he is evacuating. Dress him in his play clothes.

8:00 a.m. Now Baby may roam about the house, provided someone watches him.

8:30 a.m. Plays alone in playpen, if still content there, or in fenced play corner, indoors or outside, depending on the weather.

9:30 a.m. On toilet.
One-half cup orange juice or 1 cup tomato juice.
One teaspoon cod-liver oil, or vitamin concentrate as prescribed.

9:30 a.m. to 11:00 a.m. Nap or playtime.

11:00 a.m. On toilet, not more than 5 minutes. Sponge off after play, or give full bath now if this is most convenient time. Put on sleeping garments for afternoon nap.

11:30 a.m. or 12:00 N. Dinner:

Two to 3 tablespoons green or yellow vegetables, or soup or stew.
One to 2 tablespoons baked or mashed potato. Macaroni or spaghetti may be substituted 3 times a week.
One to 2 tablespoons meat—ground, chopped, or commercially prepared "junior" meats.
One to 2 tablespoons dessert.
Milk, 1/2 to 3/4 cup, or as much as is desired.
On toilet for not more than 5 minutes.

1:00 p.m. to 3:00 p.m. Nap.

3:00 p.m. On toilet, dressed.
One cup of milk.
Zwieback, graham cracker, or arrowroot cooky.

Outdoors to play in playpen, or if weather is bad, in playpen or playroom indoors; or taken for airing in buggy.

5:30 p.m. Allow 15 minutes for roaming about house. Watch to see that he doesn't hurt himself. Allow him to examine household objects as much as is practical. Put dangerous or breakables out of reach.

5:45 p.m. Bath (if bath is given in morning, sponge off lightly now), into bathrobe, on toilet.

6:00 p.m. Supper:

Two to 4 tablespoons custard, cornstarch or tapioca pudding, banana, or cottage cheese.
One to 2 tablespoons stewed fruit, or more if desired.
Egg, poached or soft-cooked (if not eaten at breakfast).
Milk, 8 ounces or as much as desired.
On toilet.

6:30 p.m. or 7:00 p.m. Bed.

Chapter IX

Your baby from fifteen to eighteen months

Development

Between the ages of 15 and 18 months, your baby may:

. . . cooperate in helping you dress him.

. . . build a tower of two or more blocks and fit a peg into its proper hole on a board.

. . . walk or, at least, stand alone.
. . . use a spoon to eat with.

. . . say several words that indicate to you his manner of expressing himself.
. . . establish regular bowel and bladder control.

Shoes when he walks

Don't be in a hurry to change from soft-soled shoes—or from bare feet, if the weather allows.

More important are strong, well-shaped feet for your child. Running barefoot or wearing soft, flexible-soled shoes exercises all the muscles of his toes and feet, which in turn makes them sturdy. Not until he is walking alone outdoors will he need firm-soled shoes.

For his shoes to fit properly, they should be:

1. Broad enough to allow his toes to be in their natural position. Shoes that are too narrow squeeze his toes, and ones that are too wide allow his feet to spread out of shape.

2. At least one-half inch longer than his foot. With a child this age, you can get an accurate measurement by tracing around his foot while he's standing up. Then lay the shoe on the tracing to determine the size.

3. Deep enough at the toe so his toes will not be pinched on top, and deep and full enough at the instep to allow some flexibility.

4. Broad and flexible at the sole, and straight along the outer edge from the tip of the little toe to the edge of the heel.

5. No higher in the heel than the thickness of the sole.

Scrape the sole before letting your baby wear a new pair of shoes, so they won't slip when he walks.

Baby shoes are seldom worn out, but don't pass them on to other children in your family. After they are worn for a while, they take on the shape of an individual's foot. Each child wears shoes differently, and they may cause a permanent deformity.

If there's any fault in the way he stands or

walks, special shoes and corrective exercises may be recommended by your doctor.

Walking or running barefoot exercises all the muscles in feet and toes, and helps to make them sturdy

Bladder training should begin

Within the next 3 months, your baby may begin staying dry for as long as 2 hours at a time. When he has reached this stage in the development of his bladder, you may take him to the bathroom at 2-hour intervals in addition to the before-and-after-nap-and-meal routine.

But don't worry if your youngster isn't able to stay dry as long as two hours. Many babies, especially boys, may have to urinate much oftener until they're nearly 2 years old. And don't compare your baby's progress in this respect with that of other babies.

In the first place, remind yourself that this is an accomplishment your youngster is bound to acquire whenever he's ready. Don't hurry him. Success will come whenever his muscles reach a point where he's able to control elimination, and his nervous system is capable of comprehending what is expected of him. It may be a long time before he tells you when he needs to go to the toilet, and longer still before he's absolutely perfect.

It's the mother who demands immediate and perfect results who finds this phase of learning a source of worry.

Psychologists believe that punishments, shaming, or other unpleasant associations with toilet training have an extremely unwholesome effect upon your child's later life. Whether this is true or not, rest assured that he'll learn just as quickly if he's praised as if he is punished and harangued. It will make little difference in 10 years whether he learned the lesson in 3 or 6 months, but a great deal whether it was taught with love and patience.

Pants instead of diapers

If your child has learned to control himself fairly regularly, it's time to substitute training panties for diapers. In his mind, the diaper is associated with his infant habit of urinating whenever and wherever he desired.

As a convenience for both you and your child, dress the little boy in a two-piece suit so the pants are easily removed. A girl can wear a dress over her training panties so the entire outfit won't have to be changed each time she is wet.

Keep training happy

Put your child on the toilet regularly at certain times during the day. As you have already started bowel training, he has learned what is expected of him when he's placed on the toilet, and he'll urinate at these times. Tell him what you expect him to do in terms associated with the act. Praise him for success; ignore failure or wet panties.

Place him on the toilet:
On arising.
Before and after each meal.
Before his bath.
Before and after his nap.
Just before going to bed.

In time he'll learn to wait for the expected interval. Placing him on the toilet too often will make him unhappy, and if he is not as yet able to hold his urine for two hours, he is not ready to train himself. If wet panties are changed immediately, he will become accustomed to, and like, dry clothing. This helps speed training, too.

Don't leave him on the toilet for more than five minutes at a time. If he needs to urinate, you'll usually find that he'll void very quickly after being put on.

If he hasn't performed at the end of five minutes, however, let him down. You may then watch him for signs of readiness which every mother learns to recognize. If he has an accident, show no signs of concern. Don't give him a feeling of disgust about soiling himself. Just clean him up without comment.

Some children begin rather early to indicate in some way or other when they need to go, others not until they're 2 years old. Accidents will occur for several years, during stress or excitement. In cold weather, your child will wet more than in warm because there's less evaporation through skin pores. The big, robust child who eats and drinks heartily will wet more than the one with a small appetite. All these things must be taken into consideration and allowances made.

Even after he begins to tell you, the responsibility is still yours. Keep up his same routine and have him go to the toilet at regular intervals, though these may gradually be lengthened. When you're traveling, you may have to take his nursery chair and pot with you if you're to be a very great distance from a toilet. Wherever you take your child, pay attention to the schedule he's already established and use the facilities available to help him follow it. However, don't make an issue of the matter or let it spoil the good time for both of you.

He needs space for play

Play will occupy an increasingly large place in your child's life. He should no longer be placed in the little playpen, but should have a good-sized outdoor pen that's at least 12 feet square. It's ideal if you can fence in a whole back yard. In this enclosure there should be a sand pile equipped with a pail and shovel, and a toy truck or wagon.

Both indoors and out, push-and-pull toys fulfill the need of your youngster's growing muscles. At this age, he'll enjoy putting things together, such as placing one empty box in another, or pans that fit inside other pans. And he'll also like to fit pegs of various shapes into their proper holes on a board.

Snow fence is a popular material for a temporary pen, and is usually available. Or your husband can buy wooden laths and nail them to a board frame. Fence palings also make a very neat enclosure.

For indoor play, your child needs a room, not too far away from your activities, where he can be confined with his toys for certain periods of the day. This room should contain a toy cupboard, or shelves, low enough so he can reach his playthings readily, a small, sturdy table and chair, and any other furnishings you like. A gate or other barrier which keeps your child in but doesn't shut him away from you is needed to keep him in his room. Occasionally, during the day, when you can watch him, take him for a tour of the rooms. He will then be content in his play space.

Whether indoors or out, your baby will want to examine everything he sees. At this age curiosity is proof of his alertness and growing independence. To make him stay crying in a pen or small enclosure when he wants to get out is to hold back this period of development, and shake his confidence in himself—and in you.

Try to anticipate your baby's desire to roam. Lift him out of his pen before he tires of it, so he won't get the idea that he is getting his way by crying.

During this phase of your baby's growth, it's not too difficult to combine your housework with baby-watching. You can dust while Baby wanders over the room, or carry him upstairs and shut the door while you make the beds.

In good weather you can do small chores outside while your small explorer ranges over his own back yard. And when you go for a walk, let him take his little side trips to examine the many things that catch his interest.

It's well to clear out all things in the house and yard that Baby might break, or on which he might get hurt.

Move your treasured books to the highest shelves and put your youngster's on the lower shelves where he can reach them. Make sure there are no hazards in your kitchen if you let your baby play there when you're working.

All these precautions aren't giving in too much to your baby, because to learn, he needs to handle and investigate everything he can. If you arrange these opportunities for your baby to explore, he'll be more content to stay in his crib or playpen when it's absolutely necessary.

Toy list grows

This is the period for the development of the large arm, leg, and body muscles as opposed to the smaller muscles of hands and fingers. (That comes later.) There are a number of toys which help to do this:

Small stout wagon—large enough to haul things in but light enough to be pulled. Develops large muscles.

Chairs—small, sturdy, and comfortable with fitted seat and back for correct posture. Develop large muscles.

Trains—small, without wheels, and which have a large fastening between cars. Develop large muscles.

Linenette picture books—containing simple, large pictures of familiar objects. Develop senses.

Balls—develop large muscles as child runs after them.

Large blocks—made with no sharp corners. Develop large muscles.

Unbreakable or cloth doll—develops large muscles and also senses.

Chair swing—develops large muscles.

Pull toys—stout strings. Develop large muscles.

Clothespins—develop senses.

Pans, spoons, and cups—develop large muscles and senses.

Playmates add to his fun

Your child will take pleasure now in the companionship of a youngster somewhere near his own age, although children don't begin to play together in the usual sense for some time to come. Each child will pursue his

This type of sand pile is in a box raised slightly off the ground, and has a wide edge to sit on. If you provide your child with a pail and shovel, and pans or boxes to put sand in, he'll play contentedly for a long time

own individual activities, but will like the idea that the other is around. If there are no small children in the neighborhood with whom your youngster can play, arrange to have your friends bring theirs often. Put the children together in the play yard and let them do what they wish.

They can't be expected to know how to play with each other properly—that's something they have to learn by trial and error. They'll probably maul and manhandle each other a lot before they discover that a human body can't be treated in the same manner as a shovel. If the children are approximately the same age, however, and fairly evenly matched,

He'll like the idea of another youngster in his pen

they won't harm each other and will learn by experience what they may and may not do.

To place a small child at the mercy of a considerably older or bigger and rougher one is hardly fair. Be guided by your own common sense in this matter of playmates and the regulation of play. Don't be alarmed if they seem a little rough on each other. Folks this young don't know their own power. When they get a healthy reaction from an equally sturdy playmate, they'll find out.

Keep his food list growing

Continue to widen your youngster's range of food likes by giving him more and more of the allowed foods listed in the preceding chapter. Work toward bite-sized food, except for meat, which should be chopped or ground until your child is 3 years old.

In introducing a new food or one he doesn't like very well, give him just a taste. Then allow him to eat as much as he likes of the rest of a meal which includes several of his favor-

ite dishes. Experiments conducted by nursery schools over a period of time show that if a child has a chance to become accustomed to a food, he'll like it. But he has a better chance to like it if he takes a little bit at a time.

During the present time, when food habits are still being formed, it's helpful to present the new or disliked food (usually it's a vegetable) at the first of the meal when the child is most hungry. If he has already learned to take anything that comes his way, it won't be necessary to do this. Put a fair serving on his plate—about 2 tablespoons—of each of the foods for the meal. Give him a small glass or cup of milk—about 4 ounces—and let him eat and drink as he likes. As long as he takes some of each item, it's not necessary to worry about the amounts. He may have seconds if he cleans his plate. This time, give him about 1 tablespoonful of each of the various foods, and refill his glass with milk. Give dessert in proportion to the amount of other food he has eaten. Let him have as many refills as he wants, but in small amounts.

Listed first in the schedule on the next page are the foods which tend to be slighted in child and adult nutrition. If your child eats these well and others not so well, reverse the order. If he eats all foods equally well, disregard this arrangement entirely, and set before him all the foods for the meal. In feeding him, go from one to another, or if he feeds himself, let him make his own choices.

Continue to have him eat his meals by himself. He can now have his own little table and chair, and probably wants to feed himself.

Provide a place in the kitchen that is easily cleaned if he's messy. Very likely he'll spill some of his foods and may even need you to guide the spoon to his mouth. Encourage

Your toddler will eat best at his or her own small table before your meal. Kitchen's recommended spot

honest effort, but don't allow him to play with the food. When he starts this, or tires of the eating process, take the spoon away and finish feeding him yourself.

The schedule seems to call for a lot of baths during the day, but you'll find they are needed. At this age a youngster is a heavy wetter at night, and needs a morning sponge-off until he develops night dryness. After his morning and afternoon play, you'll find he can use a thorough washing.

Schedule for baby fifteen to eighteen months old

The foods on this schedule may be selected from the list on pages 135-136.

7:00 a.m. Arises, to toilet at once for urinating. Light sponge bath. Brushes teeth, puts on bathrobe for breakfast.

Breakfast:
   Two to 4 tablespoons stewed fruit.
   Two to 4 tablespoons cereal with milk or thin cream, but no sugar.
   Milk toast or mashed ripe banana may be substituted occasionally.
   Milk, 1 cup, or as much as he'll take.
   Bacon or toast, or both, if he's still hungry. The daily egg may also be given now.

Immediately after breakfast, on the toilet for not more than 5 minutes, unless he's actually evacuating. Dressed for day, hair brushed.

8:00 a.m. Plays about the house or in his playroom, or sits in chair to eat zwieback during the family breakfast. Follow the arrangement which works best.

9:00 a.m. Vitamin D concentrate or cod-liver oil as prescribed. Four ounces orange juice or 8 of tomato juice. More if desired. On toilet again before being prepared for outdoors.

9:30 a.m. to 11:00 a.m. Plays outdoors in pen, or indoors in playroom, depending upon weather. Then on toilet.

11:15 a.m. Hands and face washed. Puts on his robe for dinner.

11:30 a.m. to 12:00 N. Dinner:
   Vegetables or vegetable soup. (See list of suitable foods on pages 135-136.)
   Meat or meat broth.
   Potato or bread. (Macaroni or spaghetti may be substituted occasionally.)
   Dessert. (See list on page 136.)
   Milk.
   On toilet.

1:00 p.m. to 3:00 p.m. Nap. Arises. On toilet. Cup of milk, graham cracker, arrowroot cooky, or fruit.
   After eating, dress to play outdoors in pen.

5:00 p.m. Toilet again. He may now stay in the house, playing with other family members.

5:30 p.m. Bath. Dons bathrobe.

5:45 p.m. Supper:
   Creamed vegetable (different from the one served at noon).
   Poached egg if none was eaten at breakfast.
   Fresh or stewed fruit, according to the season.
   Whole-wheat or enriched bread and butter.
   Milk.

6:30 p.m. to 7:00 p.m. On toilet. To bed alone with door shut and window open.

Chapter X

Your baby from eighteen to twenty-four months

Development

From 18 months to 2 years of age, your baby will probably:

. . . be walking and climbing on chairs and stairs.
. . . scribble on paper spontaneously and vigorously, and begin to imitate your strokes with a crayon.

. . . use the words he has learned to carry on a conversation, and point to nose or hair whenever he hears these words pronounced.

. . . build a high tower with a number of blocks.
. . . fill a cup with cubes as he's playing.
. . . use good control when eating with a spoon.

. . . turn pages of books to look at pictures.
. . . throw a ball into a box.
. . . never be still a minute.

"No" stage will pass

One of the most common characteristics of behavior you can expect to develop now, especially in little girls, is technically known as "negativism." All it means is that your child will "no" every suggestion you make. He won't eat his dinner, take his nap, go out in his playpen, or pick up his toys. He may even back up his remarks with a temper tantrum, and if it gets results, he'll keep right on.

Just ignore his "no" or temper tantrum. This is just another phase of development that may soon pass. Try, however, to find out what's causing his tantrums. He'll probably soon learn to do what you want him to if you avoid arguments and insist by your actions.

Don't give him a chance to say yes or no. When it's time for his nap, just announce that "we're going to take a nap." Then take him by the hand and lead him to the bed.

Often you can divert his attention by making a game out of what you want him to do. If he says he "won't" go to bed, don't agree. Just say, "Let's see who can get up the stairs first." Children are tremendously suggestible. They respond easily and quickly to play ideas when you are poised and unperturbed.

Make your commands just as few as possible. Your child can become independent only if he's allowed to take the responsibility for his own affairs. Unless it's a matter of his health and welfare, as food and sleep are, allow him as much freedom as possible.

Always let common sense be your judge. Insist upon obedience when it's absolutely necessary for your child's welfare, and let him make the decisions in other matters.

Big enough to stand on
step or box for toilet

There should be places
for all his belongings

He'll run away unless
penned up or watched

Keep good habits going

Your job really gets interesting now!

You'll be tempted to relax the routine somewhat—to let bedtime be later than it should be, to allow your youngster foods not recommended for him. But don't. It is much easier to keep good habits than to break bad ones, once begun.

Keep him in his play space at regular hours of the day, with plenty of toys. A breakfast nook or sunroom is excellent for this, but any room or corner of a room may be used. Have some barrier that will keep your child in, but which won't prevent him from seeing you and being conscious that you are near. Eighteen months is far too young for him to be shut off in an upstairs playroom, or confined behind a closed door.

Place your child in the play space when the weather is too bad for play outdoors. You can drop by and chat with him now and then, and, of course, observe his toilet times. But let him understand that you have your work to do, and he has his. Thus you'll be able to work with your mind more at ease, while son or daughter is taking another step along the path of self-reliance.

It's equally important to have regular periods each day when he's free to roam about the house, under somebody's watchful eye, and visit the family. He musn't be off in a pen all the time, by any means.

Set certain times for his exploring to eliminate his expecting you to drop your work every few minutes to entertain him.

You can manage to work in some of your daily jobs during his "free run" periods. Take him with you into a bedroom, close the door so he can't crawl away, and make a bed or dust while he investigates the wastebasket and closet under your watchful eye. This gives him a chance to learn more about his world (a very urgent need at this age) and keeps you from feeling that you're taking time needed for household tasks.

Self-help and night dryness

By the eighteenth month, your child may be dry most of the time. But this is because you or someone else has the matter constantly in mind. This will have to be the case until your child is about 27 months old, or perhaps a little older.

Now you should begin teaching him how to help himself. Use pants with an elastic waistband and let him help you take them off. In a very short time, he'll be able to show you he doesn't need your help.

If you provide a low, sturdy step stool for him, he'll climb up unassisted to the toilet stool. Your baby may prefer the low toilet chair that he can get in and out of by himself without having a feeling of height. The toilet chair may be kept in the kitchen if your bathroom is upstairs.

Between 18 months and 2 years, a little boy can be taught to urinate while standing erect, and it's a good lesson for him to learn. If he's thoroughly accustomed to the toilet, have him stand on a box before it. He may refuse for some time. But do it at least once a day and he'll presently get the idea. If he can watch his father or other boys, he will quickly imitate them.

When this lesson is learned, the pants with an opening in front can be worn. Great stress can be laid upon the fact that he's a big boy now! This is a step forward for him.

Even after your child has mastered day-time control, postpone night training until the weather is warm. Then don't expect him to achieve night dryness too soon. With some children this ability may come as early as 12 months, and with others not until the end of the second year or early in the third. It depends upon the physical development of each.

If your child wakes easily and goes back to sleep quickly, take him to the toilet just before you go to bed. If he fights against waking up or stays awake an hour or two afterward, don't disturb him at all. Nothing is gained by rousing the child any oftener during the night. Cut down the amount of liquids in his evening meal if night urination is profuse. Just give him a sip of water when he asks for a drink.

Place him on the toilet the minute he awakens in the morning even though he may be wet already. He may be ready to go again. Then he may go back to bed if it is not yet time to get up.

Don't ever shame your youngster for wetting the bed, no matter what his age. This will only make him tense about the matter and may prolong bedwetting way past the time he would otherwise achieve night dryness.

Orderliness now

Now's the time to teach orderliness. The first step is to be orderly yourself, for a child at this age sees everything and is as imitative as a monkey. If you haven't before, you should by now have a regular place for all your youngster's possessions, and be methodical in putting them back after they are used.

Clothes: There should be low hooks and hangers for your child's clothes—in his bedroom for his suits and underwear, and in the downstairs coat closet for his outdoor wraps. Have a hook for each article, and as you take off each piece of clothing, be sure to hang it on the proper hook. Your child will quickly learn where each belongs, and will run and get it as needed. The next step, to be made when your little runabout is about 2 years old, is to teach him to hang the garment on the designated hook. Observe the rule yourself, and you'll have little trouble getting him to do so.

Toys: From his first birthday on, your child has needed his own room or corner with shelves or a cupboard for his toys. Begin at 18 months to put things away as he's through playing with them, and call his attention to what you're doing. Presently he'll want to help a little. Show him where to put his toys and make a game of "running the cars into the garage," "putting Dolly to bed," etc. If he still needs assistance around the ages of 4 and 5, help him sociably.

How to teach obedience

Some conscientious parents are confused as to how much they should expect in the way of obedience. Do modern methods mean that a child shouldn't have to obey?

Not at all. To get along peacefully in the world, obedience to proper authority is a lesson everyone must learn at some time or other. You, as parents, are the first authority your child comes in contact with.

If he learns to accept reasonable desires on your part, he'll more easily adjust in later life to the authority of the school he attends. As he grows older, he'll understand why there must be rules and laws governing society as a whole. Any time you want him to do something, always make the request in a pleasant and courteous manner which contributes to his sense of security and accomplishment. Allow your child as much freedom of choice and action as is possible at this stage of development. He'll soon see why it is useless to rebel when a task is absolutely necessary, and he'll know that the sooner he gets his job done, the sooner he can use his strength and ingenuity to do anything he wishes.

Around the twenty-first month, you can occasionally ask him to do a simple task. With your gestures, show him that you want him to "pick up the paper." Make the request pleasantly and courteously, and repeat until he gets the idea.

Give few commands, now and from now on, but when you do, see that they're carried out. As much as possible, help your child feel that such requests add to his well-being and comfort.

A pitfall into which it's easy to fall is that of so-called "reasoning." At this age, children learn quickly that they can get control of the situation by arguing and resisting. They've a whole bag full of tricks! You should have a reason for your command, of course, and it's all right to explain it—once. That, however, should end all discussion. If your command is worth giving, it's worth obeying without debate. If you start refuting your youngster's objections and go into lengthy explanations, first thing you know you'll have an argument over every simple operation.

Teaching obedience doesn't mean that you should regiment your youngster and his every deed. Allow him as much freedom of choice and action as you can. Make necessary things pleasant for him. But don't be afraid to tell your child, quietly and courteously, to do the things he must do. Then see that he does them!

Fence in the runaway

Your active, bright runabout may begin running away during this period. Putting him in a fenced-in yard is the solution to this problem—not punishment. By the age of 3, when it will be almost impossible to confine him, he'll be old enough to learn to stay within bounds. Until then, it's your duty to see that he is safely confined or constantly watched.

When training hits a snag

Your youngster is now in the full swing of one of his most active periods of growth and learning. At a year, he was a baby. When he's 2, he'll be running everywhere, talking, feeding himself, making some moves toward dressing himself, helping to look after his belongings, and toilet-trained except for occasional accidents. In a year's time, he changes from a baby to a child.

With so many things for him to learn, it will be helpful to stop and look at the way youngsters this age do it. There is a time when your child is ready to take on easily and quickly each new habit, skill, or accomplishment. It's the time when his nervous system and muscular development have caught up with each other, and he's bursting to try the new powers laid open to him. When he reaches for the spoon, it's his sign that he's ready to begin feeding himself.

Thus it is with all the skills and activities, which will be opening up gradually to your child in years to come. It's your job to keep close enough to him so you'll catch the signals when he gives them. As you follow his development, you'll get more and more adept in interpreting them, and in helping develop the skill or ability for which he's ready at that time. Don't urge or rush him into an activity for which he isn't ready. But when he gives the go-ahead signal, drop everything else and go ahead with him for all you're worth!

But there's a second thing. You must understand that after your child has mastered a skill or habit, there will be periods when it seems like he has forgotten everything he has learned. Parents have been up against this since time immemorial, but haven't known what it meant. They have probably thought their youngster was being deliberately naughty because he had already shown that he understood what was wanted of him.

Lapses are just as much a sign of development as are increases in skill. Most toddlers break down in their toilet habits around the eighteenth month. To mothers and fathers, this often looks like deliberate wickedness, and as a result, countless home battles have been waged.

What else is happening? Perhaps he's acquiring a word for voiding. When he does that, he'll probably quit the gesturing upon which you've been depending. Or he may say the word for voiding all right, but only after the act has begun. It takes time for both speech and bladder control to become coordinated to the place where your child can express his need in words before he urinates.

The same is true of self-feeding. After your baby has learned to carry the spoon to his mouth, he begins throwing and splattering the food around. (That's something else that has been misunderstood by the adults. He's fascinated by a newly found skill.)

Just as soon as he starts playing in his food, his appetite has been satisfied. Lift him down from his chair, or take his plate of food away.

If you stop his meal as soon as he loses interest, he'll soon learn to pay attention when he's hungry.

Normally, around 9 months of age, he begins picking up tiny bits of food and eating them with his fingers. Part of his food should then be given in small pieces that he can pick up and eat with his fingers.

After a youngster gets to be about 3 years old, new experiences and impressions are coming so thick and fast that often he forgets to eat at all for a time, he's so busy telling you about them. But in time he'll learn to talk and eat at the same time.

Ahead of you is a long, patience-taxing period of letting your child learn to dress himself. You stand by, though it kills you, letting him feel out buttons and ties that are problems for small, awkward fingers. And then about the time he gets so he can do it pretty well, he'll lose all interest and dawdle till you'll be distracted. But that's all part of the process of growing up and will disappear in time.

Every child has an urge to exercise a newly developing function, and once he has mastered it with a fair degree of efficiency, he grows indifferent. A new type of learning will then attract his attention and use up his energies. If you understand and recognize this fact, many storms and temper tantrums will be avoided. When his developing skills seem to be going backward, look for the rapid unfolding of other aspects of behavior.

The same laws govern learning later on in sports, the arts, and all kinds of things. As each stage of development appears, you as a parent should provide the opportunity for exercising these powers. During the first 18 months, motor development is the most outstanding. Give him a chance to climb and use his arms and legs in general. As speech develops during the last part of the second year, take time to talk and read to your child.

Expect that once a new thing has been mastered, something else will come along to claim your child's interest. Don't be disappointed if he drops the first skill. Soon he'll develop to the point where he can co-ordinate the new habit with the old, and the old skill or habit is there again, good as ever.

When you understand the reason back of the training lapses, which are bound to come, it's easy to see why calmness and patience are better parental methods than crossness and punishment.

If toilet training breaks down

If your child has been toilet-trained before 18 months, he may fall back into his baby habits around this age because of new experiences, changes in times of bowel movements, growing independence, new foods, learning to walk, change in sleeping habits, etc.

This behavior may embarrass you, and your impulse may be to bear down on punishments or keep your child on the toilet for long periods of time. As a result of such treatment, many youngsters develop an aversion to the toilet itself and the whole idea of toilet training. They may go to fantastic lengths to keep from eliminating when on the toilet, only to do so immediately when allowed to get off. That is because the situation has been turned into a battle of the wills, and Baby is asserting his independence. Sometimes this behavior is not defiance on his part, but inability to release the muscles of the bowel when he should. He is learning how to control his rectal muscles, but doesn't know when to let go.

At this age, your little explorer will remind you of perpetual motion. Keep him safely within bounds in a fenced-in yard

Learning how to dress is a technique mastered by a youngster only after many long hours of fumbling with buttons and ties

Sitting on the seat intensifies the contraction. When he gets up, the muscle contraction is released. He may be helped if you will grunt so that he will imitate you and relax his muscles. Whether it's independence or a muscle contraction, don't scold or shame your baby for this behavior.

The best thing for you to do is to keep calm and unperturbed if your baby suddenly becomes balky or unconcerned about when and where he urinates and has his bowel movements. It's only a passing phase, unless you let it disturb relations between you and your baby.

Toilet training is only one of the lessons your child is learning. Don't magnify it out of proportion to its place in his development.

If he seems apparently unconcerned, continue to put him on every two hours. Allow him to get up after five minutes whether he has gone or not. But if he is actively resisting being placed on the toilet, respect his wishes and drop the matter. Don't make him try to conform to the times you select, but observe his own natural timing instead. Rather than have toilet training become an issue, it would be better to forget about it altogether for a few weeks or even 2 or 3 months. Clean panties and a diploma from the school of toilet training aren't nearly as important as a happy, well-adjusted child.

If he has an accident, pleasantly remind him to let you know when he has to go again. Always remember that your child isn't being deliberately naughty. As he becomes absorbed in some new phase of learning, the same thing is likely to happen again. In cold weather when he's playing outdoors, urination will be likely to be more frequent, and you may have to watch him more closely.

Usually by the age of 3, however, daytime cleanliness is permanently established, nighttime dryness by 5. Even a well-behaved preschool child will wet the bed when he has a cold, or some other illness, but will stop as soon as he's well again.

Time for "booster" shots

Between 18 and 24 months is the time to take your child back to the doctor to check on immunity to severe diseases.

He'll want to give your youngster the Schick test now to see if he is immune to diphtheria. If the reaction is positive, your youngster will have to be revaccinated, or your doctor may prefer to give a "booster" shot.

At this age your child will also have to have "booster" shots for whooping cough and tetanus.

When he says "I won't"

Many parents are disturbed greatly when their youngster begins saying "I won't" when they ask him to do something. A little understanding on your part is all that is needed.

As your child's powers increase, he naturally wants to try them. He'll make an all-out effort to take the control of his schedule and of his life in his own hands. If he succeeds, as too many children do at this age, he'll be as unhappy as you and the rest of the folks around him, for no child of 18 to 27 months possesses the judgment to run his own life.

He'll be as demanding as he is active

Keep perfectly calm and cheerful. Soon you'll learn that the "I won't" is only lip deep, and that he'll do what you want him to if you don't argue, but insist by your actions. If he refuses to do what you tell him, take him by the hand and pleasantly but firmly lead him through the actions.

Common sense must be your judge. As incidents arise, you'll have to decide whether they're important or trivial.

Little girls generally come out of this stage around 27 months, while boys usually start at 27 months.

The inevitable temper tantrum

The happiest and most wisely handled child in the world may have a temper tantrum sometime during this period of trying out his own powers. Pay no attention to it, unless it's to remove your youngster to his own room or some place where he won't bother anyone else. He shouldn't be allowed to get his own way by means of a temper tantrum. If he's simply trying you out, he'll quit when he finds that the tantrum gets him nothing except exile from the family circle. If the first tantrum works, naturally he'll try again and again.

Children also, however, have tantrums when they're tired, overstimulated, or ordered about too much. Have you yielded to temptation and broken his bed and nap times? Are you directing every detail of his day? If you can answer "no" to these questions with a clear conscience, just smile up your sleeve when your youngster pulls out this

Temper tantrums come with this age. Smile to yourself, otherwise ignore them. He'll soon give up

The story hour can begin any time now. One of happiest parts of day for youngsters and for you also

old trick, and make sure it wins him nothing. Have you, however, subjected him to too much excitement or stimulation? Are you treating him like a baby with no mind or will of his own? If so, take the tantrums as a signal to change your ways.

"Tell me a story"

Any time now the story hour may begin. The year-and-a-half-old child won't understand much of a story, but loves to look at pictures. The last 15 minutes before bedtime, when he's all ready to be popped between the covers, can be spent in looking at the pictures and telling what the objects are. The period can be varied with songs, either on the piano or record-player. The story and music hour will provide a precious custom both to you and your child.

When he feeds himself

Continue to feed your runabout before the family meal, and apart from the family so he'll be quiet and bothered as little as possible while he's eating.

He should have his own little table and chair. They can be in the playroom, nursery, or kitchen, whichever is most convenient. Floor coverings must be considered, for there will be a lot of spilling.

After your youngster begins to feed himself, the kitchen is an excellent place, for he can eat while you're busy getting the family meal and still be undisturbed. You're at hand to help if help is needed, but you aren't giving him your undivided attention.

As he shows an inclination to feed himself, let him do so. Help him only as he needs it, letting him carry on as long and as well as he can. When he tires, take the spoon and

finish giving him the meal yourself. Don't let him play or dawdle over his food, but don't urge or coax him to eat.

Set before him about 2 tablespoons of each food (unless he's a very hearty eater, in which case it may be more), and a small glass of milk. If he cleans his plate and asks for

A low chair which your toddler can get in and out of safely when eating alone is best. High chair may tip easily if child tries to get down

If he tires of feeding himself and plays in food, that's your signal to finish giving him his meal

more, give another round of small servings, and fill up his milk glass. If he eats all his solid foods well, it's all right to place a little pitcher on the table and let him fill his own glass if he wants more milk.

If he has a tendency to fill up on milk and slight his solids, however, give the plate of solids first, withholding the milk until a reasonable amount of the solids has been eaten.

How not to have an eating problem

A good many youngsters, trained to good eating habits, become problems at this time simply because their parents don't understand that there are normal setbacks in physical growth, just as in learning. Let's see now how children grow.

During his first year, your infant gained at least 14 pounds, which required a lot of food. But in his second year he'll probably gain only 5 or 6. It's logical, then, that his appetite will also slacken, for children eat to grow —they don't grow to eat.

Not understanding this, parents are prone to be worried when their child's interest in food lessens. They start urging, pleading, even threatening the youngster to eat more than he really wants.

Left to himself, your child at this period will probably pick at his food for a few meals. Then, getting really hungry, he'll eat everything in sight for a few days. Over a year's time, the resulting food intake is the same as if he had eaten three good meals every day.

When parents try to bribe, coax, and tease a set amount of food down every day, the child never has a chance to get hungry. Often he gets so he hates the thought of food. "I don't believe he'd care if he never ate," is a

frequent complaint of parents of preschool youngsters. To a certain extent, it's probably true.

Let your attitude from now on be "don't force him to eat." His appetite may be bird-like at times, and for some time to come, but when he reaches the prepubertal growth spurt, he'll make up for it.

And don't let him fill up between meals on bread and butter, candy, and cookies. Confine his eating to mealtimes, except for what's called for in his schedule. Then you can safely allow him to eat as little or as much as he wants of his balanced menu.

Place before him on his little, attractively set table, small amounts of each of the foods on the diet schedule. Then let him alone.

If he cleans it up and wants more, give him more in small quantities. Give dessert in proportion to the other food he has eaten. That is, if he eats only about a tablespoon of other items, give him a tablespoon of dessert. If he has refills and gets 4 tablespoons of the others, give him 4 tablespoons of dessert. Thus the food balance will be maintained, however small or large the amounts he eats.

If he tires of feeding himself, it's proper to take the spoon and finish feeding him as much of the meal as he wants. But don't urge food upon him that he obviously doesn't want.

At the end of half an hour, dismiss him quietly and pleasantly from the table even though he has eaten nothing. If he has eaten well, compliment him. If he hasn't, ignore it. Keep mealtime a pleasant, happy experience to which your child looks forward. Never let it become an issue.

Says the American Academy of Pediatrics, "Parents should understand that it is their duty to decide what and when the child should eat, but that it is the child's prerogative to decide how much of it he will eat. Missing a meal now and then is not a matter of great seriousness, but it is an excellent means of stimulating an appetite."

Between-meal sweets spoil appetite

During their child's infant years, most parents are conscientious about following the diet given them by the doctor. But when Baby turns into a runabout with teeth and the ability to eat most of the foods on the family menu, he's exposed to a deluge of candy, ice cream, soft drinks, cookies, and the like. The one idea most people have of the way to be good to a child is to feed him something,

With the proper food, rest, and outdoor exercise, the growth of your youngster will take care of itself

and in most cases it's something sweet or rich. Thus children learn quickly to want the sweet, pleasant-tasting foods, and to reject those not so exciting. The carbohydrate or energy-producing foods taste better than the body-building and body-protecting ones; so many children grow up starved in minerals and vitamins because they are gorged with sweets.

Don't make this mistake with your youngster. Keep to the foods in the schedule which follows, and request friends, relatives, and neighbors not to feed your child between meals. They mean well, but that's no reason why you should let them overthrow the splendid food habits you've built so carefully.

Weight isn't all

Little has been said about growth since the end of the first year. If your child is given the care suggested, he'll be well nourished. There'll be no need to watch the scales. If you give him the proper food, rest, and outdoor life, his growth will take care of itself.

After his first birthday, the gain is much slower. His weight on an average is 21 pounds at 1 year and 27 at 2. His height on an average is 30 inches when he's 1 year old, 34 inches when he's 2.

Much more important than weight and height are his posture, the color and brightness of his eyes, the strength of his muscles, the solidness of his flesh, and his animation and happiness. If these are all good, your child is all right, whether he's above or below the average of the tables.

Children born of tall, thin stock are likely to weigh less than the average. Chunky little folks will probably weigh more. Be pleased with your child as he is, so long as he's bright, healthy, peppy, and happy, and eats with an appetite the foods that are good for him.

Schedule for baby eighteen months to two years old

The foods on this schedule may be selected from the list on pages 135-136. When he wakens, take him up to urinate. (The time will depend upon when your child usually wakens.) Put him back to bed, in dry sleeper and dry bed if needed.

7:00 a.m. Rises, urinates, gets light sponge bath, puts on bathrobe. Breakfast, eaten at his little table, in his little chair. Let him feed himself, if he wants to.
Stewed fruit.
Cereal. Cooked, canned, and special baby cereals he has been eating. He may have a teaspoon of honey on his cereal once in a while.
Bacon and toast if desired.
Milk.

After breakfast: On toilet for bowel movement. Following this, dress him for the day. Brush his hair and teeth as part of the dressing process, hang nightclothes and bathrobe on special hook.

8:00 a.m. In playroom, or eating zwieback while family has breakfast.

9:00 a.m. Vitamin concentrate or 1 teaspoon cod-liver oil.
Four ounces orange juice, or 8 ounces tomato juice—more if desired. Urinates before going out to play in pen or fenced yard.

11:00 a.m. Brought in to toilet. May stay in now.

11:15 a.m. Wash up, with clothes hung on special hooks as taken off. Afterward puts on pajamas and bathrobe.

11:30 a.m. Lunch:
Vegetable or vegetable soup.
Meat or meat broth.
Potato. (Macaroni or spaghetti may be substituted 3 times a week.)
Milk or gelatine dessert.
Milk.

12:00 N. On toilet. Put down in room with door closed and window open.

2:00 p.m. to 3:00 p.m. Wakes, placed on toilet, dressed for play. Cup of milk.

4:00 p.m. May have another cup of milk now as it will be withheld at supper, but he need not take it if he doesn't want it.

5:00 p.m. Brought in from outdoors, urinates, plays about house, and joins family.

5:15 p.m. Bath. (Bath may be morning or evening as convenient). Puts on pajamas and bathrobe.

5:30 p.m. to 6:00 p.m. Supper:
Creamed vegetable.
Poached egg.
Fresh fruit in season.
Cottage cheese may be given often.
No milk for convenience in night bladder training.
Urinates.

6:00 p.m. to 6:30 p.m. May play while Daddy eats his dinner.

6:30 p.m. to 6:45 p.m. Story or music hour. Daddy will enjoy presiding.

7:00 p.m. On toilet again, to bed in room with door closed, window open.

10:00 p.m. Taken up, placed on toilet to urinate. Given dry sleeper if necessary and bed dried.

If the child is dry at 10 p.m., awaken and put him on the toilet. If he makes a big fuss when awakened or stays awake for a long time afterward, don't disturb him at all. You would only create a reaction which might eventually turn him against your whole training program. You won't be successful with your efforts anyway until his bladder has developed sufficiently to hold the urine.

If needed, more time may be allowed for supper. The story hour may gradually be extended to one-half hour. This schedule is only a suggested routine to give you an idea of what to do and the time to do it. Don't follow it as a railroad timetable, but make allowances for your baby.

Section III

Your child from two to six years

The world begi

beckon

Your baby has left your lap. He's an eager little runabout, going everywhere, wild for experience and adventure. You couldn't keep him sheltered in your arms if you tried. He's on his way!

You have a right to be proud and happy because the love and care *you've* lavished upon him have provided him with a healthy body, an eager mind.

Now comes the question, "How can I best fit him for what lies ahead?"

We have seen in the past that the world can change overnight from a safe, pleasant place to one of grim effort, sacrifice, and hardship. Fathers and mothers can't be blamed for wondering whether the gentle philosophies which have dominated child-rearing these past years will prepare children adequately for such a world. It's natural for you to ask yourself whether sterner attitudes and punishments are called for.

But stop and consider:

A wise man has pointed out that a gardener doesn't expose his tender spring seedlings to frost and chill just because he knows winter is coming. He doesn't keep pulling and tugging them up by the roots to get them acclimated to future hurricanes.

Instead, he cherishes them with the utmost tenderness, so they'll have a chance to grow sturdy and strong before they meet the storms. He knows such care will give them the best chance to survive.

Thus it should be with our children. The colder

and harsher the world outside, the more they need warm affection in their own homes. Don't be afraid to love and cherish your child. Don't give up trying to see things from his viewpoint. Don't give up working problems out in a gentle, understanding way. These will do for him what the glass covering of the hothouse frames does for delicate plants. Warmed and sheltered by your love, he'll have a chance to strike deep roots and to stand staunchly when the protection of his home is removed.

Adorable as he is, your youngster is going to try your patience many times during the next four years. In days of strain and anxiety, there will be a tendency to expect too much of little folks. Don't allow yourself to get stern or cross or frantic when your preschooler merely acts as any preschooler will. Keeping your poise and sense of humor for your child's sake will help you keep them in the real problems that press in from outside your home.

Enjoy him! Two to six is one of the most entertaining and intriguing of the ages of man, if you hold fast to your perspective. Let no unfounded worries rob you of the pleasure and fun you should find in your preschooler.

Strengthen your child by encouraging him to be self-reliant, independent, and responsible for his own needs. Insist that he learn health habits which will keep his body strong and fit. Provide the means for turning his interests and abilities into skills and definite knowledge.

When he passes at last through the gate of adolescence into maturity, from the shelter of your home into the unknown, he'll be strong, confident, and fearless. He'll be kind and generous because he himself is rooted in love and in gentle ways. In short, he'll be the kind of person you'd like him to be!

Chapter I

Your child from two to three years

If you've followed the suggestions in Section II, the following will be a pretty accurate picture of your youngster at 2 years.

Physically he's:

. . . about 34 inches in height.

. . . 24 to 32 pounds in weight. If a tall, large-boned child, he'll weigh more—less if short or of slender body build.

. . . the proud possessor of from 12 to 16 teeth.

. . . rosy, sturdy, running and playing tirelessly.

Mentally he:

. . . is happy and cheerful.

. . . says many words and may make a few sentences.

. . . understands much that's said to him, and sees and is interested in everything.

Good habits have gotten a start. He:

. . . eats what is set before him. Perhaps he feeds himself.

. . . goes to bed cheerfully.

. . . plays happily by himself, both indoors and out.

. . . may be bowel-trained; may have daytime bladder control, and may stay dry all night.

. . . accepts the daily routine of bathing, dressing, brushing hair and teeth.

. . . knows where objects belong and can help to put them there.

. . . obeys simple directions.

The foundations for all the fundamental habits—those things which a child should perform instinctively, without thought and without conflict—have been laid. Thus his energies are released for activities which will foster his native abilities and capacities.

From now on your child's mind will develop at a pace that will delight you. Don't force him, but give him the materials that will aid its development when the time is ripe. (See list of playthings and play materials on page 173.)

Keep him on schedule

The routine remains the same as to mealtimes, nap, and bedtime. Observe these as faithfully as you did when your child was an infant, and he'll continue to be happy, healthy, and for the most part, well behaved. It's a common weakness for parents to relax the routine as the infant becomes the toddler. And right there countless behavior difficulties get a start. Many of them can be avoided if you continue to see that your youngster eats the right things at the right time, and goes to bed at his bedtime. If you have held to regular times for these functions so far, it will

Preschoolers think it's fun to wash dishes and do similar household tasks. Provide a stool; allow them to help when they ask to

160

be easy to continue. Both you and your child will have learned the habit of regularity.

Your child's day may begin at 6, 7, or 8 a.m., and end at 6, 7, or 8 p.m., according to your convenience. By all means arrange it so that Dad can have plenty of time with his youngster. But whatever your child's routine is, stick to it as closely as possible.

Provide playmates

From 2 years on, your child needs contact with other youngsters. This is as essential to wholesome development as are food and sleep, and you must provide it in some way. If there are no children in the neighborhood, arrange frequent visits with friends who have children the same age. The ideal social contact for your youngster is in a good nursery school, if you're near one.

Social development is a learning process and, like any other, unfolds gradually. Your 2-year-old is largely nonsocial. He plays by himself, and doesn't concern himself with the children around him unless they interfere with him in some way. Yet he needs the chance to become accustomed to children his own age.

Fairly soon, you'll find him stopping to watch the others, and he'll do this more and more frequently. Next, he includes one or more other youngsters in his play. His first advances are apt to be physical—pushing, pulling, or hitting. He uses playmates as he does the rest of his environment, and with no more ill will. He must learn from sad experience—for his victim will hit back— not to trespass upon the rights of others. Presently he's playing with another child in cooperative enterprises. Gradually the group enlarges, and by the time he's 3, your little fellow should be a happy member of a neighborhood "gang" of small children.

It's an advantage for him to play with both older and younger children. In this manner he'll learn both to lead and to follow.

In your child's relations with other children, interfere just as little as possible once you have provided suitable playmates. Let him attack his problem of social learning in his own way, pick his own chums, and form his own groups.

Self-reliance the keynote

One of the principal goals of this period is to develop your child's self-reliance. He has already learned to feed himself, or he's rapidly learning. In the same way, he'll want to perform from time to time the other operations of his daily routine. He'll try to lace his shoes, put on his stockings, etc. At first, these efforts are futile and of short duration. Wait patiently. The attempt will grow more effective, and soon, with a little help, your child can really perform the function. Each accomplishment of this sort is a step forward in his development. You can't make better use of your time than to stand by while his awkward, little fingers work out the problem.

He learns to dress himself

Learning to dress himself is a long process. It must be taken gradually, or your runabout will tire of it. Undressing himself is much easier and should come first.

Your child is ready to begin dressing himself when he starts to identify the parts of his clothing and to know where they go. At first, though, he's able to do little more than get his clothes out of a drawer or closet and put them away.

Your role in this first stage is to provide clothing he can manage and to stimulate his interest in dressing himself. Keep his attention on the job in hand, prevent distraction and play, and direct him in the simplest parts of the routine. Let him think he's doing a great deal himself, even though you do practically everything. If kept busy, he'll feel he has accomplished a great deal.

When he develops an interest in dressing himself, your role becomes one of instructing and assisting only as much as is necessary. This period requires much patience, for you are able to get him in and out of his clothes more rapidly than he is himself. Only with actual practice can he advance in skill and the desire to handle the matter himself.

As he becomes fairly adept in dressing himself, he loses interest. By this time he has become good enough so that he can do it with comparative ease. Your duty now is to keep him on the job and to maintain order, without giving him more than casual attention.

If you follow these directions, your child will be able to dress himself fairly well by the time he's 3, except for difficult fastenings.

He can't be expected to manage things like back buttons before he's 4 or 5. His clothing at this time should, therefore, fasten in front, and if possible, have seats that pull down instead of unbuttoning.

Reading aloud to your child before bedtime gives him a warm, intimate feeling of companionship and a sense of security

Learning to dress himself is a long, intricate process for your youngster. You can help by stimulating his interest in it

Praise your youngster's accomplishments when they show real effort on his part, even if what he does seems trivial to you.

He'll enjoy washing himself — at first

It's easier to teach small children to wash than to dress themselves, for they love to play in water. Transfer his delight from mere dabbling in water to getting his face and hands clean. Supervision of the "washing-up hour" will be necessary until he's about 4.

The first step is to set up washing arrangements a small youngster can use without help. Provide a low bench, wash basin, and mirror in the kitchen, or put a box or steps in the bathroom on which he can climb up to the lavatory. Place a mirror where he can see himself as he cleans up, and have low hooks, rods, and a shelf which he can reach for his washcloth, towel, comb, and toothbrush. In the early stages, it's a good idea to have these articles on strings to help him return them to the proper hook, and to prevent his throwing or dropping them on the floor.

Your emphasis will be upon his finishing the job speedily and efficiently. Let him have water now and then to play in as part of his play equipment, and emphasize that washing-up times are business. Your standard of cleanliness must not be too high at first — polish him off at bathtime. So far as his own efforts are concerned, independence is more important than removing all high-water marks, and will be for some time to come.

Toilet routines

Your youngster by this time is probably dry most of the time. It's still desirable, though, for you to keep the responsibility for toilet functioning. Most lapses at this age are due to the child's reluctance to leave his play. Night control may not be established as yet, or he may call to be taken to the bathroom during the night.

Are "no" and "I won't" still with you?

Little girls are usually at the peak of balkiness at the age of 2. Continue to follow the suggestions given on page 145 for treating this phase, and otherwise ignore it. If your usually affectionate, obedient youngster suddenly stages a one-man rebellion, don't worry. See that necessary directions are carried out, and pay no attention to verbal defiance.

Allow time for dawdling

A big problem for you will be how to handle your youngster when he begins to dawdle.

It's most exasperating when he slows up on things he has learned to do so well himself, such as dressing and feeding. Now that he has mastered the task, he's no longer interested in it, and has his mind on a lot of other things. You can help him by allowing plenty of time for him to carry out the job. Keep his attention on what he's doing by gently placing his shoe in front of his foot. He'll resent your help at this stage, and will hurry through more quickly in order to do it by himself.

Picking up naughty words

Between 2½ and 3, your child may begin to pick up dirty, swear words, and expressions from the other children. To him they are very funny; to you they are embarrassing. Youngsters at this age are just now learning that

Low hooks, rods, or shelves for personal equipment help to teach children to look after their daily needs

they, as adults, can be worldly and just a little bad. If you show your child he has shocked you, chances are he'll be delighted. Don't threaten him, or he'll build up his vocabulary of such words even more. At first, just ignore his speech while diverting his attention to something else.

Dislikes interference

When your youngster is between 2½ and 3, he usually can get along satisfactorily with one parent, but flies into a rage when the other tries to interfere. At this age when he's learning to do things for himself, he's sensitive about being bossed. Instead, he'll try to do the bossing. Don't take your child's abuse seriously, and avoid interfering in situations where the other parent is assisting him. He'll soon come to you for anything he wants, and show you that he still loves you deeply.

He'll even boss you

Balkiness and contrariness reach new heights and take on new forms during this stage. Besides contradicting you, he'll probably even contradict himself. He can't seem to make up his mind, and once he does, he'll very likely want to change it again. He'll insist on doing things just as he has always done without any interference from you.

It's your job to be very understanding. Inside him, he's trying to fight two battles at once—deciding things for himself and resisting pressure from you. Don't interfere any more than necessary, and allow him plenty of time. Start him dressing himself or taking a bath when he has plenty of time and can dawdle if he wishes. Avoid pushing him into anything, and you'll find that this whole stage of behavior passes much more smoothly.

Play is part of learning

One of the important ways in which your child is educated is through his play. If directed adequately, it leads to the formation of habits of concentration, discrimination in choice of activities, and eventually to the development of individual interests and abilities.

You help his development in many ways when you furnish an adequate place for him to play, both indoors and out, and a good choice of toys and materials for him to use. His outdoor play yard should be fenced in until he is 3, if you can possibly arrange it,

Something to climb on should be included in equipment for play yard. Climbing bars are ideal, but a firmly piled group of logs furnishes much pleasure

for he can't be expected to stay within bounds much before that age, and will be constantly running or wandering away if he has the chance. If you can't have a fence, set certain boundaries and have someone there to see that he stays within them.

Have his play yard where you can see what's going on by glancing out of the kitchen or dining-room windows. Thus you can keep a check on things without interrupting your work. In planning his play yard, leave plenty of space for running and vigorous play, and include something your youngster can climb on. (Children at this age are little monkeys. You'll be picking yours down off the top of the piano, and every ladder he sees will be an invitation.) This desire for activity should be encouraged, not discouraged. Your youngster should not climb on your furniture, so you must provide things of his own that won't break or tip over. Very small children like to climb a plank supported by low boxes or on low ladders, and swing by their hands from the low bars of climbing equipment. Firmly piled logs over which your little tot can scramble will entertain him endlessly.

Play apparatus and materials for this age, and the purpose each serves in a child's development, are listed on page 173.

A good general rule for handling his play is to furnish the best equipment you can, then stay out of the picture except to keep him from actual harm. Allow him to choose his activities and to drop them when he gets tired or bored. In this way, he has a chance to pursue and develop his own individual interests.

Don't hesitate, however, to use your own good judgment in this the same as in other matters. There may be situations where a little help or a suggestion from you would enable your youngster to get more value from what he's doing. If that's the case, give it. Take care not to dominate his play, or to make him dependent upon you. If he does well, commend him, but don't overdo praise.

Your 2-year-old goes quickly from one object to another without plan. Let him alone, and by the time he's 4, he'll be making intelligent selections of play materials, spending much time on one activity, and going from one play sequence logically into another.

Should pick up his toys

Tidying up after play is part of your youngster's education. He should help at 2, even though he only puts away one toy. Gradually

All children love to dig in the dirt, and should have a small garden of their own in their play yard if it's possible. Give tiny gardeners a set of small tools and show them how to plant and tend their own seeds. For results that show up quickly, choose the seeds that sprout easily, such as lettuce, radishes, peas, and beans he can take care of more and more. In nursery schools, youngsters 3 years old and older are required to replace a toy when they're through with it, before taking down another. Few mothers, however, have time to enforce this rule, and if your child picks up his toys at the end of a play period and puts each back in its proper place, he's doing well enough for a child this age.

Young children get very intent in their play—the beginning of the habit of concentration. This is a desirable trait which shouldn't be broken. Allow your child 5 or 10 minutes in which to conclude the thing he's doing.

Taking things apart is as much a part of play to the 2-year-old as putting them together. Tearing down is as much fun as building. Give your youngster plenty of toys that he can take apart, and teach him to respect the others. Keep them in his own play places, where they can't harm your furnishings or house, and let your small experimenter carry on such researches as occur to him. (Within limits, of course, of his own personal safety and that of his playmates.)

Disciplining the runabout

Keeping faithfully to your youngster's daily routine continues to be the main prop of discipline. Providing a proper place to play indoors and outdoors, is another. See that your child gets enough sleep and rest, proper food, has plenty of opportunity to play vigorously in the open air, and plenty of things with which to amuse himself. Handle him gently, courteously, and with understanding. Do these things, and your child will be healthy, and pleasant to live with.

Being very inexperienced, he's bound to err at times. Situations are sure to arise in which you'll have to divert your youngster from unacceptable ways of doing things. And the brighter and livelier he is (the way you want him), the bigger handful he's going to be. Keep in mind that what you're after is not to get even for any annoyance he may cause, but to help him learn ways of doing things that are acceptable to society.

Various ways are acceptable in teaching your youngster how he should act in a certain situation. Always keep the same impersonal attitude. Attempt to make him understand that you require him to do a certain thing because it is the right and proper thing to do—not just because you feel he should do it.

Whenever disciplining a child, approach him with the attitude that you expect him to do what you tell him. If he fails, the best thing is to mete out the consequences according to the greatness of the act and how well he understood what he did. Any consequence should be logical, arising naturally out of the child's own conduct. Administer only a well-thought-out consequence—if it fails to accomplish what you are after, it has lost all merit. If you handle your child in a friendly way, he'll want to do the right thing.

Suppose he refuses to follow your directions? Removal from the family or play group has proved ample punishment in countless cases. If he usually gets along well with you, he'll feel just as unhappy as you do after he's done something wrong. Jumping on a child who is already sorry, sometimes reverses his feelings and makes him argue.

Help your child to love books and music

Giving your baby the best possible start from the standpoint of health and habits has been your main preoccupation for the first year or two of his life.

But now comes the time for which you've been waiting, perhaps impatiently. You can introduce him to the world of books, music, and art, and a thousand other things which give pleasure and meaning to life.

Of course your 2-year-old won't be able to appreciate Shakespeare, symphonies, and Rembrandts right off the bat, any more than he can play football. But he can and will enjoy stories, music, and pictures which are fitted to his stage of growth.

If you love these things yourself, the story or music hour will probably prove to be the happiest time of the day for you and your youngster, since there's no pleasure more keen than sharing things with those we love.

Moreover, it's one of the most pleasant times of companionship. Your little fellow is bathed and clean and all ready for bed. In slippers and bathrobe, he snuggles against you while the two of you pore over books or listen to the music.

Don't hurry him along too fast in the realm of books and music. Always remember that he has his own way of learning and his own time for doing it. Perhaps when you were young, *Alice in Wonderland* was a high spot in your life, and you couldn't wait until your child grew old enough to live it as you did. However, if you introduce it into your child's life now when he may not be ready for it, he may refuse to have anything to do with it.

A better way is to provide a plentiful supply of enjoyable books and stories for each stage of development and let your youngster choose the ones which attract him at that time. How preschoolers react to books at different ages and how to interest them in books was told most interestingly by Louise Bechtel in *The Horn Book Magazine*. Through the courtesy of The Horn Book, Inc., the following excerpts are reprinted:

First experience with books

"In my little bookroom at home, the majority of children 'before 5,' if left alone, simply slam over the pages of one book after another. They shout or sing if some single picture catches the eye. They look up away from the books for something active to happen in the room. Suppose I gather them on the sofa and read, showing them the picture slowly: then the brighter ones respond, but half still squirm and shout in irrepressible spirits about nothing at all. But if I have found a very good story and tell it, stopping frequently with a question or a chance for imitation, the audience is absorbed. That is the story they want again next time. Meanwhile, of course, an unusual child may have crept off alone with a book she loves, to apply her more mature powers of eye and mind, murmuring her own tale to herself as she fingers the lines of the pictures lovingly.

"Only the home can have the greatest pleasure of discovering books. Mothers *could* have the same fun the school has, with experiments in storytelling. But parents are still apt to push small children too fast in language process and picture appreciation.

"The first 'book,' is a recognition book of simple objects. Babies of 2 love to pull apart the big color advertisements in a magazine. Years ago they were given the Steichens' *First and Second Picture Books*, which still are popular. The objects portrayed should be those really familiar to a baby, for this book is merely a tool for talking. At this age of 2, most words are sound, not meaning; most nonsense verse and songs are not understood in the adult sense, yet can be a very soothing influence, or a source of laughter.

"Then comes the very first stories, at 2 and 3 years old. No one who has not worked daily with children will believe how simple they should be. To say that 200 words is long enough puts it too easily. The point is, much more, the utter simplicity of word and content. In these first experiments in attention, as opposed to songs and nonsense verse, there should be a delicate balance of reality— something that could happen to you—and of nonsense and action.

"At 3 and 4 years old, attention has grown in power, and we meet more sharply the problem of style. The body which has been developing an exciting lot of varied responses, the mind which has heard songs and poetry, quickly feel the wet blanket of dull prose. Then there is the matter of the 'comeback,' the question or pause for answer or imitation that lets the child actively enter the story.

"We know how the really good story has to be told over and over—how it is changed with the book upside down. It ought to be very good!

"Then, toward 5, horizons have widened; one can sit more quietly; one can listen longer. We have gathered a few criteria for style for these years: rhythm, repetition, brevity, sensory range, 'comeback.' As to content, we all agree on those elements of 'just like me,' of humor, the love of bump and fall and grimace that mark this primitive age, and we are apt to differ only on the fantastic.

"Only Mother's experiments unlock attention and imaginative response. But she must realize that these early steps are important—that it does count enormously to tell stories, each year a bit longer; to read poems, each year with more variety; to have the child treasure lovely books. With a little investigation, she will soon see how one writer speaks of 'here and now' very dully, and another so well that it is the beginning of literature.

"Mother or teacher, she will be amused at discovering the stories a child likes, those he does not, and why. As the child's sensitiveness and appreciation grow, she will know that the audience for good books has a new recruit."

Music appreciation begins

Quite as gradual will be the growth of your youngster's response to music. Heavy operatic numbers and subtle symphonies are as far beyond him now as is driving an automobile. But he'll love listening to a wide variety of other types of music. There are many classical and semiclassical pieces, tuneful and rhythmical ones, which delight quite small children. There's descriptive music, such as

"Hunt in the Black Forest" and "In a Clock Store." There are countless nursery songs.

A record-player and a selection of records he can enjoy is an invaluable aid in developing your child's love for music. He can soon be taught to run the machine himself, and can

Though you can only pick out a melody with one finger, your little fellow will prefer your playing to Paderewski's. Here's appreciation and use for your talent no mother can resist

put on the records he wants to hear. Prepare yourself to hear him play his current favorite dozens of times in a row, for that's the way he likes to do it. That's also the way he'll learn to carry a tune and get pleasure from music.

He'll be especially pleased if you sing and play to him yourself. If you can do no more than pick out a melody with one finger, here's an audience that will prefer your playing to Paderewski's!

Then there's the very simple music in which your child himself can begin to participate. Most children can't carry a tune much before the third or fourth year. But at

Youngsters like to do things to rhythm, and after a while, you'll find them singing tunes they heard on records or the radio. Thus their music appreciation soon leads to participation

any time you may find your youngster joining in when you sing a simple song, or when he hears one on the record-player. At first he may repeat only parts of songs in a monotone, and at his own rate. Let him improve at his own speed. The ability to carry a tune and to keep time develops slowly in most youngsters, and then it's largely the result of interest, imitation, and practice.

Your youngster will also learn to like doing things to rhythmic music. For this purpose, the tune should be easily recognized, the beat accentuated, and the selections short. Let him interpret this music in his own way—running, jumping, trotting, or galloping like a horse, "flying," "swimming," or "skating."

Simple instructions help keep up the interest in rhythm—drum, tom-tom, cymbals, triangle, bells, and tambourine. One or several may be acquired to help your youngster express what the music makes him feel.

Whether he has any musical ability or not, and whether or not he does anything with music in later years, he can get infinite pleasure from it if it has been presented to him as a pleasurable experience in early childhood.

Another baby on the way?

Perhaps it will be your good fortune to learn that another baby is coming your way. The second arrival often appears at just about this time. Your wish should be to handle this matter in the best possible manner from the standpoint of your first youngster, who up to now has ruled as an absolute monarch in your affections and household. A child this young is not likely to notice anything different about you. Shortly before the time you expect to have the baby—very shortly, for 2- to 3-year-old memories are brief indeed—tell him that a small brother or sister is expected, and that you'll go to the hospital for the event. Show him the things you and he and Daddy have ready for the new arrival; make him a full partner in the relationship. Emphasize that it's "our" baby; Johnny's as much as anybody's. If he asks questions about where the baby came from and how it's going to get here, that will be your first opportunity at sex instruction. Answer each question very matter-of-factly, but briefly, and tell no more than he has asked for. (See "When Your Child Asks About Life," page 187.)

If the new baby is to usurp his place in your room, or his crib, make the change sometime before the baby is born. Your first youngster will be delighted with his new room or new youth bed then, but may resent them and the baby if he is put out of his accustomed place after the baby is brought home.

When you bring the new baby home from the hospital, you'll take pains, of course, to see that Big Brother or Big Sister isn't crowded into the background. Yet don't go so far as to crowd the new arrival into the background to avoid jealousy. Some parents, anxious to keep the first from feeling slighted, have actually slighted the newcomer. That develops selfishness in the older child, and therefore, he's quite as unhappy as though he had been ignored.

Visitors to your home may unintentionally hurt the feelings of your older child. They're very likely to ignore him in their enthusiasm to see the new baby. Make it a point to bring in the older youngster for conversation and praise *before* guests inspect the new baby.

Your first-born must learn that life is a process of sharing. Consider his rights and feelings, but not at the expense of the baby's place in the family. Give each his deserved affection, and make the elder a sharer, insofar as it's possible, in the pleasures and tasks

arising out of a new baby in the house. Such a course builds happy relationships and is the best insurance against jealousy.

Jealousy over the new arrival may show up in many ways. Perhaps your older youngster will hit or slap the baby. He may even feel so resentful of you that he'll request you take the infant back to the hospital. Other youngsters, forgetting all about what they can do, resort to baby habits such as bedwetting and thumbsucking to draw attention. Some become so occupied with the newcomer that they talk baby talk to everything they come in contact with.

Feelings of some children show up in indirect ways. While around you inside the house, your child may be deeply fond of the baby, but the minute a stranger on the street admires him, he's rude. He may appear to be so affectionate that he hugs the infant until he cries. This is no accident—at this point he doesn't know his own feelings and which way to turn.

Your job now is to protect the baby, at the same time reassuring your older child that he still has your love. Make him feel that you are still on his side. You must realize that some of

Problems of jealousy are avoided if older children are permitted to help care for a new baby in the family

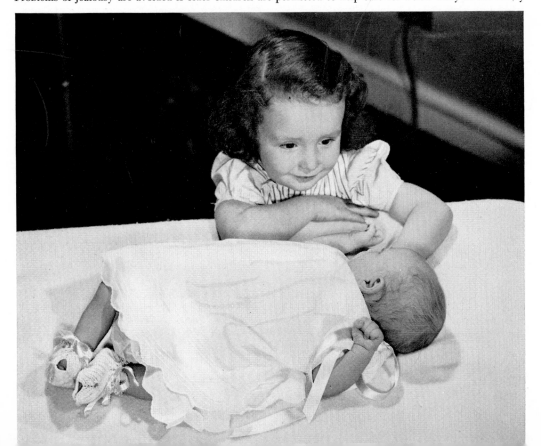

his acts are done out of pure despair and bitterness and try to curtail any conduct of yours that might lead him to act the way he does.

As the baby gets a little older, give the first child a room by himself where he can keep his toys and possessions undisturbed. Never make him share anything against his will, or he may feel even more insecure.

Feeding your preschool child

Your youngster's diet is altered very little from what it has been throughout the last six months, and will change very little for four years more. Continue to choose his foods from the lists on page 135-136. He should still be guarded from rich, greasy, spicy things, from pastries, and from any but the simplest sweets and desserts.

Keep his foods easy to manage

In preparing foods for your child from 2 to 6 years old, continue to make them as easy to handle as possible, and as appetizing as you can. A child of 2 with sufficient teeth may eat raw vegetables and like them this way. Wash carrots, lettuce, celery, turnips, cabbage, rutabaga, and cauliflower, remove any tough spots or woody leaves or fibers, and cut into attractive sticks or break into leaves and flowers. Soak them in cold water until very crisp, then serve as one vegetable at the meal.

Preschoolers gobble up tiny sandwiches of whole-wheat bread, buttered (cut a regular-size piece of bread into quarters), and filled with bits of raw vegetable or fruit. Any you have on hand may be used this way—apple, carrot, tomato, lettuce, cabbage, and celery. Prepare the vegetables or fruits as above, and cut into thin slices or easily managed bites. Such sandwiches should be passed only after your child has eaten a fair amount of his meal, for the preschooler will fill up on bread at the expense of other foods if you let him.

Make cream soups thick enough so they won't slip from the spoon. Cut or chop such foods as tomatoes and spinach to make them easy to manage.

Cereals and starchy desserts such as cornstarch, tapioca, and rice puddings shouldn't be made too thick. Children like these dishes best when made with about one-half the amount of cereal or starch called for in adult recipes.

In seasoning, use no pepper or spices. Use one-half the amount of salt you would for adults and limit the amount of sugar added.

Make meat, liver, and fish loaves very moist with plenty of milk and several eggs. Place the loaves in a pan of water in the oven while cooking.

Your child at this age needs an egg every day, two vegetables other than potato, and two fruits (unless there's a tendency to loose bowels).

Include three-fourths to one quart of whole milk in his diet every day. It's not necessary that all this be drunk as a beverage; part may be used in cooking.

Serve fish once a week; liver about twice a week. Two teaspoons of cod-liver oil or the amount of concentrate prescribed by your doctor should be given daily during the winter, and 1 teaspoon, or concentrate as prescribed, in summer. If the milk is fortified with 400 International Units of vitamin D and he drinks a full quart of it daily, this may be sufficient vitamin D for him without any additional as a supplement. Be sure to ask your doctor about this.

As a general rule, serve no food between meals. If your youngster's hungry, however, a snack is permissible if you're sure it won't interfere with the next meal. A cup of milk, an apple, or a graham cracker make the best "snack." A whole-wheat sandwich is good also.

Planning his meals

Menus for two weeks are listed on the next two pages, one for winter and one for summer, to show how your child's daily food needs may be combined appetizingly into three meals. Dinner menus were taken from the book, *Your Child's Food*, by Miriam E. Lowenberg, published by Whittlesey House, McGraw-Hill Book Company, Inc.

These are only suggestions, and the menus may be varied greatly according to your preferences and the food you can obtain. These menus give the principal meal at noon. This is not necessary, unless you find it more convenient at noon. If you serve your main meal at night, your preschooler may have his then also. The sort of menu suggested for supper may then be served him at noon.

Because of seasonal conditions, it may not be possible to get all the variety of fruits and vegetables you want at all times of the year. In such cases, substitute others which will supply the needed vitamins and minerals. Substituting tomatoes for oranges is an example.

One week of winter menus for child from 2 to 6

Monday

Breakfast:

Orange or tomato juice — Buttered graham toast

Oatmeal with whole milk — Milk

Dinner:

Meat loaf — Creamed carrots

Buttered green beans — Tomato sandwich

Crisp celery — Chocolate corn-starch pudding

Milk

Supper:

Soft poached egg on toast — Cottage cheese

Baked apple — Cookies (2)

Milk

Tuesday

Breakfast:

Prune and orange juice or prune juice or tomato juice — Milk toast

Milk

Dinner:

Scrambled egg — Celery sandwich

Buttered potatoes — Scalloped tomatoes

Rennet custard and peaches — Milk

Supper:

Cooked cereal with whole milk — Crisp bacon

Graham crackers (2) — Applesauce

Milk

Wednesday

Breakfast:

Sliced orange or canned fruit — Buttered whole-wheat toast

Cooked cereal with whole milk — Milk

Dinner:

Salmon loaf — Scalloped potatoes

Raw cauliflower — Buttered peas

Whole-wheat sand-wich — Graham cracker

Milk — Stewed prunes

Supper:

Coddled egg on toast — Crisp lettuce

Milk — Tapioca pudding

Thursday

Breakfast:

Stewed apricots — Scrambled egg

Buttered whole-wheat toast — Milk

Dinner:

Broiled liver — Scalloped tomatoes

Parsley potatoes — Celery

Whole-wheat sandwich — Fruit cup

Milk

Supper:

Cream of pea soup — Toast sticks

Milk — Banana custard

Friday

Breakfast:

Sliced oranges or canned fruit — Cooked cereal with whole milk

Buttered whole-wheat toast — Milk

Dinner:

Creamed codfish — Buttered broccoli

Scalloped tomatoes — Banana custard

Toast — Milk

Supper:

Vegetable soup — Toast

Crisp lettuce — Fruit gelatine

Milk

Saturday

Breakfast:

Stewed peaches — Buttered whole-wheat toast

Cooked cereal with whole milk — Milk

Dinner:

Liver en casserole — Crisp lettuce

Onions, peas, carrots (cooked with the liver) — Animal cookies

Toast — Fruit cup

Milk

Supper:

Soft-cooked egg — Baked potato

Chocolate-Bread pudding — Milk

Sunday

Breakfast:

Orange or tomato juice, or sliced fruit — Cooked cereal with whole milk

Buttered whole-wheat toast — Milk

Dinner:

Creamed chicken on rice — Brown rice

Buttered carrots — Whole-wheat sandwich

Apple wedges — Orange betty, orange sauce

Milk

Supper:

Vegetable soup — Toast sticks

Stewed cherries — Sponge cake

Cocoa

One week of summer menus for child from 2 to 6

Monday
Breakfast:
Orange or tomato
juice
Buttered whole-
wheat toast

Bananas with
whole milk
Milk

Dinner:
Cream of tomato
soup
Fruit cup
Milk
Graham cracker

Buttered green
beans
Hard-cooked egg
Toast

Supper:
Rice with cheese
sauce
Sandwiches

Fresh apple
Sugar cooky
Milk

Tuesday
Breakfast:
Stewed cherries
Milk

Prepared cereal
with whole milk

Dinner:
Creamed liver
Carrot sticks
Tomato sandwich
Milk

Buttered potatoes
Buttered green
beans

Supper:
Poached egg on
toast, or scrambled
egg and toast

Fresh fruit
Cookies (2)
Milk

Wednesday
Breakfast:
Applesauce
Milk

Milk toast

Dinner:
Scrambled egg
Graham cracker
Bananas with
whole milk

Buttered cabbage
Buttered carrots
Tomato aspic
Toast

Supper:
Broiled porterhouse
steak
Baked potatoes
Milk

Whole-wheat
and lettuce
sandwich
Fruit cup

Thursday
Breakfast:
Sliced orange
Prepared cereal
with whole milk

Buttered whole-
wheat toast
Milk

Dinner:
Fish timbale
Parsley sandwich
Crisp lettuce
Milk

Buttered potatoes
Scalloped tomatoes
Fruit gelatine

Supper:
Cream of spinach
soup
Milk

Baked egg
Sponge cake

Friday
Breakfast:
Tomato juice
Buttered whole-
wheat toast

Coddled egg
Milk

Dinner:
Soft-baked egg
Tomato sandwich
Crisp celery
Milk

Beets with lemon
butter
Creamed peas
Orange ice

Supper:
Green beans
Fresh fruit
Milk

Cottage cheese
Graham crackers

Saturday
Breakfast:
Prepared cereal
with peaches,
whole milk

Buttered whole-
wheat toast
Milk

Dinner:
Scrambled egg
Peanut butter
sandwich
Milk

Buttered potatoes
Tomato wedges
Applesauce

Supper:
Potato soup
Rennet custard
with fruit

Toast
Milk

Sunday
Breakfast:
Orange juice or
tomato juice

Milk toast
Milk

Dinner:
Broiled lamb chop
Crisp lettuce leaf
Whole-wheat
sandwich
Milk

Buttered wax beans
Broiled tomatoes
Grape sherbet
Animal crackers

Supper:
Bread and milk
Cookies (2)

Crisp carrot
Cocoa

Schedule for child two to three years old

6:00 to 7:00 a.m. Rises, goes to toilet. Cod-liver oil or amount of concentrate prescribed by doctor.
Juice.
Breakfast:
Fruit.
Cooked cereal with whole milk.
Milk.
If this is eaten, toast and bacon may be added, if desired. Milk toast, banana, or prepared cereal may be substituted for the cooked cereal occasionally.
Dresses for day.
Brushes teeth, combs hair.
Plays outdoors, if weather permits. In cold weather, an hour outdoors will be enough.
9:00 a.m. Brought in to toilet. (Continue doing this throughout the day at intervals you've found best suited to his needs.)

12:00 N. Lunch:
Vegetable soup or green vegetable.
Meat.
Potato, macaroni, or rice.
Simple dessert.
Milk.
12:30 p.m. to 2:30 p.m. (not later than 3:00 p.m.). Nap or rest in room alone with door closed.
3:00 p.m. (On arising from nap or rest.) Graham crackers. (Cup of milk also, if child is underweight.)
5:30 p.m. Supper:
Creamed vegetable.
Poached or soft-cooked egg.
Fruit.
Milk.
Bath, story hour.
6:00 or 7:00 p.m. Bed. (Depends upon the time of rising.)

Play equipment and material for child two to three years old

These develop and teach control of large muscles:

Chair swing	Broom
Board swing	Snow shovel
Rocking chair	Garden tools
Board to walk on	Large floor blocks
Tricycle	Balls of all sizes
Slide	Heavy train
Large wagon	Heavy truck
Sled	Heavy automobile

These develop large muscles and senses:

Sandbox	Shovel and similar
Pans	toys

These develop muscles and teach cooperative play:
Balls of all sizes

Materials that encourage self-expression and skill:

Block nest	Blunt scissors and cutting paper
Hammer and nails of different sizes	Blackboard and chalk
Large dominoes	Easel and water colors
Crayons and paper	Beads to string
Building blocks in brick shapes	Color cubes
	Modeling clay

These stimulate imitative play and develop imagination:

Picture books	Doll furniture
Telephone	Laundry equipment
Dolls and animals	Unbreakable or cloth doll to dress
Outdoor tools	Toy dishes
Household utensils	Small table and chairs

At three years, children are independent and delight in doing things for themselves. Toys and bubbles help to make bathtim

Chapter II

Your child from three to five years

Development

Around the age of 3 years your child may:

. . . measure 36 to 40 inches in height.

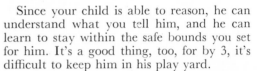

. . . weigh 28 to 38 pounds —more if tall or large-boned, less if short or of slender build.

If dressing routines have been followed, he can:

. . . unbutton and button side and front buttons, if buttons and buttonholes are big enough.

. . . put on panties and dresses, with a little help.

. . . put on and pull up leggings and snowsuits with a bit of help or advice.

. . . unlace and take off his shoes.

. . . put on his shoes if someone holds the tongues down, and if the shoes are marked to distinguish right from left. (A thread on one will do.)

. . . put on and take off galoshes, if they're large enough to slip easily over his shoes. (Tightly fitting galoshes will be too hard for him for a long time.)

Physical development

Once again physical development slows down. Your youngster may not gain more than three or four pounds a year for the next year or two. Mental development, however, leaps forward.

Since your child is able to reason, he can understand what you tell him, and he can learn to stay within the safe bounds you set for him. It's a good thing, too, for by 3, it's difficult to keep him in his play yard.

His active little body, plus an equally active mind, will carry him into many things that may look to you like mischief, but to him are really explorations of his world. During the next year or two—maybe it has already happened—your lively little chap may get into your perfume and cosmetics, cut his own or some other child's hair, ransack your bureau drawers and cupboards, and decorate your wallpaper after his own artistic fancy. The healthier, stronger, and smarter he is, the more

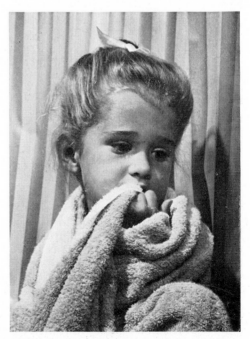

Active little minds are concerned with many things. Everyday tasks such as getting dressed become uninteresting once they have learned how

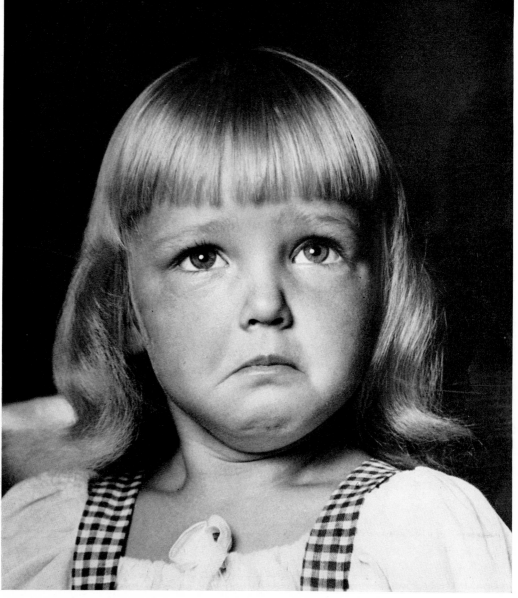

Undesirable behavior traits may show up in youngsters no matter how wisely they've been trained. Instead of punishing your child for generally unsocial or rebellious behavior, find out what is causing the trouble. If your doctor rules out all physical causes, something in the emotional environment is wrong

ways he'll find to upset the household routine.

He'll be the world's champion "why-er," for his whole environment to him is one big question mark to which he tries to find the answer. He'll run so fast and so hard in his quest that he'll always be falling and bumping himself. But that won't slow him down.

He'll go through various phases of behavior which may annoy you unless you understand that it's all a sign of growth. In a few months he'll forget a trick you don't like, but it may be replaced by another one which is just as distasteful to you.

At the same time, he'll have settled down in his habits. He'll be able, at last, to look after his own toilet needs. He can wash himself and get in and out of his clothes, except for the more difficult fastenings. You realize suddenly that he isn't a baby any more.

Three, in fact, is an age of transition from infancy to childhood. One authority calls it the "adolescence of the preschool period."

Like the adolescent period of the teens, it often keeps parents guessing, simply because they don't know what is normal behavior for the period and how to treat it.

Give him leeway

Once more keep habits and routine going. It will be your job to supervise these until your youngster is through high school. But aside from necessary matters, allow your little fellow as much leeway as you can in his explorations. Your aim should not be to suppress his eager interest, but to supply plenty of legitimate material on which it can grow.

Develop his self-reliance and independence by having him do everything for himself that he possibly can at each stage of growth.

Behavior problems from 3 to 5

At this age your youngster will exhibit one annoying phase of behavior after another, no matter how wisely you handle him. It's a little difficult sometimes for a bewildered parent, going through this for the first time, to know what behavior is normal curiosity and what has more serious implications.

A broad rule may be set up. If your child gets plenty of sleep and rest, eats the right food, is healthy and happy, and has plenty of interesting things to do, you can be pretty sure that he is basically all right. If his undesirable behavior is accompanied by a generally unhappy, rebellious, or unsocial attitude, then it's wise to look further into the matter. Try to understand why he cooperates under some conditions and rebels under others. Then remove the cause of the trouble, if possible, or help him understand it.

It may mean disciplining yourself, for doing for him is such a pleasure! He'll grow sturdy, though, only as he looks after his own needs.

Many otherwise well-behaved children become peevish or have temper tantrums late in the afternoon after a hard day of play. Or they become unmanageable when a meal is long delayed. The real problem in such cases is not how to treat peevishness or temper tantrums, but to see that the child doesn't get overtired, and that his meals aren't overly late.

Here are some of the more common problems of the preschool period and suggestions for handling each. Many occur earlier, but they seem to come to a climax from 3 to 4.

Don't forget that quite often physical condition is the cause of naughty behavior. When you're confronted with a problem that refuses to yield to gentle but firm methods, take your child to his doctor for a thorough physical examination. Even if your child is perfect physically, medical advice will be a great help in tackling a behavior problem that has baffled you for some time.

You must not feel that you've failed or are disgraced as a parent if your youngster displays any or all the following traits during the next year or so. It would be rare, almost abnormal, for a 3- to 5-year-old to exhibit none of them.

Mannerisms and tics

Thumbsucking. Has your child carried this habit over from baby days? If he's happy, well adjusted, and isn't nagged, he'll usually drop it of his own accord as soon as his developing social consciousness shows him that it brings derision from playmates. Just before giving up the practice, however, some thumbsuckers go at it harder than ever. It's best to ignore the habit, as calling your youngster's attention to it may prolong the thumbsucking.

A youngster who continues thumbsucking much past the age of 5 should have some special consideration (see Chapter III of this section). But at 3, thumbsucking may be treated as a phase of development.

"Bumping" and "rocking." If your youngster is a tummy sleeper, he may have become a "bumper" or "rocker." Since he is able to lift himself up on hands and knees, he develops a rocking motion, or bumps his head on the bed. Enthusiastic "rockers" propel their beds clear across the room and all but shake them to pieces. This usually does no harm, and is a habit that will pass if ignored. Try to divert his energy to another activity that you know is equally satisfying to him, and easier on your nerves. Three-year-olds can even understand

There's no harm in "bumping" or "rocking" the bed, but if your 3-year-old's an addict, it's probably getting on your nerves by now. He's old enough now, though, to stop, and will if you ask him to quietly

a request to stop, whereas it is asking a bit too much of the 2-year-old.

Nailbiting, earpulling, nosepicking, and face-twitching. Life is so exciting for the 3-year-old that he often develops little nervous habits. If yours does, check his routine to be sure he's getting enough rest, the right food, isn't playing too hard or getting too tired, and isn't upset emotionally.

Having made these things as right as you possibly can, you needn't worry about the mannerism. Just suggest quietly that he stop whenever you see him doing it.

Stammering and stuttering. Somewhere around the age of 3, many children begin to stutter. There is no particular need to be worried.

Between 2 and 6, your boy or girl will make enormous strides as a conversationalist. It's during this period, however, that he may get pronouns mixed up ("me" for "I"), may be unable to say certain letters or combinations (he may say "free" for "three," "widdle" for "little," etc.), may stutter some, and may repeat words and sentences over and over.

None of these things should cause you any concern. It's better not to try to correct your youngster's speech except by speaking correctly yourself. These difficulties will usually disappear as your boy or girl develops talking ability. If you call your youngster's attention to any of these defects, you may fix the habit in his mind and it will persist and become a problem. Above all, don't nag or ridicule him for his mistakes. If a defect such as stuttering continues after 6, there is probably some emotional tension causing it, and the help of a specialist in speech correction should be sought.

Let him talk. Between 3 and 5, your budding talker will probably become a chatterbox. He's discovered the pleasure of communication through words, has become sociable, wants to attract attention and tell you things.

If his chatter starts to wear you out, direct his interest to something else—a game or some physical activity. *Don't* scold or squelch him for talking too much.

At this age, you should see that he has other children and grownups outside the family to talk to. In this way, he'll learn to talk to others before he starts to school.

Toilet accidents

Involuntary urination is common throughout the whole preschool period, and should be treated casually. Any small child, when excited or interested in play, may have an accident. This is particularly true when he's playing outdoors in cold weather. Don't shame or punish your little fellow if this happens. Take him to the toilet, change him without comment, and make the intervals between toilet trips shorter for a time.

However, if your child of 3 or older has been trained for a long time, and then has extended lapses of control, some emotional upset or lack of adjustment may be suspected, and you should find out what it is.

Bedwetting

Many a first-born child takes to wetting the bed after a new baby has been added to the household. A perfectly trained youngster who finds himself in a strange place may wet the bed. And some continue to do this after they're old enough for camp and boarding school.

A youngster may wet the bed as a bid for adult attention or to "get even" for having been punished for something.

If he's physically capable of bladder control, treat the toilet lapse casually, but try to find out what emotional causes are behind this behavior. In your own mind, determine what your child hoped to accomplish by his actions. Then you can more easily correct this condition.

For a time, remind him again to go to the toilet at regular intervals. You may get him up in the night for a few weeks if he is easily wakened or doesn't cry or stay awake for a long period afterward.

If he's big enough, however, it's best to let him get up by himself. Speak to him to encourage him when you hear him getting up. He may need help returning to bed. Have a low-watt night light in the bathroom. Place a gate at the top of the stairs if your bedrooms are on the second floor.

However, if your child fights or cries at being awakened, or is unable to get up by himself, don't force him to do so. This will only make an issue of the bedwetting and it may continue for a much longer time than if you treated it as just another phase of behavior that will soon pass.

Protect his mattress with a waterproof sheet and pad. Have him sleep in a heavy night diaper, or panties that are padded with several thicknesses of material, and wait out the period of bedwetting as something lots of the little boys and girls do but soon outgrow.

You can put waterproof pants on the youngster so he won't be "floating" by morning. The heavy night diaper and waterproof pants cut down the amount of laundry that results from bedwetting, and eliminate the strong, unpleasant odor of urine in his room. Be sure the waterproof pants aren't airtight, or a rash may develop.

Cut down on the amount of milk or water your youngster drinks late in the day. This should not be done abruptly. The milk at the evening meal can be gradually reduced and just a sip of water offered when he asks for a drink at bedtime.

Destructiveness

With the 2-year-old, tearing things down is quite as much a part of play as building them up. At 3, your child will be an even more accomplished wrecker than he was at 2, but for the most part there's no malice in his destructiveness. The lively little fellow who threw Grandmother's book over the garden wall, and hid Grandfather's favorite magazine behind the bookcase, was merely carrying out what had seemed like good ideas at the time. There will be plenty of this when there's a 3-year-old in the house. Adults have to learn to be good retrievers.

But if all his play seems to be the destructive kind, you should investigate the situation. Maybe your youngster hasn't enough opportunity for activity, and gets bored. Perhaps his toys are so flimsy they invite being torn to pieces. Perhaps his destructiveness is a sign of rebellion and unhappiness.

If your study shows that the fault is with poorly made toys, buy better ones. If the difficulty lies in your child's environment, try to correct it. Then lead him into constructive play, and help him succeed at it. Children should have their own sturdy books to look at when they wish. Their good books, and adult books, magazines, and newspapers, should be handled only under supervision.

Lying

Rapidly developing imagination will probably lead your 3-year-old into telling tall tales. This isn't lying, and should be entered into as a game which both of you enjoy. Let him see that you know there's no giant in the bedroom, but you can laugh together at his vivid description of one. Help your child learn to distinguish between the real and the imaginary things.

You may also expect your child to make the discovery one of these days that he can escape consequences by saying he didn't do something which he really did. Harsh punishments increase a child's tendency to "lie out" of things. Our scheme of discipline, of course, doesn't call for harsh punishments. Nevertheless, your child has to be taught truthfulness the same as he must be taught other things.

Take care that your own attitude in questioning him doesn't frighten him into a denial. Don't ask him if he did something you're pretty sure he did, or you'll make it too easy for a small offender to resort to falsehood. Say quietly, "Johnny, where did you put the nozzle of the hose when you took it off?" rather than "Johnny, did you take the nozzle off the hose?"

Johnny's whole reaction will be to tell you where he put it—if he remembers. Then you can have him get it, and explain, as he puts it back on, why he mustn't remove the nozzle again.

If he does something he knows he shouldn't, however, don't withhold deserved consequences as a reward for truth telling. You want your child to tell the truth, not to escape punishment, but because telling the truth is the only way in which people can have confidence and trust in one another.

Explain to him that if we tell the truth always, people will believe what we say, and that's a much more satisfactory state of affairs than to be doubted.

Your youngster should learn to take the consequences of his unsocial acts. If the matter is approached impersonally, and your attitude is one of trying to get at the facts rather than of prejudging your youngster, you'll help him to admit his wrong and, at the same time, be prepared to take his punishment when it's coming to him.

Showing off and bullying

Such manifestations at this age are often stages of your child's social development. Most youngsters aren't ready to be leaders in group play until they're 4 or 5 years old, because they don't as yet have the qualities which induce other youngsters to follow them.

An ambitious child may want to lead before he has the ability. He may then try to win his place by showing off, or by interfering with and bullying the other children.

If he carries this to an extreme, he may need some help in finding a part in the group play that he'll enjoy, and that will satisfy the other children. If he interferes with them too much, try isolating him from play for a time.

Sleeping

In the period between 2 and 5 years, most children go through three stages in regard to their afternoon nap. Until 2½, your child will probably fall asleep almost immediately if all conditions are made right for him, and may continue to do so until he's around 3.

Around 4, he may stop sleeping in the afternoon. Have him rest, but he may enjoy quiet diversions such as looking at a picture book

Any time after 2½, however, he's likely to begin staying awake at his nap time. He has so many things to think about that he can't take time out for anything as prosaic as sleeping.

Whether your child sleeps or not, have him lie down in his bed for two hours right after lunch. He is more likely to be sleepy then than if he plays awhile after the meal. Close his door and keep everything quiet.

You may insist that he stay in his bed after you've put him there, but leave it to him whether or not he sleeps. After a period of staying awake during nap time, most youngsters go back to sleeping again until they get to be 4½ or 5. Then they'll sleep some days and stay awake on others. At this age, it's proper to let your youngster take a picture book or toy to bed with him, so he can amuse himself quietly if he doesn't sleep.

If your child spends 12 hours in his bed every night, has the right food and plenty of outdoor play, there's no need to worry about

Bedtime is likely to come too early for active youngsters at this age. Do try to keep them on the same schedule as much as possible

the amount of actual sleeping he does. Until he starts to school, have him go to bed every afternoon for two hours of sleep, quiet play, or relaxation. He'll sleep or not as he needs to. Don't let him nap past three o'clock as this may interfere with his night's sleep.

Eating

It's quite natural for your youngster's appetite to slacken as his growth rate slows down. At 3, moreover, the excitement of developing mental impressions often makes children forget their hunger. You must also allow for the inevitable period of boredom, or regression, after your youngster has learned to feed himself well.

Aside from these factors which may enter into the most nearly perfect eating situation, there are six ways in which your child may become a mealtime problem between the ages of 3 and 5:

1. Too much interest in what's going on around him. This is particularly true if a 3-year-old eats at the family table, or in a room where he's surrounded by toys and playthings.

2. Too much food. You've seen already how discouraging that can be to a little fellow with a limited stomach capacity.

3. Dislike for foods offered.

4. Trying to get adult attention.

5. Too tired.

6. Too much insistence on your part that he eat.

Treat your child's problem according to its cause. If his appetite has dropped off, cut his helpings in two. He can always have another if he wants it, but don't try to urge more food upon him than he needs.

If he's bored with feeding himself, let him help set the table and serve himself. Serve his milk in a small pitcher, and let him pour it himself into a tiny cup or glass. A straw for drinking may stimulate his interest. When he's through, let him remove his dishes and help himself to dessert, according to the amount of the other food he's eaten at the meal.

If his mealtime environment is too stimulating, remove him from the family table to a little table of his own, and have him eat ahead of the adults. Don't leave toys or other diverting objects where he can see them when he eats.

If there's more food on his plate than he can manage, you may "divide" it. That is, take the plate away, remove part of the food, let him finish the rest, and then have as much

Debby quickly cleans up her plate when it's filled with her favorite foods, so she can have dessert

dessert as he has had other foods at the meal.

If he dislikes a number of foods, try to find substitutes that will appeal to him. Then let him eat as much as he likes of favorite wholesome foods, without urging that he eat more.

Attempts to get attention usually go hand in hand with a family table situation. Removal to his own little table should help to cure it. Ignore his bids for attention.

Serve him small portions. If he doesn't eat them, remove the food without comment and let him go hungry till the next meal.

If he's tired, have him come in from his strenuous play and lie down for a while before dinner and supper, or at least engage in some quiet occupation.

Don't show any concern whether your child eats or not, and particularly don't let eating become an issue between you. Mealtimes should be treated as pleasant interludes in the day when everyone eats as a matter of course —not because he is forced to eat.

Understand that there will be times when your youngster has very little appetite, times when he will want to eat several helpings of one food and none of any others, and times when he will not really care whether he eats at all.

Don't worry about these fluctuations. If he doesn't feel compelled to eat, he will make up at another meal for the small amount taken previously. He'll balance his diet by switching

to another food when he has had his fill of a favorite. If he wants to skip a meal, he's sure to be ravenously hungry at the following one. Always remember that there are times when you and other grownups, too, aren't as hungry as usual.

That eternal "why"

When he gets to be 3 years old, your child will expect you to be a walking encyclopedia. By all means answer questions that are asked with a sincere desire for information. But your youngster is apt to find this new game so amusing that he'll ask a million senseless questions.

If he already knows or can easily figure out the answer to his question, have him answer it himself. Otherwise he may have you do all his thinking for him.

"Why" oftentimes becomes almost automatic. When you have replied to one question, he'll ask "why" again.

There's no need to answer this kind of "why." You'll only wear out your patience if you try. Very often the "why" is just a way of putting off necessary functions like dressing, undressing, going indoors, and so forth. It's best to phrase your remarks so that there's no chance for your youngster to ask "why." For instance, when it's mealtime, just say, "Let's go in now and eat lunch," and take his hand to go indoors.

Early sex instruction

Any time after your child is 2½, 3 is the usual age, you may expect the question, "Where do babies come from?" Nearly all children ask it in just this form. Answer simply and matter-of-factly, "They grow inside their mothers." This will in most cases suffice for some time. Then they will ask some other question, usually one which elicits the information that the baby was once a tiny egg, which grew until the baby was ready to live in the world.

These first questions are often as simple as can be, and can be answered without difficulty from your own knowledge. Answer each time only as much as is asked, unless an opportunity is given to expound some point you think desirable. See p. 187, "When Your Child Asks About Life," for more detailed answers.

During this preschool period, it's natural for children to exhibit interest in the opposite sex. Don't look upon this as some degraded or

Shortly before entering school, your child will begin to show an interest in the opposite sex. Look upon this as a natural curiosity. Show by your attitude that you're not alarmed, and treat the matter tactfully

perverted manifestation, but as a purely natural curiosity. Handle it tactfully and without alarm. Small children in the same family may have their baths together, and it's not necessary to separate the sexes for dressing and similar operations.

If yours is an only child, when a small playmate of the opposite sex comes to visit, treat the two in the same way you would a brother and sister. A perfectly legitimate curiosity will thus be satisfied in a natural and matter-of-fact way, and will then pass.

Don't be alarmed, either, if you discover your youngster handling his genital organs. This is called "masturbation" and is quite common to childhood. It is quickly forgotten if tactfully managed. See that the boy or girl is happy and has plenty of activity and interests. The healthy, normal child can be easily diverted if the matter isn't stressed in any way.

Time for tuberculin test

Tuberculosis is not an uncommon disease among children, and it's time now to take your youngster to the doctor for a tuberculin test. If your doctor thinks it's necessary, he may wish to give the test again before your youngster enters school.

Schedule the same

Your child's schedule does not change, except that you can shift to seven o'clock, if you've been putting him to bed at six o'clock.

Play equipment to add at 4 years

These materials develop the body, teach muscular control, encourage quick thinking, and keep your child out of doors: Swing; rings; bars; trapeze; sled; coaster wagon; jumping rope; ice skates; roller skates; boxing gloves; football; punching bag; beanbag; pushmobile; merry-go-round; seesaw. Some additional materials for indoor play are: Toy tool chest and tools; real cooking utensils; sewing material; construction sets; block printing sets; games; blocks; builder-boards; electric train; art tools; stamp books; real tools; large doll for which a girl can sew.

Chapter III

Your child from five to six years

Development

Probably your child at 5 years will:

. . . weigh 36 to 50 pounds.

. . . measure 41 to 46 inches in height.

He should be able to:

. . . button and unbutton all buttons except the most difficult (small ones with tight buttonholes, or small buttons in the middle of his back).

. . . put on and take off all his clothing.

. . . handle his toilet needs without assistance (except for hard-to-reach buttons).

. . . wash his face and hands and comb his hair without supervision.

A big boy now!

Now, at last, your youngster definitely puts baby days and baby ways behind him and proceeds to take a more mature role. He's ready for kindergarten, if there's one in your vicinity.

Before he starts to school, check over the list of accomplishments which heads this chapter and be sure your Mary or Johnny has mastered them all. A kindergarten teacher has enough to do without buttoning and unbut-

toning, and putting galoshes and rubbers on 30 to 40 children.

Some months before it's time for him to start to school, you should take your youngster to his doctor for a thorough physical checkup, including examination of his eyes, ears, and teeth. He'll probably need to be re-vaccinated for smallpox and have a "booster" shot for diphtheria. If there's anything wrong which might affect his comfort or efficiency, you should find out in plenty of time so that you can correct the trouble before he starts to school.

Your 5-year-old still needs 11 to 12 hours of sleep every night, although this varies considerably with different children and with the same child during different seasons. Many children are better off if their afternoon nap is continued after they start to kindergarten.

If your child goes to school in the morning, have him lie down to rest in the afternoon for a time, at least, while he's adjusting to the exciting new experiences of going to school.

Even though your child of this age goes through the day well without a nap, he'll benefit if you'll have him rest for 15 or 20 minutes before his dinner and supper. This relaxes him and helps his appetite. Have him get up early enough in the morning so he'll have plenty of time to eat breakfast and have his bowel movement before going to school.

Baby days are over

Just as 3 years is a transition age between infancy and childhood, 5 years is gradually marking an end to the baby period.

Not on his fifth birthday, necessarily, but

Healthy and happy five- and six-year-olds are quick to drop infantile ways and take on adult habits

during his fifth to sixth year, your child is expected to say good-bye to baby ways and to take on a more mature role.

While he was under 5, lapses into infantile traits were not taken too seriously. You gave annoying habits a chance to correct themselves with some gentle and indirect help from you.

However, if thumbsucking, bedwetting, and stammering show themselves, or persist into the fifth to sixth year, give them more attention.

The first step is always to take your youngster to his doctor for a thorough going over, and for a review of his life and habits. The physical side must always be taken into account when dealing with a behavior problem. Psychology can't help bedwetting, for instance, if the youngster has some malformation which makes control impossible.

If your doctor rules out physical causes and approves your child's pattern of sleep, eating, and play, then you must look to the emotional environment. The child who sucks his thumb much past 5, except for a little sleepy-time indulgence, is unadjusted in some way and quite often unhappy. It may be something at

186

home or school, or an inability to get along with playmates, that causes his unhappiness. Whatever it is, help him as much as you can.

Take care, moreover, not to shame or worry the youngster about it. He's none too secure as it is, or he wouldn't be sucking his thumb. Don't add to his unhappiness and feeling of insecurity.

Explain that while thumbsucking probably did little harm up to this point, if he continues it may cause crooked teeth which would impair his appearance. Approach the matter reasonably and understandingly. Re-

mind him with a look or an upraised eyebrow to stop when you see him doing it, and you'll help far more than by making him the butt of family attention and criticism.

The stammerer should have expert help, if possible, before he starts to school. See your doctor about this.

If bedwetting (enuresis) continues to this age, there should be a physical examination to see if there is any organic trouble. If there isn't, try to find the emotional difficulty and follow the rules in Chapter II of Section Three for dealing with bedwetting and toilet training.

Schedule for child five to six years old

(Going to morning kindergarten)

6:30 a.m. to 7:00 a.m. Rises; goes to toilet. Washes face and hands. Dresses for school. Has fish-liver oil or concentrate as prescribed, followed by fruit or tomato juice.

Breakfast:
Fresh fruit, stewed prunes, or applesauce
Cooked cereal with whole milk
Milk
If this is eaten, buttered whole-wheat toast and bacon may be added if desired. Milk toast, banana, or prepared cereal may be substituted for the cooked cereal occasionally.

Toilet for bowel movement

Off to school

*12:00 N. Dinner:
Vegetable soup, stew, or green vegetable
Meat (include liver and boneless fish once or twice a week)
Baked or mashed potato, macaroni, or rice
Slice of whole-wheat bread with butter
Simple dessert
Milk

1:00 p.m. to 3:00 p.m. Rest or nap in his own room.

3:00 p.m. Arises. Fish-liver oil or vitamin

concentrate as prescribed by his doctor.
Cup of milk
Graham cracker
Plays outdoors

5:30 p.m. Comes in from play, washes face and hands, and combs hair for supper.

*Supper:
Creamed vegetable or vegetable soup
Poached, scrambled, or soft-boiled egg
Whole-wheat toast, or whole-wheat sandwich with fruit or vegetable filling
Milk
(Cottage cheese may be given often)

6:30 p.m. Bathes, gets ready for bed.
Story hour

7:00 p.m. or 7:30 p.m. Bed

If your child goes to kindergarten in the afternoon, he'll play in the morning. He'll probably be hungry by midmorning and may have a glass of milk and a whole-wheat cracker. Have him come in at 11 or 11:15 and lie down for 20 minutes or more. Then have him wash and get dressed for school. He should be ready to eat dinner by 12 o'clock, so that his meal need not be hurried.

*Note: If the main family meal is at night, the dinner and supper menus given here may be reversed.

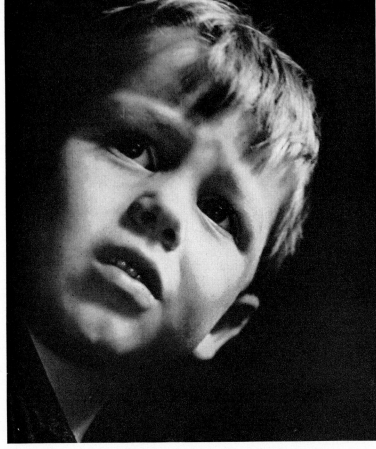

When your child asks about life, he's entitled to honest and simple answers

When your child asks about life

When your children ask you where they came from and other questions about human reproduction, they're entitled to honest answers. You're on the spot. How you help them at this point is a measure of your success as a parent.

You must know your facts—not guess—and state them clearly. Give the essentials; don't overload with details.

If your answers don't quite clear things up for your child, he'll ask more questions. When he does, keep on answering.

He'll probably ask about pregnancy, birth, fertilization, and mating, usually in that order. Most of his questions will arise from something he observes in everyday life. Some may seem to come out of a clear sky.

In answering, be friendly, not evasive, not vague, certainly not jocular or frivolous. Be serious, but not sentimental. Never conclude with, "That is the reason we love you so." And *never, never,* say, "That is the reason

why you should love your daddy and mother."

You can expect the first question about birth and pregnancy before Johnny or Nancy is 6, perhaps earlier. Most children know something about human reproduction by the time they enter first grade.

Here are the questions you're most likely to get and how to answer them.

Babies

Q. Where did Mrs. Graham get her new baby?

A. The baby grew inside of her in a special place mothers have for babies to grow in.

Chances are you can answer this first question without going into much detail. Don't generalize about birds or butterflies. Young preschoolers just aren't interested. In fact, they'll probably change the discussion from Mrs. Graham's baby to themselves.

Q. Did I grow like that in you, Mother?

(Or did I grow in Mother like that, Daddy?)

A. You certainly did! (Mother can pat herself to indicate the region.)

Don't confuse a small child at this point with names, either fanciful or scientific. No "cradle" or "nest," no "vagina" or "uterus," and no "under Mother's heart," though the affection and welcome indicated in that old-time answer were not misplaced, even if the baby was. When your child is older, you can tell him the correct names—"uterus" for the sac in which the baby grows, "vagina" for the birth passage.

Q. Where was I when you were a little girl? (Or when Mother was a little girl?)

A. The beginning of you was hidden away in Mother waiting for her to grow up and find Daddy, and make a home ready for you to come into.

Avoid the quick answer. "When Mother was a little girl, there wasn't any you." Your child has a strong feeling for the continuity of life. So don't abruptly deny him any existence before he came into the world. Here's an answer that's less harsh, still truthful.

Q. Is there a baby growing in you now, Mother? (Or in Mother now?)

A. No, not right now, but I'll tell you where there is one this minute. In Aunt Barbara. You notice Aunt Barbara is much rounder than she used to be. That's because her baby takes up a lot of space. The bigger her baby grows, the rounder Aunt Barbara will get.

You can never predict how questions about babies will be asked. It depends largely on what inspired them—a radio program, a movie, a photograph or painting, a chance remark, a new baby in the neighborhood. Whatever your answer, always establish one fact: *Babies grow in their mothers*.

Birth

Q. How does the baby get out?

A. Every mother has a little passageway just made to bring the baby out into the world when he is ready to be born. This passageway has a small opening at the lower part of the body, where the legs begin. The baby grows for nine months in a small sac which stretches a little bit at a time to make room for him. (You can make a little pantomine by cupping your hands together with wrists and fingers touching.) At last, when he is old enough and strong enough to live out in the world as a separate little person, his head swings around into the passageway and he is ready to be born into this big world, a little tiny baby.

At this point, with your hands still cupped, you can demonstrate, moving your finger tips apart and pushing downward with your wrists, how the canal begins to open. You can show how the muscles begin to press on the baby, carrying him farther and farther along the passageway until at last he reaches the opening and there, ready and waiting for him, are the doctor's strong and skillful hands. This coming down the passageway and out into the world, you explain, is called being born.

Q. Does it hurt the baby (or the mother)?

A. No, when a baby is born it is just about the size of your doll, Susan, or Friskie, your puppy. Besides being very tiny, the baby is all folded up. His little arms are folded across; his little legs are drawn up. He's like a little jack-in-the-box. As for the mother, she may feel tired, but the doctor takes very good care of her and the baby.

Fertilization

Q. How does the baby get in the mother in the first place?

A. The baby didn't get in there as a baby. It started from a tiny speck of living matter inside the mother. (If the child is old enough to grasp scientific names, give the correct term, "egg cell" or "ovum.") By itself, this little cell cannot grow to become a baby. It must be joined with a father cell. These two cells must come together inside the mother before the baby starts to grow.

Someday when you're going to have a hen for dinner, show Johnny or Nancy the mass of tiny eggs at the mouth of the oviduct. Explain that human babies, puppies, kittens, and the like are born without a hard shell around them, while little chickens and birds continue to grow for some time in their shells before they hatch out. When you open an egg and find the dark stringy particle in it that indicates the egg has been fertilized, take the opportunity to explain that here is a baby chick which has just started to grow. Explain that this egg was fertilized by a sperm cell of the rooster before the shell formed around it.

Another question asked by both girls and boys arises almost as often as questions on reproduction and may come any time from pre-school on. It concerns menstruation.

With the very young children, the question is usually prompted by some puzzling object.

Q. Mother, what is that big package? May I open it?

A. If you wish. They're just a lot of sanitary pads that take up moisture. Mothers and big girls wear them to protect their clothing from a discharge that appears now and then. The discharge is part of being able to be a mother and contains some blood and other substances that she doesn't need at the time. So Nature lets them drain away at certain times and sends her more after a while. The pads are used like a bandage.

Mating

To answer questions on mating clearly and without embarrassment, you must have laid a foundation of several facts. Before children can understand mating, they must know the difference between boys and girls. Little brothers and sisters should be allowed to dress and undress together so that they can observe casually that one is made differently from the other. If your child has no brothers or sisters, work out some casual way for him to see a baby of the opposite sex. Don't be surprised if Nancy asks:

"What is that on Dougie?"

If you're prepared, you'll answer:

"That's a penis. Little boys are made differently from girls. Dougie's penis shows that he is a boy. On your body the part is called the vulva." (If Dougie asks a similar question about a little girl, you can merely turn the answer around.)

This familiarity with bodily parts and differences is essential for an understanding later of your answers to the question about the actual mating process. Sooner or later, Johnny or Nancy is going to ask:

"How does the baby get started?"

Here's how you can answer:

"Men and women are made so that when they grow up and get married they can be fathers and mothers. The father's penis fits into the inner passageway of the mother, the one the baby comes down. Then the father, or sperm, cells pass up into the mother in a white fluid. If one father cell joins with a mother cell (or ovum), a baby may begin to grow."

A family of puppies, kittens, or rabbits is the best possible source for observing the principles of reproduction, and may provide just the opening you need for a discussion.

Then, too, there are books, written for elementary school children. Leave them on the table in the living room as you would any other book. If a book disappears, don't send out a tracer. If it remains apparently untouched, don't quiz or fuss. Keep your relationship with your children free and open, and they will discuss the book with you if they feel the need.

If they don't ask any questions, perhaps it's because you've missed their first expressions of interest, or have put them off, or shown displeasure. They probably found their answers elsewhere.

It's best not to probe to find out how much a child already knows. But if your boy or girl is approaching 10 and has not discussed human beginnings with you, you might throw out a leading remark or two and see what happens. Even if it produces no response, at least you have shown yourself to be open to the subject.

Confidence between you and your children must be established before puberty—the period when they start to mature. You'll find it difficult if you wait until then! By the time they're adolescents, they may shrink from your comments and cautions.

There is one question that bothers parents from the very beginning of their children's sex education. . . .

"Should I caution my child not to discuss sex matters with other children?"

The answer is "No."

Give your instruction in simple terms and to the best of your ability. Do this; then trust your child with it. His associates are bound to talk about sex and reproduction. (We adults do the same thing when we get together.) If children have the matter well in hand, without a feeling of guilt, they are very good teachers of each other. The child whose talk and conduct we disapprove is the one who has had to get his teaching hit-or-miss. If you inform your own child properly, you need not worry about the influence of a child whose knowledge is garbled or incomplete.

You need not fear exploration or sex misconduct as a result of good teaching. Sex education wisely carried out is the best possible assurance of a balanced, happy play life among growing children, and the best possible preparation for a happy adjustment to the problems they'll face in the future.

Common diseases and complaints

Changes in your child's usual physical appearance or his behavior often signify that something is wrong. And you should be able to recognize quickly the symptoms of common illnesses and ailments which these changes denote, and what to do for them.

Listed in this chart are the signs by which you can tell when your child is ill or has only a minor complaint, and the treatment that can be given.

Some of the more serious diseases require a doctor's care; call him at once. Below are recommendations for temporary treatment to give while waiting for him to arrive.

Disease	Cause	Appears	Symptoms	Duration of illness	Things to guard against	Treatment
Allergies (See Hives, Asthma, Hay fever)	Sensitivity to foods, dust, molds, pollen, dog's hair, cat dander, etc. Exact cause sometimes unknown.	After exposure to allergy-causing items. May be year-round if sensitizer is food or household object.	Red, swollen, watery eyes; sneezing; headaches; spasmodic coughing; hives; rash; gas pains in abdomen; vomiting; diarrhea; eczema; nose rubbing; constant cold; asthma. Child may be fatigued, cross, depressed, restless, and jittery.	Until sensitizer is removed. Seasonal if due to pollen.	Year-round allergies may cause sinus infections.	Have doctor determine cause and remove offending substance. Treatment may be given to decrease sensitivity. Anti-histamine drugs give some relief, but must be prescribed by physician.
Asthma	Allergy to foreign substance, or infection.	Whenever irritating substance reaches bronchial tubes.	Thick mucus is secreted; breathing becomes difficult, labored; wheezing; coughing. Attacks most common at night.	Short or long. Some cases clear up by puberty.	Repeated attacks may have harmful effect on lungs.	Have doctor determine cause. Remove offending substances. Drugs may be prescribed or an injection given.
Blocked tear duct	Tear gland from eyes to nose be-	Disease not detected until babies are several	Tears overflow from eye on cheek. Mucus gathers,			Bathe eyes with warm boric acid solution. Doctor may prescribe eye drops. Massage

Disease	Cause	When	Symptoms	Duration	Complications	Treatment
Bronchitis	Pneumococcic or streptococcic bacteria. Due to several germs or irritants as dust and gas.	When mucous membranes of bronchi become inflamed.	Temperature may rise to 100 degrees or higher for 2 or 3 days and drop back to normal; headache; wet cough most severe in morning and evening; vomiting; diarrhea.	Seven to 10 days.	Complications leading to pneumonia.	Keep child in bed in warm, moist room (68-70 degrees). In acute stages, inhalations may be given for 30 minutes every 6 hours from a croup tent filled with steam. Drape a sheet and blanket over crib. Lead steam into tent by heating a kettle over gas or electric hot plate at side of crib. Use cardboard or rolled paper pipe to carry steam from kettle to crib. Protect child from burning or scalding himself. Doctor may give sulfa or penicillin treatment. Infants frequently require hospital care.
Chicken pox	Filterable virus transmitted by direct infection or articles soiled with discharge.	Two to 3 weeks after exposure.	Fever; irritability; pink, blister-topped lesions appear in crops for several days on body, face, scalp, sometimes on legs and arms. Blisters break, forming itchy crusts or scabs on spots.	About 14 days.	Scars from scratching. Well-cared-for child rarely has aftereffect.	Keep child in bed as long as pox appears or fever continues. Relieve itching by giving soda or starch bath for 10 minutes, 2 or 3 times daily. (Cupful of starch or soda for small tub of water.) Do not rub scabs. Doctor may prescribe lotion to relieve itching. After scabs drop off, bathe and shampoo child thoroughly.
Chorea	Thought to be aftereffect of rheumatic fever, caused by streptococcic infection.	Between 6 and 15 years; more frequent in girls than boys.	Jerky, spasmodic, irregular body movements; worse if attempt is made to suppress them; nervousness develops gradually; child is irritable, fretful, and fatigued.	One to 4 months, or longer.	Recurrent attacks. Death may result from exhaustion if heart is weak.	Put child to bed and call physician at once. Sedatives are required in severe cases. Warm baths may help quiet patient.
Colds	Virus	After becoming chilled, or exposure to person having infection.	Sneezing; running or stuffy nose; flushed cheeks; dull-looking eyes; little appetite; may have slight fever and cough.	Two days to a week.	Bronchitis, pneumonia, ear infections, and sinusitis.	Isolate infant in well-ventilated room in which temperature is 70-72 degrees. Give boiled, lukewarm water, or fruit juices, often. Don't force food down. Keep crusts cleaned off nose with cotton dipped in sterile water. If symptoms persist, consult physician.
Colic	Indigestion; gas in intestinal tract. May be allergy	Between 2 weeks and 3 months of age. Attacks common in late afternoon and night.	Severe pain; face and body turn red; feet and hands become hard; hard crying; child repeatedly draws legs up and straightens them out.	Attacks may be very infrequent, or regular until 3 months of age.	Does no permanent harm.	Try bubbling infant. Then lay him in bed or across your lap on a wrapped hot-water bottle or hot flannel cloth. Warm enema may be given. If pain isn't relieved, call your doctor.
Conjunctivitis	Infections, chemicals, allergies, foreign objects.	Inflammation of inner eyelids, accompanied by itching, tears, or discharge of pus.	Sore, red eyes; yellow discharge.	From 1 to 3 weeks; may become chronic.	Chronic infection.	Doctor may prescribe sulfa, penicillin, or bacitracin drops or ointment. Keep the child's eye clean. Bathe often with sterile water or boric acid solution.
Constipation	Lack of water in intestinal tract; too little sweetening in formula; underfeeding; persistent vomiting.	When bowels move infrequently or with difficulty.	Blood-streaked stools; movements hard and passed with straining.	Depends on individual response to treatment.	Chronic constipation.	Offer cooled boiled water between feedings. One or 2 teaspoons of prune juice or prune pulp may be given each day. Check milk content of formula and add to sweetening if necessary. Don't give laxative, enemas, or use suppositories unless recommended by doctor.
Croup	Infection from cold.	Most often in children under 5 years of age. Larynx becomes inflamed.	Barking cough; hoarseness; rapid breathing; little or no fever; spasmodic attacks, chiefly at night, from ½ hour to 3 hours duration.	Spontaneous recovery after about 3 nights.	More severe forms of croup.	Call your physician at once. Then get warm, moist air into child's room. (See Bronchitis.)

Disease	Cause	Appears	Symptoms	Duration of illness	Things to guard against	Treatment
Diaper rash	Ammonia formed in diaper and bedclothes by bacteria acting on the urea in urine; or skin may be irritated by sweat, urine, feces, soap powders, etc.	Usually, in early months of baby's life or hot weather when bacteria works quickly on wet diapers; when diapers are not sterilized; when plastic or rubber pants hold in moisture.	Small red pimples or patches of rough, shiny, itchy, red skin. Pimples may develop white heads or become raw. Rash on end of penis is called ulcerated meatus; end of penis may ulcerate and bleed. Tissues may swell so urination is difficult.		Allowing baby to remain in wet diapers. Rubbing of irritated areas.	Boil or rinse diapers in a special rinse. Rinse boiled diapers 3 times, adding 4 tablespoons boric acid to a gallon of water. Zinc ointment or baby lotion may be patted on area. If rash involves end of penis, set child in warm bath for ½ hour. If difficulty persists, call physician.
Diarrhea	Improper formula or food; allergies; upper respiratory infection; infectious diseases; poor hygiene; unsterilized bottles, nipples, and formula; overfeeding.	In sick and undernourished children. When digestive system is upset by formula, vegetables, or other food; cold or other germs. Commonly in hot weather.	Loose, watery, frequent, green-colored bowel movements, may contain mucus and blood; scanty urine; vomiting; irritability; restlessness.	Depends on treatment and severity of disease.	*Do not give laxatives!* If stools are watery after 24 hours, consult doctor. Continued loss of water in bowel movement endangers life. Acidosis may develop.	Cut down food or offer none at all for a day or two. In artificially fed babies, cutting down on sugar, or sugar and fat (cream) may help. Urge child to drink cooled boiled water or weak tea frequently. Restore food gradually when watery stools cease, starting with smooth cereal, gelatine, or rennet.
Diphtheria	Germ in discharges from the nose and throat of person having disease; in secretions from nose and throat of "carriers"; can be transmitted by direct contact or articles soiled with discharges; infected milk or food.	Two to 7 days after exposure.	Fever; sore throat; membranes of throat, tonsils, palate, and nose slightly grayish.	Isolated until several nose and throat cultures show bacteria no longer present.	Obstruction of larynx; membranous croup; paralysis of the palate; peripheral neuritis; severe heart damage.	Antitoxin given as early as possible. Keep child in bed from 2 to 3 weeks. Modify diet to throat condition. Advance protection provided by shots. Schick test determines immunity after exposure.
Discharge from ear (See Ear infection)						
Discharges from nose (See Colds)						
Discharges from vagina (See Vaginal discharges)						
Ear infection	Colds; sore throat; measles; scarlet fever.	After child has cold for several days.	Cold, may or may not have fever; may discharge thin pus; child sleeping 10 or 15 minutes, awakening and crying.	Drugs most effective in early stages.	Abscess, mastoiditis, deafness. (Deafness during a mild case will clear up in a few days.)	Apply heated pad or hot-water bottle to inflamed area. If that doesn't relieve pain, try an ice pack. Doctor may prescribe ear drops.
Eczema	Food allergy or substance irritating to skin, as wool or powder.	When irritating food gets into blood, or skin comes in contact with wool, silk, rabbit's hair, etc.	Patches of light red or tannish-pink rough, thick, scaly skin on face, in folds of arms, and backs of knees. Scales like dried salt. Scales later become moist,	Most cases in infancy clear up in 1 or 2 years, or become milder.	Scratching lesions, as serum will ooze out and form crusts. Secondary infection such as impetigo. Never vaccinate	Have doctor find cause. Lotions and ointments may cure mild cases. Give child oil baths instead of soap and water. Other treatment will depend on age, location and type of rash,

Condition	Cause	When it appears	Symptoms	Duration	Complications	What to do
(Bed-wetting)	child under 5 may mean bladder control is not yet complete; or due to physical disease; or due to tenseness, excitement, uneasiness, or fatigue.	...where one or both parents were bedwetters.		...years old.		Have physical examination and urinalysis. Examine your attitude toward child.
Eye infections (See Blocked tear duct, Conjunctivitis, Pinkeye, Sty)						
Fever blister		Sometimes when child has fever from some disease or cold.	Small area on lip, causing slight swelling. Later forms blister.			Small applications of camphor ice will dry blister up in a few days.
German measles (See Rubella)						
Hay fever	Allergy to pollens. Allergic rhinitis, condition like hay fever, caused by sensitivity to dust, animal hair or dander, molds, etc.	In mid-August when ragweed pollen gets in wind. In early spring or summer from tree and grass pollens.	Stuffed-up, itchy, running nose; red, itching eyes.	Depends upon effectiveness of treatment.	Asthma, sinus infections.	Frequent injections over a long period. Remove cause of condition if possible.
Hernia			Slight bulging, about the size of hazelnut, at navel (called umbilical hernia) or in area of groin (called inguinal). May be noticeable only when child is crying or straining himself.			Consult physician for treatment immediately.
Hives	Sensitivity to serum injection; plants, foods, and drugs; exposure to heat or cold; emotional stress.	Within few seconds to several days after exposure.	Raised welts, pale in center, may itch unbearably; swelling of eyelids, lips, feet, or hands.	Can be once in a lifetime or repeatedly.	Scars from scratching.	Bathe child in starch or soda water. (Cupful for a small tub or 2 cupfuls for large one.) Have physician prescribe medication.
Impetigo	Contagious skin infection.	After personal contact with infected child.	Starts as small, runny blister, often on the face. Sometimes develops into infected sore. Generally has light tan or honey-colored crust.	Each sore may last week or more. Reinfection may develop other spots for weeks.	Reinfection from hands, clothes, bedclothing. Boil clothing and bed linens every day.	Consult physician immediately. If none is available, soften crusts with warm boric acid solution. Then scrub with soap, water, and cotton to remove crusts. Paint each spot with 2-percent aqueous solution of gentian violet.
Infantile paralysis (See Poliomyelitis)						

Disease	Cause	Appears	Symptoms	Duration of illness	Things to guard against	Treatment
Lice	Parasite on scalp.	Transferred through use of articles of person having lice.	Itching scalp; tiny pearly nits (eggs) clinging to hair strands.		Persons having infection; using another's combs and brushes.	Apply kerosene or tincture of larkspur to hair. Cover with turban for 12 to 24 hours. Wash hair thoroughly, apply a large quantity of vinegar, and rewrap head. Comb thoroughly with fine-tooth comb after 5 minutes. Wear covering cap and gown when giving treatment. Boil garments afterward.
Lockjaw (See Tetanus)						
Mastoiditis	Serious inflammation of mastoid system of skull from ear infection.	After draining ear of 2 to 4 weeks' duration.	Fever; tender over mastoid bone, may be swelling back of ear; vomiting; diarrhea.	Clears up with proper surgical treatment.	Serious complications if treatment is delayed.	Ear must be drained adequately. Penicillin and sulfa drugs.
Measles	Virus in respiratory tract, transmitted from person to person.	Seven to 18 days after exposure, usually 10 to 14.	Fever; running nose; red, watery eyes; harsh, dry cough; Koplick's spots (fine, white, milklike spots) on inside of cheeks; red rash around hairline and behind ears on fourth or fifth day. Gradually spreads over body.	Rash disappears in about five days. Keep child in bed until cough and cold clear up completely.	Pneumonia; eye and ear infections; encephalitis. Complications are common and serious. Disease can be fatal, particularly in small children	Notify doctor as soon as you know child has been exposed. An injection of immune globulin can prevent or modify disease. If symptoms appear, put child to bed in a warm, well-ventilated room. Subdue light if necessary. Steam inhalations will relieve cough. Sponge baths with water containing baking soda relieve itching. Consult physician for further treatment.
Mumps	Virus transmitted by contact with person who has disease.	Ten days to 3 weeks after exposure.	Fever; pain; swelling about jaw angle on one or both sides, frequently under chin and jaw.	Swelling usually disappears in 7 to 10 days, but keep child in bed for 48 hours afterward. Patient should be isolated until swelling has subsided.	Involvement of sex glands after puberty; meningitis; encephalitis; nerve deafness.	Bed rest; light diet, mainly liquids and soft solids. Avoid acids, hard or chewy foods, any with strong seasonings. Hot or cold applications on swollen portions may relieve pain.
Penis, Sore on (See Diaper rash)						
Pinkeye	Infection by bacteria, usually pneumococcus.	White of eye becomes red and inflamed with discharge of mucus or pus.	Itching; increase in flow of tears; sensitiveness to light; blurred vision.			May disappear spontaneously. Bathe eyes frequently with sterile (boiled) water and cotton. If condition persists, consult physician.
Pneumonia	Serious inflammation of lung from bacteria or virus.	May have abrupt onset in previously well child, or occur after cold, measles, or whooping cough.	May start without warning; temperature of 103 degrees or 104 degrees; harsh cough; rapid, grunting-like breathing; vomiting; sometimes convulsions.	Depends on cause, child's resistance, and effectiveness of treatment.	Disease causes high mortality rate in infants. Fatigue and overplay when child gets up. Follow physician's advice.	Sulfa, penicillin, and other antibiotic drugs frequently control infection promptly. Call physician just as soon as disease is suspected. Rest is essential. Feed child bland, easily digested foods. Hospitalization and administration of oxygen may be necessary.
Poliomyelitis	Virus infection. Method of transmission unknown.	Frequently in summer and autumn. Strikes every age, although commonly from 1 to 5 years.	Fever; headache; vomiting; stiff neck and back; pain in legs or arms; profuse sweating. Paralysis may set in suddenly after 3 days or develop by degrees for 3 or 4 days.	Isolate child for 2 weeks. Virus remains in body for 2 or 3 weeks.	Do not become panicky during an epidemic.	Call your doctor at once for accurate diagnosis and treatment. Spinal fluid must be examined before a diagnosis can be made. Hot packs and physiotherapy are used during

Disease	Cause	Where and when it occurs	Symptoms	Duration	Complications	Treatment
Prickly heat	Excessive perspiration.	In hot weather when baby is sweating from too much clothing or extreme summer heat.	Clusters of small pink papules, usually on neck or shoulders. Tiny blisters form on the pimples. Tan-looking rash appears later.	During hot weather.	No serious trouble.	Sponge area with cotton soaked in baking soda solution (1 teaspoon to a cup of water); bathe child frequently, dusting body with cornstarch. Remove excess clothing.
Rheumatic fever	Thought to be caused by streptococcic throat infections, particularly in poorly nourished children.	In children between 7 and 10 years of age, frequently in winter and spring; 10 days to 2 weeks after throat infection.	Fatigue; irritability; loss of appetite; fever; fleeting pains in joints; acutely inflamed joints with swelling and redness; skin rashes; nosebleed; anemia.	Acute phase may last from 1 to 3 months. Complete recovery may require many months of bed rest and medical care.	Damage to heart. Each recurrence may more seriously damage heart.	Absolute bed rest until temperature and pulse remain normal, nutrition improves, blood count normal. Child may have to stay in bed for 6 to 9 months for complete recovery. Follow physician's advice.
Ringworm	Contagious fungi in skin; frequently on scalp.	Anywhere on body.	Circular lesions, outer part slightly raised and pale.	Depends upon treatment.	Lesions spreading to other parts of body. Ringworm of scalp may produce permanent areas of baldness.	Consult physician for proper treatment.
Roseola infantum	Thought to be caused by virus; apparently contagious.	Chiefly in infants or children under 3 years of age.	Onset is abrupt; fever of 102 to 105 degrees in a few hours; restlessness; irritability; poor appetite. May be playful. On fourth day, fever drops to normal. Blotchy red rash forms on trunk and neck (resembling measles). Lesions become bluish in color. May be convulsions at onset.	Disappears within 48 hours after rash appears.	Complications or fatalities do not occur.	Bed rest; liquids; light diet; sponge baths.
Rubella (German measles)	Virus in upper respiratory tract.	Epidemic disease. Appears 14 to 21 days after exposure.	Slight fever, may last for 2 days; may be slight redness and swelling of throat; pinhead-sized, red spots on palate; glands back of ears and in back of neck swollen and tender; flat, pink, pin-point rash appears and spreads over body in a few hours, sometimes fading before reaching legs. May resemble rash of measles or scarlet fever.	Rash disappears in 2 to 4 days.	Encephalitis. Keep child isolated until all symptoms disappear. Pregnant women should entrust care of child having or suspected of having rubella to someone else. Rubella in early pregnancy may cause defects in unborn child.	No treatment other than brief isolation and bed rest during period of fever.
Rupture (See Hernia)						
Scabies	Itch mite buries itself in skin to lay eggs.	After personal contact with person having disease, or bedding.	Burrows in skin caused by mite crawling under surface. Areas become inflamed, itch intensely, become infected, may be filled with pus. Itching more severe at night and may disturb sleep. Infection usually on underside of wrists, armpits, around waist, between fingers. May spread over body.	Depends upon treatment. Not more than 2 weeks if child does not scratch it.	Sulfur or other skin reactions may develop from ointment used and require special treatment. Scratching lesions may cause secondary infection.	Apply sulfur ointment at night after thorough, hot soap-and-water bath. Have child wear underwear with long sleeves and legs. Thoroughly sterilize all clothing and bedclothing.
Scarlet fever	Streptococcus in discharges from nose, throat, or ears of person having disease. Transmitted by direct contact or contaminated milk or other food.	Two to 7 days after exposure. Seldom contracted during first year. Frequently between 5 and 8 years of age. Chiefly in fall and winter, seldom in summer.	Fever; vomiting; sore throat; appearance within 24 to 48 hours of fine, pin-point, red rash; most severe under arms and around groin.	Fever for several days, gradually returning to normal. Rash lasts from 3 to 7 days, followed by peeling of skin. Length of quarantine varies, usually from 2 to 3 weeks.	Swollen glands of neck; ear infections; nephritis; heart damage.	Notify doctor immediately after exposure. Patients are ordinarily quarantined and kept in bed for 2 weeks. Physician may give penicillin or sulfa treatment, or convalescent serum.

Disease	Cause	Appears	Symptoms	Duration of illness	Things to guard against	Treatment
Smallpox	Highly contagious disease caused by virus.	Nine to 14 days after exposure.	Abrupt onset with severe headache; backache; fever; temperature of 103 to 104 degrees; rash appearing 5 to 7 days after onset, consisting of separate papules filled with clear fluid, later pus. Crusts form and often leave pitted scars.	Crusts loosen and fall off in 4 to 6 weeks.	Encephalitis; erysipelas; septicemia; pneumonia. May be fatal.	Vaccination is adequate prevention. If exposed, have the child vaccinated immediately. If smallpox is suspected, isolate patient and call physician at once. Sedatives may be given for headaches, hot-water bottle applied to back, and ice packs applied to head. Boric acid compresses are soothing after pustules appear.
St. Vitus's dance (See Chorea)						
Sty	Infected gland of eyelid.	Infection in hair follicle of eyelid.	Red, tender swelling of eyelid; may come to a head, break, and require no treatment.	Infection clears up in a few days. Recurrences common. If another occurs, consult physician.	Not serious.	Apply hot, moist boric acid packs to relieve soreness. Doctor may prescribe antibiotic ointment.
Tetanus (lockjaw)	Tetanus bacteria in soil and fecal discharges of man and animals.	Particularly following puncture or dirty wounds, compound fractures, or burns. Usually 5 to 14 days after a wound. May be 3 to 5 weeks.	Stiffness of muscles in neck and jaw; inability to open jaw: difficulty in swallowing and speaking follow rapidly; severe, repeated convulsions; some fever.	Two to 4 weeks.	Disease highly fatal, but preventable. Have child immunized against tetanus (inoculations) in last half of first year. Booster inoculations should be given at 2 and 5 years. Also after puncture or dirty wounds for protection. If child had not been immunized, tetanus antitoxin is given at time of injury.	Patient with tetanus must be hospitalized. There is a high death rate.
Thrush	Fungus infection in mouth.	May be transmitted by unsterile nipples; carried into child's mouth by adult's hands; acquired at birth if fungus is in mother's vagina; in poorly nourished child.	Small, white sores in mouth like spots of milk. Spreads gradually. Mouth sore and inflamed. May cause loss of appetite, restlessness, difficulty in nursing.	One or 2 weeks with no treatment. Few days with treatment.	Spread of infection by using unsterilized nipples.	Give baby drink of water after feeding to cleanse mouth. Soak nipples in soap solution, wash, boil in separate container. One-percent aqueous gentian violet may be applied to mouth twice daily.
Tics (habit spasms)	Spasmodic, irregular movements of separate muscle groups repeated over and over. May be copied from another person.	Usually in late childhood or preschool age.	Blinking of eyes; sniffing; throat-clearing; dry-coughing; grimacing; shoulder-shrugging. Begin as voluntary movements, later habitual.	Until underlying tension and nervousness are relieved.	Excitement and noise. Do not call attention to tic or suggest methods of stopping.	Adjustment of home or school environment to relieve pressure. Help child attain self-confidence and gratification from accomplishment. Scolding and punishment increase difficulty.
Tonsillitis	Bacteria and infections of various kinds. May be transmitted to other children.	As part of upper respiratory infection or distinct disease.	Acute onset of sore throat and fever; headache; vomiting; difficult swallowing; abdominal pains; convulsions. Tonsils are usually red, swollen, with white spots or white membrane.	Five to 7 days.	Abscess of tonsils; involvement of lymph glands in neck; rheumatic fever. Diseased tonsils may jeopardize health of child.	Physician may prescribe sulfa or penicillin. Hot salt-water gargles and sprays may give relief. Apply hot or cold compresses to neck.
Tuberculosis	Infection by tubercle bacillus. Most often caused by intimate contact with adult having tuberculosis or raw milk from infected	In lung and lymph glands at root of lung. Except in small children, first infection usually heals and becomes surrounded with lime deposit. Infection may spread through blood or lymph vessels to brain	First infection may occur without child's being ill. May be some fever, irritability, loss of appetite. Early symptoms of reinfection are fatigue, slight rise in temperature, pain in chest from pleurisy. When patient loses weight, coughs, and has night sweats, disease is usually well advanced.		Meningitis or generalized miliary tuberculosis in infants. Intimate contact of baby or child with adult having disease. Often fatal in infants.	Diagnosis by skin tests, X-ray, and finding tubercle bacillus. Treatment must be directed by doctor.

Disease	Cause	When it appears / Incubation	Symptoms	Duration	Complications	What to do
	son who has had first infection is later re-exposed, or if there is lightening up of first infection, reinfection tuberculosis develops. First infection in some individuals is progressive and continues into reinfection.					
Typhoid	Typhoid bacillus, generally carried into body by contaminated water or food.	One to 2 weeks after exposure.	Fever; diarrhea; vomiting; prostration; stupor; delirium; thirst; low pulse rate. Symptoms vary.	Usually only 2 or 3 weeks in young children. More serious after 10 years of age.	Intestinal hemorrhage and perforation; dehydration (loss of water in the tissues), especially in infants; anemia; bronchitis; relapse or reinfection.	Vaccine provides immunity for 2 or 3 years. If child develops disease, he will need complete rest, good diet. Antibiotic drugs are effective.
Urination, frequent	May mean nothing or due to infection or disease.				Emotional tension and pressure.	Have doctor determine cause and urinalysis made.
Urination, painful and scanty	Infection, bladder stone, or highly concentrated acid urine.					Have specimen of urine examined. Follow physician's advice.
Vaginal discharges	Handling of genitals; pushing objects into them; mild infection; lack of cleanliness.	Generally before puberty.	Discharge from vagina which may consist of pus and blood, or pus. Vulva may be inflamed.			
Vomiting					Accompanied by abdominal pains, vomiting may be a symptom of serious disease.	Consult your physician at once.
Whooping cough	Specific bacteria transmitted by direct contact with patient.	One to 2 weeks after exposure. Child with whooping cough is infectious for about 4 weeks.	Paroxysmal cough increasing in severity and frequency. Occurs after meals, usually worse at night. When coughing, child chokes, gags, gets red in face, frequently vomits. Coughing spell usually ends with inspiratory whoop.	Four to 8 weeks.	Pneumonia; hemorrhage; malnutrition. Have child immunized early in life. Whooping cough is serious in infants.	Physician will prescribe new antibiotic drugs. Serum given soon after exposure may prevent or lessen attack. Keep child warm in well-ventilated room, or outdoors in fresh air if weather permits. Give solid foods immediately after vomiting. During whooping spell, place young baby on his side to prevent his swallowing mucus or vomited food. Abdominal support may prevent hernia. With an older child during coughing spell, hold his abdominal muscles with one hand and forehead with other. Keep child's nose free of secretions.
Worms	Intestinal parasites or their eggs, carried into body by food, hands, or picked up from soil through feet when barefooted (hookworm).		Itching around rectum; moderate indigestion; disturbed sleep; worms in stool.	Depends on type of worm.	Reinfection; anemia; malnutrition.	Doctor will prescribe treatment. Varies with different types of parasites.

First aid

Here's what to do in case of minor injuries, and while
waiting for the doctor in serious emergencies

Abscess

If a tender, inflamed, throbbing infected area develops on a finger tip, around a toenail, or at the site of a cut, apply a wet compress to the area constantly. Place a thick sterile bandage over the area, wetting it with a solution made from a cup of boiled water and a tablespoon of Epsom or table salts. The compress will soften the skin, allowing it to break and release the gathering pus. If the child has a fever, a noticeable swelling around the area, or red streaks appear up the limb or arm involved, consult your physician immediately. The infection may be spreading.

Artificial respiration

If the child stops breathing because of smothering, electric shock, drowning, or gas which he has inhaled, begin artificial respiration at once. Continue until the child starts to breathe again or a doctor arrives.

Rest an infant on his back on a table or across your knees. Place one hand under his thighs and the other under his neck and shoulders. Arch his body until thighs are pressed against chest. Straighten his body and repeat movements about 30 times a minute.

Use the regular method of artificial respiration for an older child because he can stand the weight of an adult's body on his. Lay him on his stomach, with one arm extended above his head, and the other bent at the elbow. Rest his face, turned outward, on his hand, so that his nose and mouth are free for breathing.

Straddle the child's thighs with your knees placed beside his. Place palms of hands on the small of his back with your fingers resting on his ribs. Your little finger should be touching his lowest rib, and the rest of your hand in a natural position.

Hold your arms straight and swing forward slowly, applying the weight of your body to the child. At the end of the swing, your shoulders should be exactly over the heel of your hand. Do not bend your elbows. Allow about 2 seconds before releasing pressure and swinging backward. Wait another 2 seconds, then repeat. Continue about 12 to 15 times a minute until breathing starts or a physician arrives. Keep the child warm. Do not give any liquids.

Bites, animal

Wash the wound with soap and water to remove saliva, holding the wounded area under running water if possible. Dry with clean gauze. Then bandage like any other wound. Consult a doctor at once, as he may want to give the Pasteur treatment or antitetanus serum. Notify police or health department so the animal can be observed for rabies.

Bites, bees, wasps, and hornets

Apply a paste of wet baking soda, moistened with ammonia water. This can be held in place by a bandage, but should be kept moist. Cold compresses reduce swelling and pain.

Bites, chiggers, *See bites, mosquito*

Bites, human

Cleanse thoroughly with soap and water and dry with gauze or cotton. Take the child to the doctor if the skin has been broken. Human bites often become infected and need close attention.

Bites, mosquito and chigger

To relieve discomfort, apply weak ammonia water or a paste of baking soda and water.

Bites, snake

Apply a sterile gauze dressing and bandage and call a doctor. Although most snakes are nonpoisonous, there are certain precautions you can take while waiting for the doctor if you think the snake is poisonous. Keep your child lying down and quiet. Wrap a band tightly around his limb, about an inch above the wound. You can use a stocking, necktie, or any strip of material. About every 20 minutes, release band for 1 minute, then retighten. Then, with a sharp knife or razor blade (sterilized if possible), make an X-cut at each fang mark, avoiding large veins or arteries. The cuts should be from $\frac{1}{4}$ to $\frac{3}{8}$ inch deep. Suck on the wound, spitting out the fluid.

Bruises

Apply iced or very cold cloths immediately to keep down the swelling, relieve the pain, and prevent discoloration. If the skin has been broken, treat as an open wound.

Burns, chemical

Such substances as lye, caustic soda, etc., should be kept far beyond the reach of small children. But if an accident happens, strip off all clothing which has come in contact with the chemical. Flood the burned area immediately with a large quantity of sterile water until the chemical is washed away. Then apply wet packs and take the child to the doctor or call him at once. Carbolic-acid burns should be washed with rubbing alcohol if it's available.

Burns, fire, dry heat, and scalds

For a slight burn, in which the skin is reddened but not broken, spread petroleum jelly on sterile gauze and cover the burn. For a more extensive one, cut clothing from around the burn and apply several layers of sterile gauze (or freshly laundered cloth) which have been spread with petroleum jelly. Bandage the gauze lightly in place. Cover the child lightly with blankets.

If he's badly burned, undress the child quickly. Apply petroleum jelly and sterile dressing and get to a physician immediately. If the burn covers his entire body, you may put him into a warm bath while waiting for the doctor or ambulance, leaving his clothes on if they are too hard to remove. Epsom salts or soda may be used.

Don't use absorbent cotton directly on a burn as it will stick and cause further injury when it's removed.

If wax or metal-like substances have caused the burn, don't attempt to remove any portion that sticks. Leave that to the doctor.

Burns, powder

Exploding firecrackers and blank pistols are the common causes of powder burns. They should always have the attention of a doctor since he may want to give antitetanus serum. Try to get the wound to bleed as freely as possible to clean it out.

Burns, sunburn

The skin of the baby or small child is tender and burns easily. Don't expose him to the direct rays of the sun for more than a short period at a time. If the sun is hot, he should be protected by a hat and an old shirt over a sunsuit or bathing suit.

If he happens to get sunburned, cold cream, petroleum jelly, olive oil, or cocoa butter give relief. These should be applied liberally, with as little rubbing as possible. Calamine lotion is also soothing and doesn't stain clothes.

If burns are severe, take the measures described for burns from fire. A bad sunburn can be very serious, especially with a baby.

Cuts. *See wounds in which bleeding isn't severe*

Drowning. *See artificial respiration*

Drugs and medicines swallowed, *See poisons*

Earache. *See "ear infection" page 192*

Eyes, specks, foreign objects, and caustics.

Keep the child from rubbing his eye, since the object may scratch the membrane covering the eyeball. Small specks can be removed by flushing the eye with a boric-acid solution. (Add a teaspoonful of boric acid to each pint of boiled water.)

You may also draw the upper eyelid down and away from the eye, holding it by the lashes. Tears will wash the speck out. Or examine the upper eyelid with clean cotton. Call a doctor if not removed in a half-hour.

If the child gets lime, plaster, or cement in his eyes, wash it out immediately with great quantities of water. Milk is also satisfactory for washing out the eyes. Then consult the doctor at once.

Eye wounds. See wounds

Falls

If the baby falls from a high place, put him to bed, keep him as quiet as possible, and have the doctor examine him to be sure he's all right. This is especially important if he vomits or seems dazed and unlike himself.

Food poisonings. See poisons

Frostbite

Gently cover the frozen part with your hand until it's thawed and circulation is restored, or cover with extra clothing. Keep the child away from heat for some time. Frozen part may also be thawed very gradually in cold water.

Gas, inhaled. See artificial respiration

Gun wounds. See wounds

Hiccups

Often clear up spontaneously with no treatment. Mild cases can often be stopped by getting the child to hold his breath as long as possible, or making him drink slowly a glass of water to which a pinch of baking soda has been added. Pulling his tongue out as far as possible may give immediate relief. Breathing in and out of a paper bag which fits tightly over the face may stop them. Persistent cases must be treated by a physician.

Hives. See allergies, page 190

Infections from cuts. See wounds, infected.

Infected wounds. See wounds

Insecticides, swallowed. See poisoning from drugs

Ivy poisoning. See poisons

Nosebleed

Have the child sit with his head slightly back. Apply cold wet compresses over his nose and face. A pack of sterile gauze or cotton may be inserted gently back, not up, into the nostril, leaving an end outside so the cotton can be removed easily. Or press the nostrils together firmly with your fingers for at least 4 to 5 minutes.

Objects swallowed

A round object, such as a button or small coin, usually goes into the stomach and does no harm. If the baby chokes, however, call the doctor. While waiting, hold the baby up by the legs, head down, and gently pat the upper part of the back to help him get rid of the object. Don't stick your hand down his throat in an attempt to recover it.

If the baby swallows a pointed object, such as an open pin or a needle, give him some food such as spinach or string beans. This may surround the point and keep the object from doing damage until it can be removed or has passed through the intestinal tract. Get in touch with your doctor at once. Never, under any condition, give a laxative if something has been swallowed.

Poisoning from drugs, medicines, caustics, insecticides, sedatives, and animal poisons

Call the doctor at once, as he may want to have the stomach washed out immediately. While waiting for him to arrive, try to get the child to vomit by sticking your finger into his mouth and tickling the back of his throat. Or give 2 teaspoonfuls of baking soda or salt in a glassful of water. You may have to give as many as six glassfuls before he'll vomit. If you don't have either of these, try milk, soapy water, or dishwater.

After the stomach is well washed out, give

an antidote of 3 egg whites in a glass of milk, or a heaping tablespoon of Epsom salts in a glass of water.

Do not make the child vomit if he has swallowed a corrosive acid such as carbolic, sulfuric, hydrochloric, and oxalic acids, Lysol, or a solution containing phenol; or alkali poisons such as lye, ammonia, drain or toilet-bowl cleaners.

Neutralize an acid poison by giving an alkali such as milk of magnesia, chalk, or baking soda in water, or lime water. Follow up with milk, olive oil, or egg white.

For an alkali, have him swallow a tablespoon of olive, mineral, or corn oil, and diluted vinegar or lemon juice.

If the child has swallowed plant or insect sprays or rat pastes, induce vomiting by any of the methods described in the first paragraph of this section.

Induce vomiting if he has taken opium, morphine, or sleeping tablets. Keep the child awake by giving him a cup of strong coffee every half hour. If breathing stops, apply artificial respiration until the doctor can get there.

In all cases of poisoning, keep the patient warm.

Poisoning from food

Sometimes children eat poisonous mushrooms or berries, or food that has partly decayed. The symptoms of food poisoning are pain, cramps, nausea, and vomiting. Treat as for drug poisons. Induce vomiting with syrup of ipecac. Always get in touch with a doctor immediately.

Poisoning from plants

Wash the skin with plenty of soap and water, lathering five or six times. Then wash again with rubbing alcohol, rinse in clear water, and dry.

If rash develops, wash as above. Make a paste by heating soap with a little water until about the consistency of lard. Apply thickly over the part; allow to dry and leave on the poisoned area overnight.

Or apply dressings wet with a solution of Epsom salts, as strong as can be made with cold water. Keep the dressing wet.

Powder burns. *See burns*

Puncture wounds. *See wounds*

Scalds. *See burns, fire*

Sedatives, swallowed. *See poisoning from drugs*

Shock. *See artificial respiration*

Smothering. *See artificial respiration*

Splinters. *See wounds*

Sprains

Apply cloths that have been soaked in cold water as soon as possible after the wrist or ankle has been sprained, and continue to apply them for at least 30 minutes, or longer. Have the child lie down with the sprained part on a pillow. Then call the doctor, as he may wish to tape the sprained part, or it may be a fracture.

Stings. *See bites, bees, etc.*

Sunburn. *See burns*

Toothache

Take the child to the dentist as soon as possible. It may be necessary to apply home relief while waiting. If there's a cavity in the tooth, put a small bit of cotton around the end of a toothpick and clean it out. Then plug the cavity with another small piece of cotton dipped in oil of cloves, using end of a toothpick to insert the cotton. If there's no cavity, apply packs of sterile gauze on the outside. Sometimes hot ones will give more relief, sometimes cold. You'll have to experiment.

Wounds in which bleeding isn't severe

Wash your hands with soap and water before touching the wound. Using sterile gauze or cotton, clean the wound carefully. Grease and oil may be removed with benzine, naphtha, oil of turpentine, or ether. For other kinds of dirt, soap and water or rubbing alcohol is the best cleanser. Begin at the edge of the wound and wash away from, never toward, it.

If an antiseptic seems desirable, alcohol may be used. Spread it well over the wound and the skin around it for a distance of $\frac{1}{2}$ to 1 inch. Let the disinfectant dry, and then apply a sterile dressing of folded gauze if it's a cut or deep bruise. Hold the dressing in place with adhesive tape. Change the dressing every day.

Wounds, infected

Signs of infection in a wound are redness around it which soon develops into a swelling, accompanied by a feeling of heat and throbbing pain. If the wound is in a part of the body which can be dipped into a pan, soak it in water (as hot as the child can stand) in which has been dissolved 2 teaspoons of boric acid, or 3 heaping tablespoons of table salt, or 6 heaping tablespoons of Epsom salts to each quart of water. Keep soaking for at least an hour, adding more hot solution as the water cools. Soak again at intervals. If the injured part can't be immersed, apply cloths wrung out of the hot solution, changing them often enough to keep them hot. Cover the wet cloths with a large dry towel to keep the heat in. Apply the treatment continuously until all signs of inflammation have subsided.

Consult a doctor about an infection, for a seemingly insignificant one may prove dangerous. This is especially true of infections in or about the nose and forehead.

Wounds of the eye

Have the child close injured eye. Cover with a sterile gauze dressing, bandage lightly to avoid pressing on eyeball, and take the child to the doctor at once. Don't try to remove foreign objects imbedded in the eye.

Wounds in which foreign bodies remain

Splinters are the ones most commonly acquired by children. If the foreign body is near the surface, it may be picked out. First clean the skin with soap and water. Then sterilize a needle, knife point, or tweezers by passing through a flame. Don't touch the point after you've sterilized it. Use this to remove the splinter. Make the wound bleed if possible. After the bleeding has stopped, apply an antiseptic down into the wound. If the object is buried deeply or is quite large, simply apply alcohol and a bandage and take the child to the doctor. Tetanus antitoxin may

be needed, especially if it is a deep puncture wound or there is dirt in the wound.

Wounds, puncture and gunshot

These should always have the attention of a doctor because germs may be carried into the body. He may want to give antitetanus serum. Home care consists only in getting the wound to bleed as freely as possible in order to clean it out.

Wounds with severe bleeding

Bleeding from wounds of the scalp and face can be stopped by placing a compress over the wound and bandaging tightly. Most wounds on other parts of the body can be controlled the same way. If a large artery or a vein is cut, however, apply a tourniquet until you can get the child to a doctor.

A tourniquet should be a flat band at least one inch in width—never a rope, wire, or string. A triangular bandage folded into an inch-wide strip is best, but a belt, stocking, or handkerchief will do.

For a wound in the arm, tie the tourniquet around the upper arm about a hand's breadth below the armpit. For a wound in the leg, tie the tourniquet around the thigh about the same distance below the groin. A pad underneath the tourniquet places additional pressure on the artery or vein.

Wrap the material twice around the injured limb and tie a half knot. Place a short stick or similar article on the half knot and tie a square knot over it. Turn the stick rapidly to tighten the tourniquet, but don't tighten more than is necessary to stop the flow of blood. Hold the stick in position by the ends of the bandage already applied, or by another tie looped around the ends of the stick and tied around the limb. Get the child to the doctor as soon as possible.

A tourniquet must be used with care, since it cuts off the supply of blood to the limb. So don't use it unless it's needed to stop severe bleeding. Loosen the tourniquet every 15 to 20 minutes, but don't remove it. If the bleeding has stopped, let the tourniquet remain loose. If bleeding starts again, retighten the tourniquet.

Index

RECORD SECTION

for keeping a permanent account of your
child's physical and mental development,
personality traits, interests, and abilities

Why this record is important
to you and your child

Records of your child's development from birth onward have become far more than a matter of sentiment. They are proving a treasure house of valuable information as well.

Doctors are asking mothers to note down in permanent form their youngster's physical development so that physicians who take care of them in later life will be able to follow constitutional tendencies or acquired susceptibilities. Records of your child's mental progress will assist his teachers and counselors at the high-school and college level.

The whole trend today, in fact, is toward more and more detailed knowledge of each individual. When you fill out the succeeding pages, you will be making a contribution to science, and to a better understanding of your own youngster.

These records will serve another purpose, too. Some space has been left for problems and difficulties when they occur. And they will arise! But you'll find it's a wonderful help to write them down. First, just what happened and how it happened; and what you did and said; and finally, how your child responded. In the very act of writing, you'll begin to get an inkling of the causes and of the solution. Soon you'll acquire a technique not only for meeting problems serenely and competently, but for keeping them from coming up.

So that you may reap full benefit from these records, ample space has been left for noting down anything in your child's development which may (1) interest his doctor or medical examiner in the future; (2) be a guide to his school counselor; (3) help you to a better understanding of your youngster, and (4) be a source of personal pleasure to you in years to come.

For the convenience of doctors, vocational-guidance experts, and others who may refer to them in later years, the records have been arranged so physical development may be followed through without a break; and mental, personality, and character development likewise; yet they're so planned that physical and mental development can be compared easily at any given age.

The nicest thing about these records is the pleasure you'll receive from them. It will surprise you to find out how unreliable even your memory can be. It will be a never-ceasing thrill to look back over these pages.

Keep these records, not for your sake alone, but to help those who will be interested in your youngster later on.

Personal Record of

....
(Baby's name in full)

Born......................................
(Year, month, day, hour, and minute)

At.........................Hospital.................
(City)   (State)

Father....................................
(First name   middle name   last name)

Mother....................................
(Full name, including family name before marriage)

Address...................................
(At time of Baby's birth)

Subsequent addresses:

....
....
....
....

Birth Certificate

Paste photostatic

copy of certificate

here

The birth is officially recorded at . . . .
(City)

. . . .
county   state)

Original birth certificate is kept . . . .

Identification

Hand- or footprints

Paste copy of prints here

Any distinguishing marks—list and describe them and their location on Baby's

person . . . .

. . . .

. . . .

. . . .

. . . .

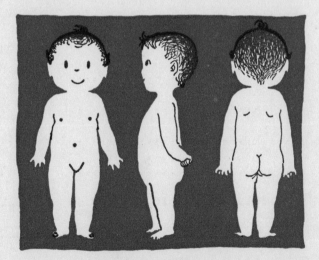

Mark location of distinguishing marks

Birth announcement

Mount birth

announcement here

Gifts received: From:

. . . .

. . . .

. . . .

. . . .

. . . .

. . . .

. . . .

. . . .

. . . .

. . . .

Other mementos

From birth to six weeks

Birth

Labor began at......................

Mother went to hospital

  at...............................

Delivered at........................

Anesthetic (if any)...................

Type of delivery....................

Baby's weight......................
                    Pounds   Ounces

Baby's height......................

Circumference of head..............

Circumference of chest..............

Condition at birth..................

Describe fully any circumstances of birth or of Baby's condition which departed in any way from the normal....................................

....

....

Baby's appetite—   Good.........Poor..........

Diet—   Breast milk.........Formula.........Both..........

First physical examination

Name of Baby's doctor...

This record may be of interest to medical attendants in later years. It
should be filled out by a physician, and his findings listed in detail

Head
  Circumference...............
  Symmetrical.................
  Size of fontanels............

Eyes
  Crossed....................
  Discharge..................

Nose
  Free breathing..............
  Discharge..................

Mouth and Throat
  Tonsils....................
  Adenoids..................

Neck
  Lymphatic glands............
  Thyroid gland..............

Skin
  Texture...................
  Color.....................

Chest
  Circumference..............
  Shape....................
  Thymus...................
  Heart.......Size...........
    Rate......Murmurs........
  Lungs....................

Abdomen
  Size......................
  Shape....................
  Liver.....................
  Spleen...................
  Hernia...................

Back
  Posture...................

Arms
  ....

Fingers
  ....

Genitalia
  ....

Legs and Feet
  Knees....................
  Nails.....................

Reflexes
  ....

Nutrition
  ....

Height
  ....

Weight
  ....

Hemoglobin
  ....

....

Signature of Physician

First few days

First put to breast at

....
(Give time of day and interval after birth.)

Any difficulties in nursing?

Describe..

How dealt with...

Was 3-hour, 4-hour, or self-demand schedule employed at first?

....

If bottle feedings were given—

When begun? After breast feeding, or in place of it?....................

....

First formula...

....

....

Weight lost...

Regained birth weight at.........................days...........

Note any problems or difficulties encountered in getting Baby started, together with methods found effective in solving them: ....

....

....

Went home from hospital

....
(Give date and time of day)

Chart of natural rhythm during first week

Every baby has his own individual pattern of times at which he is hungry and sleepy. It's important to know these times so that he won't cry for long periods from hunger, or be kept awake when he wants to sleep.

Using the key letter given below, mark down for approximately one week the times at which the baby sleeps, cries, seems to be hungry, and is given his bath. After a week's trial, you will know the schedule that fits your baby most satisfactorily.

S—Sleeps	W—Wakens
N—Nurses	C—Cries
F—Bottle feeding	B—Bath

	1 AM	2 AM	3 AM	4 AM	5 AM	6 AM	7 AM	8 AM	9 AM	10 AM	11 AM	12 M	1 PM	2 PM	3 PM	4 PM	5 PM	6 PM	7 PM	8 PM	9 PM	10 PM	11 PM	12 PM
1st day																								
2nd																								
3rd																								
4th																								
5th																								
6th																								
7th																								

If a crying, feeding, waking, sleeping, or bath period occurs at the quarter or half hour (1:15, 2:30, etc.), jot down "15" to indicate 15 minutes past the hour, "30" for half-past the hour, or "45" for 45 minutes past the hour.

Vitamin record

Vitamin D begun at. . . . . weeks

Kind and dosage prescribed by doctor. . . . .

First given. . . . .
                                        (Date)

        Amount Baby took. . . . .

        Describe method used, Baby's reaction:

        . . . .

        . . . .

        . . . .

Vitamin C begun at. . . . . weeks

        (Orange, grapefruit, sweetened lemon, or tomato juice or ascor-
        bic acid tablets)

Kind and dosage prescribed by doctor. . . . .

First given. . . . .
                                        (Date)

        Amount Baby took. . . . .

        Describe method used and Baby's reaction:

        . . . .

        . . . .

        . . . .

Thiamin (Vitamin B_1)

        (If your doctor prescribed any in addition to amount supplied by
        his food.)

Kind. . . . . Dosage. . . . .

When begun. . . . .

Growth record

	pounds	ounces
At birth...............................		
On leaving hospital....................		
At two weeks..........................		
At three weeks........................		
At four weeks.........................		
At five weeks.........................		
At six weeks..........................		

Physical examination at six weeks

By...
(Doctor's name, city)

Doctor's comments..

....

....

Illnesses

Describe symptoms, severity and duration of attack, and treatment.

. . . .

. . . .

. . . .

. . . .

. . . .

. . . .

Special problems

Write down circumstances in detail. What had happened before, how Baby acted, and what you did.

Describe method of handling which seemed to be successful.

. . . .

. . . .

. . . .

. . . .

. . . .

. . . .

. . . .

. . . .

From six weeks to four months

Growth record

	pounds	ounces
At seven weeks..		
At eight weeks..		
At nine weeks..		
At ten weeks..		
At eleven weeks..		
At twelve weeks..		
At thirteen weeks..		
At fourteen weeks..		
At fifteen weeks..		
At sixteen weeks..		
Further comments:..		

....

Development

weeks

Noticed light at.. ....

Followed bright object with eyes at...................... ....

Held head up when placed on abdomen at............... ....

Turned head in the direction of sound at................ ....

Reached for an object at................................ ....

Recognized parents at.................................. ....

Smiled at.. ....

Further comments:......................................

....

....

```
┌─────────────────────┐   ┌─────────────────────┐
│                     │   │                     │
│                     │   │                     │
│        Snap         │   │        Snap         │
│                     │   │                     │
│                     │   │                     │
└─────────────────────┘   └─────────────────────┘
```

First solid food

Solid foods

First solid food was . . . . Begun at . . . . weeks.

Describe method used and Baby's reactions:

. . . .

. . . .

. . . .

. . . .

Second solid food was . . . . Begun at . . . . weeks.

Describe method used and Baby's reactions:

. . . .

. . . .

. . . .

. . . .

Third solid food was . . . . Begun at . . . . weeks.

Describe method used and Baby's reactions:

. . . .

. . . .

. . . .

. . . .

. . . .

Illnesses

Describe symptoms, severity and duration of attack, and treatment.

. . . .

. . . .

. . . .

. . . .

. . . .

. . . .

Special problems

Write down circumstances in detail. What had happened before, how Baby acted, and what you did.

Describe method of handling which seemed to be successful.

. . . .

. . . .

. . . .

. . . .

. . . .

. . . .

. . . .

. . . .

From four to six months

Growth record

	pounds	ounces
At seventeen weeks..		
At eighteen weeks..		
At nineteen weeks..		
At twenty weeks..		
At twenty-one weeks..		
At twenty-two weeks..		
At twenty-three weeks..		
At twenty-four weeks...		
Further comments:...		

....

Development

weeks

Laughed out loud at. . . . .

Held toy at. . . . .

Held head up well at. . . . .

Rolled over at. . . . .

Giggled at. . . . .

Coughed artificially (a polite little cough to get attention) at. . . . .

Pulled self forward in an attempt to sit up at. . . . .

Offered fluids (including occasional sips of milk) from cup at. . . . .

Accepted fluids from cup reasonably well at. . . . .

Further comments. . . . .

. . . .

Snap

Snap

Illnesses

Describe symptoms, severity and duration of attack, and treatment.

....
....
....
....
....
....

Special problems and difficulties

Write down circumstances in detail. What had happened before, how child acted, and what you did.

Describe method of handling which seemed to be successful.

....
....
....
....
....
....
....

Six to twelve months

Growth record

	pounds	ounces
At six months..		
At seven months..		
At eight months..		
At nine months...		
At ten months..		
At eleven months...		
At twelve months...		

	weeks
First tooth appeared at...................................	
Second tooth appeared at.................................	
Third tooth appeared at..................................	
Fourth tooth appeared at.................................	
Fifth tooth appeared at...................................	
Sixth tooth appeared at..................................	

Development

	weeks
Grasped toy by curving fingers around it at..............	....
Sat up alone at.......................................	....
Held two objects, one in each hand, at....................	....
Reached for.........immediately on seeing it at........	....
Expressed pleasure by crowing or cooing at...............	....
Sounded definite syllables ("na-na," "da-da," etc.)........	....
Banged spoon or patted table...........................	....
Became shy with strangers at...........................	....
Crawled at..	....
Pulled self up to standing position at....................	....
Picked up objects with thumb and index finger at.........	....
Poked and examined with index finger at.................	....
Brought two objects together at........................	....
Learned to pat-a-cake at...............................	....
Learned to wave bye-bye at.............................	....
Showed signs of temper at..............................	....

Snap

Snap

Illnesses

Describe symptoms, severity and duration of attack, and treatment.

....

....

....

....

....

....

Special problems

Write down circumstances in detail. What had happened before, how Baby acted, what you did.

Describe method of handling which seemed to be successful.

....

....

....

....

....

....

One to two years

Growth record

	weight	height
At one year.........................		
At fifteen months................		
At eighteen months..............		
Further comments................		
....		
....		

Snap

Development

Showed preference for.....right or.....left hand in reaching at....months.

Held cup to drink at.....................months.

Bowel training begun at...................months.

Developed fair control at..............months.

Daytime bladder training begun at.........months.

Developed fair control at..............months.

Used spoon with good control at...........months.

Pointed to eyes, nose, or hair at............months.

First tantrum at.........months.   First said "I won't!" at...months.

Began to feed self at......months.   (Beginning of negativism.)

Used sentences at........months.   Snipped with scissors at...months.

Story hour begun at......months.   Identified pictures at.....months.

Snap

Snap

Development

Walked with help at....months.

Lowered self from standing to sitting position at....months.

Stood up without help at....months.

Walked alone at....months.

Threw a ball at....months.

Climbed stairs with help at....months.

Climbed stairs unaided at....months.

Climbed into chair unaided at....months.

Ran with confidence at....months.

Jumped down at....months.

Further comments:..
....
....
....
....
....
....
....
....

Illnesses

Describe symptoms, severity and duration of attack, and treatment.

....
....
....
....
....
....
....

Special problems

Write down circumstances in detail. What had happened before, how youngster acted, what you did. Describe method of handling which seemed to be successful.

....
....
....
....
....
....

Two to three years

Growth record

	weight	height
At two years..		
At two and one-half years...............................		

Development

Favorite outdoor play apparatus:..................................

....

New physical skills and age at which acquired:.......................

....

Development

Vocabulary at two years......words.

List several typical sentences or sayings:

. . . .

. . . .

. . . .

Fed self whole meal unaided at......months.

Began to dress self at......months.

    Able to do reasonably good job at......months.

Began to wash self at......months.

Put toys away after play at......months.

List favorite songs and stories:. . . . .

. . . .

. . . .

. . . .

. . . .

List favorite indoor toys and amuse-

ments:. . . . .

. . . .

. . . .

. . . .

. . . .

Snap

Illnesses

Describe symptoms, severity and duration of attack, and treatment.

....

....

....

....

....

....

....

Special problems

Write down circumstances in detail. What had happened before, how youngster acted, what you did.

....

....

....

....

....

....

Three to five years

Growth record

	weight	height
Three years		
Four years		

Development

List favorite outdoor play apparatus and special physical abilities:

At three years..

At four years...

Development

Vocabulary at three years contained......words.

List typical comments:...

....

....

....

Attitude toward other children:

Friendly toward all..

Friendly with a few...

Shy at first..

Painfully shy..

Takes lead in social relationship.................................

Overaggressive..

Describe special traits and skills, favorite indoor play materials, stories, and

songs, at three years:...

....

....

at four years:..

....

....

....

Five to seven years

Growth record

	weight	height
At five years...		
At six years..		

List favorite outdoor activities, any special physical skills:

At five years...

At six years..

Illnesses

Describe symptoms, severity and duration of attack, and treatment prescribed.

....

....

Development

Describe reactions at entering kindergarten, any adjustments required, how worked out. . . . .

. . . .

Describe reactions at entering first grade, any adjustments required, how worked out. . . . .

. . . .

List favorite indoor games and play materials; special skills; favorite books, songs, and stories:. . . . .

. . . .

At five years . . . .   At six years . . . .

. . . .

. . . .

. . . .

Special problems and difficulties

Write down circumstances in detail. What had happened before, how child acted, what you did. Had there been late bedtimes or overstimulation? Describe method of handling which seemed to be successful.

. . . .

. . . .

. . . .

. . . .

Immunization record

	Date	Booster doses Date
Pertussis (whooping cough)	1st dose..........	1st dose..........
Diphtheria	2nd dose.........	2nd dose.........
Tetanus (lockjaw)	3rd dose..........	3rd dose..........

A combination vaccine is generally given to obtain simultaneous immunization against these three diseases. The immunity obtained is not permanent and should be renewed by stimulating (booster) injections at the ages recommended by your doctor.

If separate immunization is given for pertussis, diphtheria, and tetanus, use record below:

	Dates of 1st dose	2nd dose	3rd dose	Booster doses	
Pertussis (whooping cough)	......	......	......	......	......
Diphtheria	......	......	......	......	......
Tetanus (lockjaw)	......	......	......	......	......
Smallpox	......	......	......	......	......

1st vaccination.........................
(*date*)   ("*take*")   (*no* "*take*")

Revaccination...........................
(*date*)   ("*take*")   (*no* "*take*")

Revaccination...........................
(*date*)   ("*take*")   (*no* "*take*")

The following immunizations may not be done routinely in your vicinity. Your doctor will advise you concerning their desirability.

Scarlet fever	Date of 1st dose......	2nd dose......	3rd dose......
Typhoid	Date of 1st dose......	2nd dose......	3rd dose......
Tuberculosis (B.C.G. vaccine)	Vaccination......	Revaccination..........	

Tests for immunity

Schick test (to test susceptibility to diphtheria); usually given between 18 and 24 months and repeated at 6 and 12 years:

Date of test.......... Age..... Reaction......

Date of test.......... Age..... Reaction......

Date of test.......... Age..... Reaction......

Dick test (to test susceptibility to scarlet fever):

Date of test.......... Age..... Reaction......

Date of test.......... Age..... Reaction......

Tuberculin test (to test susceptibility to tuberculosis); recommended at 3 years of age and at 3-year intervals thereafter up to the eighteenth year:

Date.....Age.....Reaction..... Date.....Age.....Reaction.....

Date.....Age.....Reaction..... Date.....Age.....Reaction.....

Date.....Age.....Reaction..... Date.....Age.....Reaction.....

Record of diseases

Disease	Date	Mild or severe	Antitoxin, serum, or antibiotic given	Complications
Chicken pox	....	....	....	....
Measles	....	....	....	....
German measles	....	....	....	....
Mumps	....	....	....	....
Scarlet fever	....	....	....	....
Whooping cough	....	....	....	....
Diphtheria	....	....	....	....
Asthma, hay fever, or other allergy	....	....	....	....
Rheumatic fever	....	....	....	....
Polio (infantile paralysis)	....	....	....	....

Describe any other
diseases, surgery, fractures, or unusual condition your child may have:

....	....	....	....	
....	....	....	....	
....	....	....	....	

Teething

Indicate on the chart below the order of their appearance and the age in weeks and months at which each tooth appears. The order of the appearance and the age at which they come through is expected to vary with each child. A dentist should be consulted when there is unusual delay.

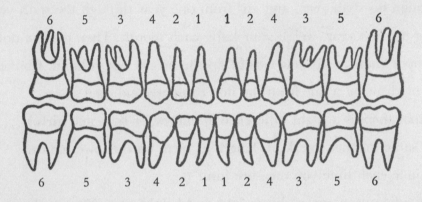

1. Central incisors: usually appear during the sixth to ninth months.
2. Lateral incisors: usually appear around the eighth to tenth months.
3. First molars: usually appear between the twelfth and fourteenth months.

4. Cuspids: usually appear from the eighteenth to twentieth months.
5. Second molars: often appear by the twenty-fourth month.
6. Molars: these are the first of the permanent teeth, known as the "six-year molars."

Age teeth appeared

Upper teeth		Lower teeth	
Right	Left	Right	Left
1.............................		1.............................	
2.............................		2.............................	
3.............................		3.............................	
4.............................		4.............................	
5.............................		5.............................	
6.............................		6.............................	

Weight and height charts

On the next four pages are charts on which to keep a record of Baby's weight and height gains. There are separate charts for a baby boy from birth to one year; a baby girl from birth to one year; boy from one year through his sixth year; and girl from one year through the sixth year.

During the first year, weigh your baby each month. Then place a dot on the upper chart at his new weight, in the proper age column. Connect the dots by drawing a line from the first to the second, and so on. (Notice that there is a slight difference in curves for boys and girls.)

In the same manner, mark his length at birth on the lower chart, and continue each time you measure him.

After the first year, record his weight and height every six months in the same manner as on the first-year chart.

The shaded section on each chart is the "average" zone. The height and weight curves for about 80 percent of all children will be within this zone. However, if the curves for your youngster follow the same general course as those shown, you may consider his growth normal, even though the curves do not fall in the center section.

Consult your physician about any abrupt change or irregularity. For example, if the child's weight line goes up rapidly while his height for the corresponding period remains the same, he is probably gaining too fast. Or if his height line continues to creep up and his weight remains the same, he may not be gaining fast enough. Your doctor will make a thorough examination and tell you what to do.

Baby boys from birth to one year

Weight

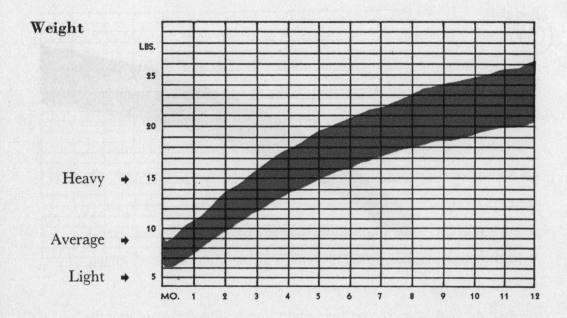

Height

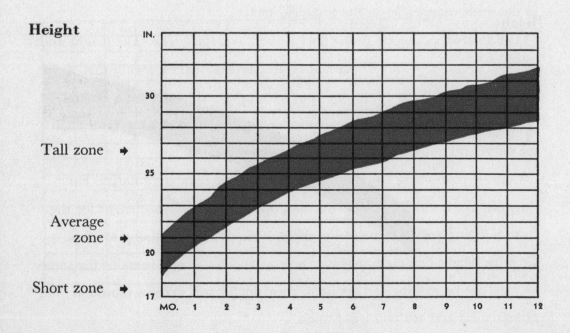

Baby girls from birth to one year

Weight

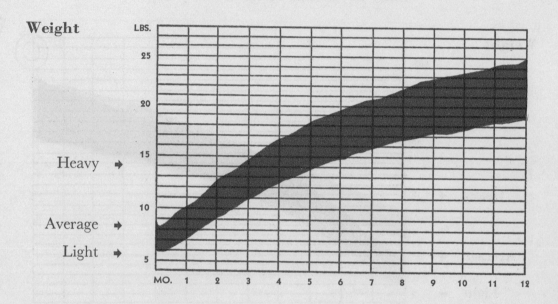

Height

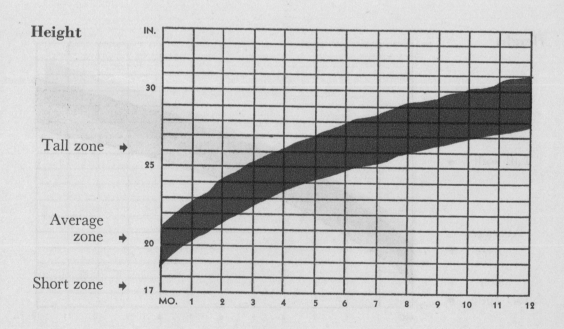

Boys from one year through sixth year

Weight

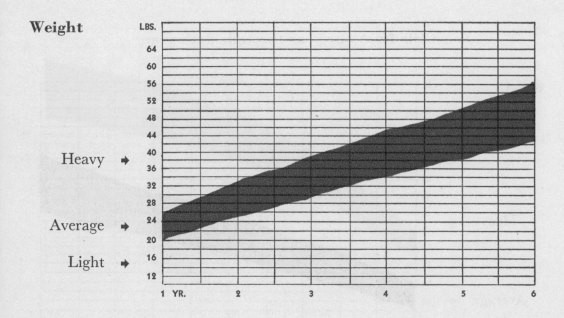

Heavy ➡

Average ➡

Light ➡

Height

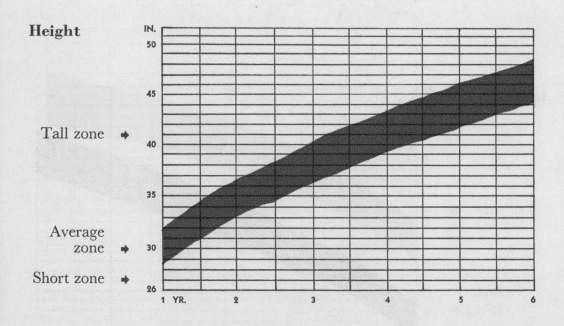

Tall zone ➡

Average zone ➡

Short zone ➡

Girls from one year through sixth year

Weight

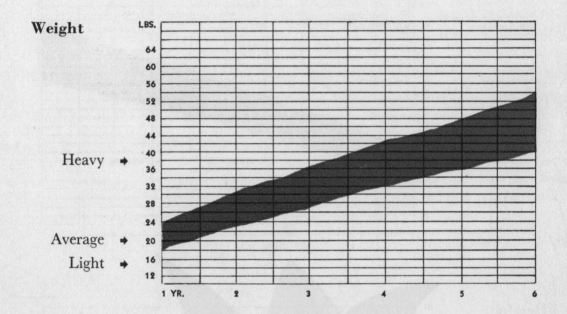

Heavy ➡

Average ➡
Light ➡

Height

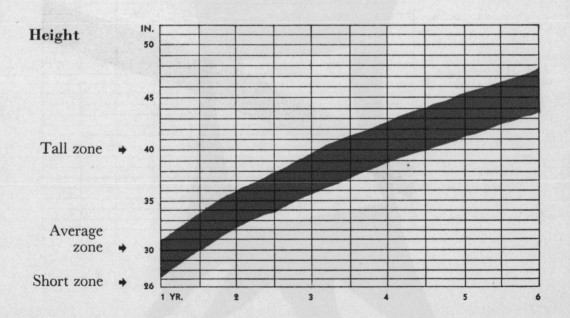

Tall zone ➡

Average
zone ➡

Short zone ➡

Family Tree

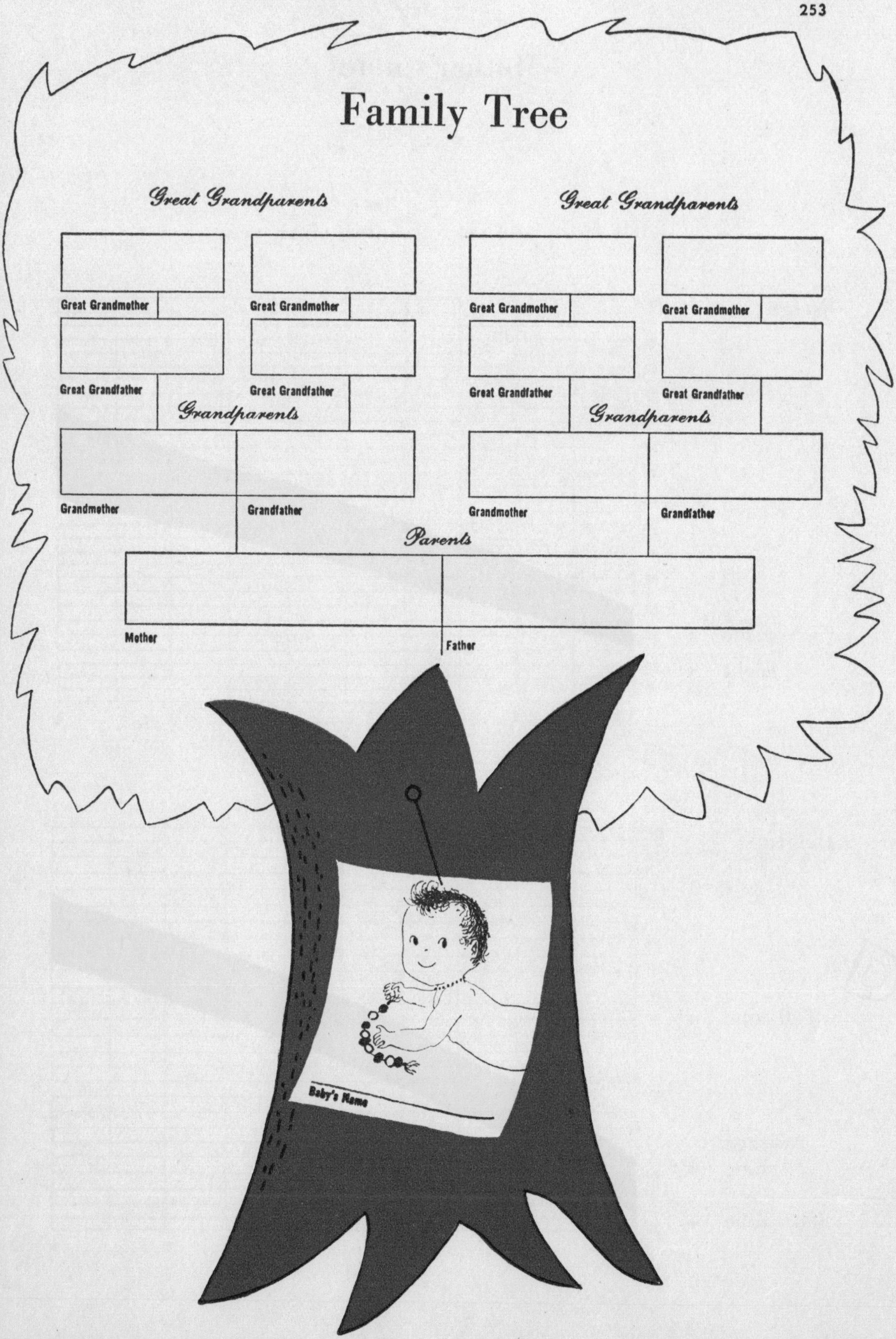

Great Grandparents

Great Grandparents

Great Grandmother

Great Grandmother

Great Grandmother

Great Grandmother

Great Grandfather

Great Grandfather

Great Grandfather

Great Grandfather

Grandparents

Grandparents

Grandmother

Grandfather

Grandmother

Grandfather

Parents

Mother

Father

Baby's Name

Mother's notes

....

....

....

....

....

....

....

....

....

....

....

....

....

....

....

....

Snapshots

Snapshots